So Sorry, No Peace

So sorry,

NO PEACE

Royal Arch Gunnison

THE VIKING PRESS · NEW YORK

1944

COPYRIGHT 1944 BY ROYAL ARCH GUNNISON
PUBLISHED BY THE VIKING PRESS IN OCTOBER 1944

PUBLISHED ON THE SAME DAY IN THE DOMINION OF CANADA
BY THE MACMILLAN COMPANY OF CANADA LIMITED

Some of the material in this book has
appeared in *Collier's*.

PRINTED IN U.S.A. BY AMERICAN BOOK–STRATFORD PRESS, INC., NEW YORK

To

My Wife, MARJORIE,

*whose calm sureness that we would
somehow come through right side up
will always be an inspiration*

Foreword

"You can't do this to me. I'm an American!" But they did. For the first time the word "American" held no magic. The Japanese did what for generations they had wanted to do. They seized American civilians, poked them with bayonets, slapped old women and children, stole their belongings, burned their household goods, ransacked their homes, and pilfered their businesses. They threw us, the hated "foreigners," into primitive, filthy, overcrowded concentration camps, with barely enough to eat. They had waited a long time for this opportunity!

Correspondents who, like myself, had been covering the Far East in 1940 and 1941 had seen it coming. We had huddled in caverns in bomb-blasted Chungking, lay half covered in rice paddies along the Burma Road, as Japanese bombardiers were being trained for the Pacific war with the helpless countryside as a target. Others like myself had found themselves helpless for an answer when General Chiang Kai-shek had asked how, as Americans, we could justify the course of the United States Government which, having promised aid to China, sent her only Bibles, while sending bombs, in the form of scrap iron, to Japan.

We had watched Nazi sea raiders refueling and being refitted at Japanese ports. Flying on patrol in a Dutch Dornier seaplane off the Netherlands East Indies in October 1941, I had seen a Japanese "fishing" boat—not fishing, but marking waters.

We knew that hundreds of Japanese Shinto priests in Burma were holding special religious meetings, keeping at white heat the seething antagonism to "British Imperialism" which "prevented independence." We heard, and found it not too difficult to believe, that Burmese "patriots" were ready, at a moment's notice, to revolt and massacre every Britisher—and welcome every Jap.

We knew that Singapore, the famed "fortress," was protected only by a high, electrically charged, steel picket fence. This was no impregnable bastion, but wide-open Singapore, where no one knew better than the Japanese agents that in all Malaya there weren't more than 250 aircraft, including Link trainers.

Yet our stories of Singapore, Burma, French Indo-China, and Hong Kong were blocked by stupid censorship.

These things and more had prepared me for the electric shock of Pearl Harbor, for the attack on Clarke Field on the Island of Luzon —the attack which destroyed most of MacArthur's available Flying Forts on the ground.

Yet when Japanese forces streamed into the Philippines like ants after honey and I went to the beachheads with the Filipino-American defenders of the Island of Luzon to watch the well-trained and over-whelming Japanese expeditionary forces make their landings in the face of brave but inexperienced defenders, I learned what little comfort intellectual preparation can be. With our inadequately equipped boys from New Hampshire, Texas, Utah, New Mexico, Massachusetts, Arizona, South Dakota—infantrymen, submariners, gunners, navigators, ground crews—I cursed in a sense of utter futility at our lack of military preparation. Few people in any war could have felt so completely frustrated as we, sitting helplessly in the Philippines while Hirohito struck confidently, successfully, with a plan which had obviously been perfected years before.

As American families were dumped out of horsecarts into a Manila concentration camp, with no food and only small bundles of clothing, I stood by helplessly watching, clenching and unclenching my hands, biting my lips. These Americans—some of them so aged or so young they could scarcely walk—dragged their few belongings through the gate, bowed to surly Jap guards, and stood glassy-eyed and bewildered in their new, confusing prison surroundings.

To most of these Americans and British the end had come so swiftly, caught them so unprepared physically and mentally, that it took months of rugged, dirty camp life before they actually grasped what had happened, before they realized it actually *was* more than just a bad dream. They couldn't seem to get the idea that they weren't free to say and do what they wished. Japanese hate thrived on this attitude. Japanese soldiers enjoyed slapping the "arrogant white men."

People cracked up, then found themselves. Men slowly deteriorated; others seemingly thrived and grew in conditions that at their best were terrible. This wasn't an example of what college professors call applied psychology. This was humanity in the raw.

I saw Japanese atrocities, heard about others, and saw results of still others. Discouraging black reports came firsthand of how Japanese soldiers had bayoneted faint and sick American soldiers who had surrendered at Bataan and were being cruelly marched, without rest and food, hundreds of kilometers in the blazing, tropical Philippine sun. I witnessed the horror "gloat" march through the streets of Manila of worn-out, shell-shocked, American and Filipino soldiers who had surrendered at Corregidor.

My wife and I lived in two different American prison communities—Manila and Shanghai—and watched the reaction of native populations to the treatment meted out to the Americans, the British, and the Dutch.

Serving on internee committees, negotiating almost daily with the pugnacious, greedy, brutal Japanese military gendarmerie and consular officers, I watched the American, the Britisher, the Dutchman under some of the worst possible conditions. Their story is one of spiritual victory over overwhelming odds of discouraging filth, lack of food, lack of hospitalization, lack of humane treatment.

For two years I watched the new Far East history unfold from within the enemy's camp. For a newspaperman it was an unusual opportunity to cover a war from a new angle, although I would have skipped the experience gladly had Marjorie and I been able to get out to Corregidor and away from Manila after our communications failed in the Philippines on the last day of 1941.

For some, plans for escape succeeded; ours failed. We had to stay. In the meantime there was a story to get, even though we were imprisoned. So we set out as carefully as possible, constantly under the threat of Japanese atrocities and army bayonets, to get that story. You'll read it as I saw it happen, as accurately as I can put it down, and with no punches pulled.

Here it is.

R. A. G.

Contents

PART ONE

Before Pearl Harbor

I

MORE than a year before the attack on Pearl Harbor I was in the Far East watching the events which preceded the beginning of the Pacific war. Perhaps the day early in 1940 when I prepared to leave Hong Kong to fly across the Japanese lines to Chungking is as good a time as any to begin the story of what I saw and heard and felt. It was during this period that I began to be fully aware of the devilish thoroughness of Japanese preparation, of the ingenuity and completeness of their espionage, of the almost unbelievably brutal cruelty of Japanese soldiery, and of the inevitability of our approaching war with Japan.

I had been very careful to tell no one of my plans to visit Chungking, the war-blasted capital of Free China, nearly 1000 miles into the interior from the coast. Of course, there were a few who knew —those who were actually engaged in the preparation for my night flight over the Japanese lines—but these, I thought, were all.

From the CNAC (Chinese National Aviation Corporation—55 per cent Chinese, 45 per cent Pan American Airways-owned) office in Hong Kong where I had just completed arrangements to make the flight, I went directly to call on the Japanese Consul General to check on a visa to go to Japan. His first words to me were: "So, you are flying to Chungking tomorrow to interview President Chiang Kai-shek!"

I jumped. Less than half an hour previously, a CNAC official had told me he couldn't tell me what day or what hour the plane for Chungking would leave the airport. This information was withheld in order that the flight might be made in relative safety—that is, to escape being shot down by patrolling Japanese planes. Now here was the Japanese Consul General telling me that he not only knew of my plans to visit the China capital but he knew the day. I wondered if he knew the hour too.

"What makes you think that?" I parried.

He smiled knowingly. "Come in and see me when you get back. I may have some interesting news for you."

My only answer to the Consul General, who was obviously enjoying the situation, was: "I take it your invitation to call on you when I return guarantees my safety."

He merely smiled again. That smile still haunted me as I stood in the waiting room at Hong Kong's Kai Tak airport at three the next morning. (The Consul had been right about the day.) That knowing, overconfident smile came to symbolize for me the official Japanese attitude toward their entire activity in China and Southeast Asia.

My typewriter and small bag had been inspected for forbidden firearms, secret documents, "small bombs placed there by the Jap." As I looked at the murky weather I was grateful that the pilots on this airline were top-notch American fliers, some of whom had been flying in China for eight or ten years.

There were about twenty Chinese around me, jabbering and shoving—waiting to find out whether or not they could get seats aboard the Chungking-bound plane. I noticed a short, stocky man look in at the door from the hangar. His hair was tousled and his white shirt rumpled. His khaki trousers bagged at the knees as though he had been seated for a long time. This was Chuck Sharp, chief pilot for CNAC. Chuck was one of the first Americans to do any serious commercial flying in China. He waved and beckoned to me to follow him through the heavy mist to the big hangar. As we ducked under wings of dilapidated ships, streamlined Vultee dive bombers and two Douglas DC-2's, I asked if he were to take this flight out.

"No," he said. "I just got in from Kweilin. This is a swell night to fly. It's good and foggy. Foxy Kent is going to be your pilot."

By that time we were in the pilots' quarters at the far end of the big hangar. There was a tremendous map hung across one wall of the room, a low, worn-out couch on the other side. W. C. ("Foxy") Kent was seated at a small table at the far end of the room checking on weather reports. I could see that he was very tall, though a bit on the heavy side. Foxy was from Texas, and redheaded.

As we waited for more weather reports we talked about the early days of the China war. We stood at the wall map and Chuck and Foxy reflew many of their "more tricky jobs" for me. Foxy told me of the night he had flown the Generalissimo and Madame Chiang out of Hankow, the former temporary capital—a flaming city—just as the Japanese entered from the other side.

A boy came in with a weather report. Chuck glanced at it as he handed it to Foxy. "Good news," he said, "the bad weather is holding."

"I guess we're the only airline in the world that doesn't seek publicity and prays for bad weather." Foxy laughed as we made our way out to the field. "I don't know as you can see them, it's so dark, but there are patches on the wings and the tail," he helpfully offered just as I was about to climb in. "This is the plane that Woods was shot down in not so long ago."

That's the sort of thing that makes you feel good.

I stumbled up the steps, found my seat, and managed to fasten my seat belt. The Chinese were jabbering excitedly . . . motors roared. I was wondering all the time if there might not be some high Chinese official aboard whom the Japs would like to intercept. There was, but I didn't find out until after we arrived in Chungking.

After a little more than five hours in the dark, we flew into a lusty red Chinese dawn, over a mountainous but an intensely cultivated portion of Free and Disputed China. Before landing, we circled over what looked a little like lower Manhattan. On one side was the historic Yangtze and on the other the smaller Chailing River. The two meet at the south tip of this peninsula. And on this peninsula, which is a 400-foot high bluff rising nearly perpendicular from the two streams, was spread, rather thinly, what was left of a valiant and ancient city—Chungking.

The first time around I could scarcely distinguish the city. It was ashen gray in a hazy, leaden morning. Circling lower, the damage done by the bombs was unmistakable. It looked as though moths had got at a cloth map and had eaten great chunks out of it. Here and there clumps of buildings stood vertically with clusters of people staring up. Elsewhere stood only jagged shells of what had once been office buildings, homes, shops . . . not one a military objective. Eighty per cent of the city of Chungking had been destroyed. Even Rotterdam's ruins couldn't compare with Chungking's. This was what 3000 tons of bombs dropped in thirty-eight raids from May to September 1940 had done.

We landed on a long sandbar in the middle of the Yangtze. Foxy loaded up with gas, took on some freight and a couple of passengers, and waved good-by. He was off to Hanoi and Rangoon. I was to go back with him in a few days—if he got back.

I was ferried across the river and carried in a swinging-swaying sedan chair up the steep 400-foot rock cliff upon which the city is built.

At first the physical damage that I was viewing completely blocked out the human activity going on about me. Then I became conscious of the bright and faded indigo-blue-jacketed men and women working like honey bees to repair the damage done by the bombing raids of the day before.

There were soldiers in every type of uniform, from muddy khaki to faded chartreuse and purple, clopping along in wooden sandals or mat shoes. Here a little boy with a reed broom was sweeping off a cobblestone sidewalk. I walked along with Hollington Tong who had come from the ruins of the government offices to the airport to meet me. "Holly"—now Vice-Minister of Information, a brilliant Chinese with a Ph.D. from the University of Missouri—is well known in the United States now, after acting as aide to Madame Chiang on her 1943 trip here. As we walked up the rutted streets, we saw an old man seated squat-legged with a hand cycle cropping grass on what had once been a public square and which was being re-landscaped by a crew of eight or ten.

Everyone had a cheery word for his neighbor or a lusty cry of welcome for some friend crossing the other side of the street. A gang of workmen passed, headed for some job on the outskirts of town. Two boys were having trouble pushing a great rock out of an air-raid dugout that was being blasted into the hill. The gang of workmen stopped, watched the boys, laughed heartily at their puffing and straining with the rock, and then helped to hoist it out of the mouth of the dugout. Co-operation is the key to Chungking's—to China's—defense.

There were over 500,000 people living in Chungking when the Government moved there. When I first arrived in the fall of 1940, there were only a little over 150,000 people left. Many had fled from the city and scattered back in the hills. More than 12,000 were killed either by direct hits or by concussion, which is by far the worst way to die. As I write this, Chungking's population is estimated at nearly 900,000.

Walking down the rock-strewn streets that morning, I found the air pungent with the odor of burning timber, dank with the smell of wet plaster and debris after a rain. I watched the patient coolies neatly piling the scattered bricks from the jumble of the houses and stores, and saw the fire and health departments working, slowly but successfully, to maintain sanitary conditions.

A few hours later I was seated in the study of the "Great Man of Asia." Hollington Tong had escorted me down the muddy road from Chialing House, about the only livable quarters left in the city for "visiting firemen" (as the local correspondents usually call visiting correspondents). An air raid had delayed the interview and piled up the Generalissimo's work. Chiang Kai-shek even then used to take his "paper work" with him down into the deep and dank dugout. There's nothing complacent about the Generalissimo. He keeps his staff going half the night.

The Generalissimo was taller than I thought he would be—and thinner. But more affable. He started out by interviewing me.

What did I think of Chungking? What did I see in the faces of the people on the street?

Hollington Tong was translating quickly, nervously. Everyone was high-strung in Chungking those days—that is, everyone but the Generalissimo.

"Yes," the Generalissimo admitted, "things look bad. But actually they are nowhere nearly as bad as they look. Things have looked bad in China for centuries."

He rose from his chair and paced across the darkened room. The only light came from a window behind his chair. There was a deep red glow from a fireplace on the other side of his chair. There was a snap to his speech, just as to his movements. For the first time I noticed his uniform. No fancy decorations. No insignia of any kind. In those days there was no time for much ceremony.

Then Hollington Tong translated what the Generalissimo had been saying.

"If the world thinks we are losing this battle—you tell them this. Tell them that I say: 'We can go on losing the war much longer than Japan can go on winning it—if that is what Japan is doing now.'"

Then I put a question I'd been thinking about since I'd talked with Hong Kong's Governor General, Lieutenant General E. F. Norton, and Major General A. E. Grasett, Commanding Officer of the Hong Kong Crown Colony defenses.

Within the past year 1939–40 the Chinese General Staff, through War Minister General Ho Ying-Ch'in, had sought to establish the basis for a joint defense of Hong Kong and the surrounding territory with the British. This was to have had a twin motive. From China's angle, it would have meant that Britain would have provided war material through Hong Kong for China. The Chinese would have "run" this through the Jap lines isolating Hong Kong on the land side. From the British angle, China would have attempted to knife through the Jap flank that cut around in back of Hong Kong "if Japan ever attacked Hong Kong." The number of Chinese troops to have been utilized in such an action was suggested by the Chinese as "about 400,000."

But the British didn't even want to talk about the plan at the time it was suggested. This the British had admitted to me. Now that Japan was acting more aggressively (mid-1940), the British were thinking Chinese assistance might not be inopportune. So I asked if the Generalissimo would consider reopening the question of the 400,000 troops at this time.

That touched off another spark. He continued to pace up and down as he talked rapidly and feelingly for several minutes. Holly Tong seemed agitated. I looked questioningly at Holly.

He hesitated. Then replied: "The Generalissimo says, 'No'!"

I'd have given a great deal to know exactly what Chiang really did say. I often thought of this incident during the hectic days just before Christmas 1941 when Hong Kong was fading fast and Chungking troops were reported closing in on the Kowloon Leased Territory just outside Hong Kong.

In the questions about the war that were to follow, a reference was made to the approaching Tokyo-Berlin agreement. This was before Tokyo joined the Rome-Berlin Axis. I immediately asked about it and the Generalissimo said any mention of it must be off the record. He continued to talk about it for a few minutes saying that he for one "hoped the pact would be signed quickly." I was surprised at this and wondered why.

The Generalissimo said he felt "the more irons Japan had in the fire," the harder it would be for the military dictatorship to use any one iron effectively for a long period. His prediction was that Japan's contribution to the "questionable success of the totalitarian cause" would be an attempt to spread South-Asiaward in pursuit of Japan's announced "New Southeast Asia Policy." That meant increased action in French Indo-China, Thailand, and Burma.

When I talked with War Minister Ho Ying-Ch'in later about this he expanded the idea to say it looked to him as if Japan would draw many troops out of China to enable her to force her way into Singapore and Sumatra with seasoned soldiers. New recruits would be put into China, and this, General Ho thought, would weaken Japan's position so that China, with American aid, could drive the Japs back toward the China Sea rather quickly.

It is not revealing anything now that should not be told, when I tell of the Generalissimo's foresight in analyzing what was then the unannounced Tokyo adherence to the Rome-Berlin world dictatorship trust.

The Generalissimo said he believed that the Nazis had persuaded the Japanese that the most fruitful policy Japan could pursue was in South Asia, not China. If this analysis was correct, Chiang said, it would be China's tactics to keep attacking the Japs along the Yunnan-French Indo-China border, the Kwangsi-French Indo-China border, and in Kwangtung Province, even providing for American, British and Chinese airforce attacks at Hainan Island in the Tongking Gulf. That, he outlined, would weaken Japan's position during any Jap attack against Singapore and the Netherlands East Indies.

Chiang said he believed the United States would be drawn into the war in the Far East just as soon as the Japs came close enough to threaten the United States sources of tin, rubber, and other vital raw materials in Malaya and the Netherlands East Indies. And as things turned out it looks as though Chiang Kai-shek had figured the Jap out pretty thoroughly.

I asked, too, about the future position of the Occidental in China. Like his other answers the Generalissimo pointed this one sharply.

"That greatly depends upon how quickly and to what extent the Anglo-American powers assist China in its fight for freedom. Quite naturally," he said, "some day we will have to insist on a Chinese China with no foreign concessions, no extraterritoriality, no special foreign privileges. That may be soon. Or it may be some generations away. But the Occidental may be relatively sure that any successful support given to China will be repaid in economic profit. But also it must be understood that we Chinese are developing China for ourselves; that we are not helping you develop it for your own profits."

Chiang would not discuss China's relations with Soviet Russia. I asked him how China's friendly relations with Russia fitted into the Tokyo connection with Berlin, especially since Hitler and Stalin were apparently on good terms.

"The Generalissimo will not comment," was Hollington Tong's reply.

Actually at that time Russia and China had signed a new trade agreement whereby Russia continued to send in certain military and non-military supplies by caravan across from the Northwest via the Sinkiang (Urumchi-Hami-Lanchow) route.

Other Chungking leaders with whom I talked on this first trip of mine into Free China—especially Dr. H. H. Kung, Vice-Premier and

Finance Minister—believed that the Soviet Union's natural enmity against Japan would keep the Russians "as neutral as possible; not caring who keeps Japan out of possible northward aggression along the Siberian Coast."

"If Japan is going to be busy with China and perhaps America and Britain in the South," the heavy-set Buddha-like Kung told me, "it's unlikely Japan will want to fight Russia in the North."

My first flight into Free China was short, but to me fully worth any risk taken. My talks with our Ambassador, then Nelson T. Johnson, at the Embassy over on the south bank of the Yangtze; with Sir Archibald Clark Kerr, Britain's Ambassador (now in Russia); and my long discussions with Dr. Wang Chung-hui, (not to be confused with the Japanese puppet Wang Ching-wei) then Foreign Minister —a man with a broad vision and wide foreign experience—left me with few illusions about what China wanted from us, and a better grasp of what our diplomats out there thought and told the American and British Governments should be done to help China.

This is the tone I took in reporting during those last months of 1940 while covering my "beat" from Melbourne to Shanghai. The Jap wasn't particularly concerned with Europe—except only as it drew his two major enemies' attention away from him. He just grinned to himself, sucked in his breath politely, and was "so pleased with immeasurably satisfactory manner in which war situation developing. . . ."

After my flight to Hong Kong from this first Chungking visit, I felt I had an even more personal interest in this war to come. I felt that my stories of "put up or shut up in the Far East" had a closer to home touch.

II

AFTER returning from Chungking—still in 1940—I made a trip to Shanghai. Since Pearl Harbor I have often thought of that week's voyage up the China Coast, when, between Formosa and the China Mainland, our tiny Butterfield and Swire China Coaster passed through the center of a giant Japanese naval force of seventy warships.

"Is it still maneuvers, or are they on their way?" we asked ourselves. For at that moment there was trouble in Indo-China. American citizens had been jailed by the Japanese in French territory.

Our coaster stopped at Swatow and Amoy, both occupied by Japanese forces. I hadn't then become accustomed to seeing Japanese atrocities, as I was to later. But somehow you learn to control the pit of your stomach so that you aren't too obviously nauseated. It was in Amoy that I saw a Jap officer whirl around and shoot a harmless Chinese "hey-ho" coolie for bumping the officer with one end of the "hey-ho" bamboo shoulder pole.

And down at the lace port of Swatow, where the Japanese had made several "practice landings" against defenseless Chinese guerrilla forces—just a rehearsal for the real fight to come a year or so later against the "foreigner"—I watched a gendarmerie customs inspector show us "foreigners" lined up at the rail of the coaster how the Japanese was winning the "friendship and respect of his Asiatic brother—the Chinese."

Our ship was merely putting into Swatow to show the Japanese, at this stage in Anglo-Japanese relations, that the British were still keeping their flag flying in the face of every conceivable annoyance and delay Japanese port authorities could think up.

Although we carried little freight (the Japanese refused to permit much freight to be carried by foreign bottoms between Occupied China ports; almost everything had to go in Japanese bottoms, or not at all) we were carrying a fair number of Chinese coolies as afterdeck passengers.

As these deck passengers filed down the board gangway to the pontoon dock which floated in the muddy river, baggy-uniformed Japanese gendarmes ordered them to line up along the pontoon in two lines, and undo all the bundles and bags in which they were carrying their only possessions.

These, I learned, were the Chinese who were coming to Swatow —then nearly a ghost city, for the Chinese had filtered out after the Japs had arrived—with the assurance of the Japs at Canton that they would be welcome.

Anyone who has ever seen a Chinese family traveling knows the amount of incidental food stuff and trinkets carried in small paper bags, in sacks, in blanket rolls, and in dilapidated bamboo suitcases. This assortment was spread along the pontoon by some seventy-five people—all opened up for the gendarmes to inspect. The Chinese stood respectfully, patiently, hats in hand. (The Japanese insist on this in all occupied areas.)

There was a bustle at one end of the pontoon. A diminutive Jap-

anese officer appeared in dark green uniform and highly polished
black boots, holding the scabbard of a sword nearly half his size. He
would do the inspecting.

Aided by two pugnacious soldiers, he started sorting the sundry
articles of the first family, scarcely deigning to soil the tips of the
fingers of his cheesy white cotton gloves. Instead of looking into the
several paper bags, he tore them open, scattering beans and rice clear
across the pontoon. The husband scrambled to retrieve the rice, for
there was a rice shortage. As the Chinese knelt to scrape up his
precious food, the officer stepped over and gave the stooped figure a
boot that sent him sprawling half the width of the pontoon. Just as
the surprised Chinese started to rise to his knees, another gendarme
rushed up and for no apparent reason struck him a hard blow across
the teeth. Blood trickled out of the corners of his mouth as he rose,
but only half-way, to one knee.

At this obvious caution the gendarmes burst into boisterous laughter. Then they looked up at the rail of the ship to see how the few
English officers, and the single American passenger, liked the "show."
Then back to their "duty." Each family on down the line suffered in
some such way. One man owned a cheap Chinese thermos bottle.
The cap stuck. The gendarme inspecting it whacked the bottle
against the iron railing. Then he unscrewed the top and shook out
all the broken glass. More loud laughter.

One family's bag full of apples—Chinese are among the world's
greatest apple munchers—was scattered across the pontoon; rice and
bean sacks were broken; and the mother, who said something in a
pleading tone to the officer, received a sharp blow in the face with a
closed fist. When her husband bent to help her, a gendarme struck
him a rabbit-punch on the back of the neck, lifted him up and
shoved him reeling toward the iron rail, then knocked him over
backward. The Chinese caught the rail with unexpected agility but
the gendarme kicked his knuckles, and the man fell into the mud
and water. No one helped him pull himself back onto the pontoon—
a mess of mud and blood.

"This sort of thing happens every trip," the captain of our ship
snorted, "and what you've seen here isn't bad at all." He stormed
into his cabin and slammed the door.

"He really should not be so upset at an officer merely doing his
duty," observed a smooth voice at my elbow. I turned quickly and
saw a stocky, middle-aged Japanese, who looked like the average
Japanese businessman you'd meet in San Francisco or Los Angeles.

This was the start of a queer "Mr. Moto" business that lasted for several days until we got to Amoy. I've never quite figured it out. But what I learned from this Japanese, who claimed he was also a journalist, later proved to have significance. He said his name was Nishikawa; that he had lived in the United States at one time; that he was now "doing journalistic duties" for a Tokyo newspaper group. When I suggested it might be the Nichi Nichi he just smiled blandly. I never did get the name of his "newspaper group."

Nishikawa-san was exceedingly frank. He told me all about myself as we sat in the ship's small social room that was also its dining salon. He was a lot like Nazi press-propagandist Schmidt in Berlin, who once warned me to stay out of Germany, after I'd written a piece on Nazi training of German youth ostensibly for war against the British and us.

Nishikawa told me I'd just returned from Chungking, and that I'd interviewed Generalissimo Chiang Kai-shek; and he told me whom else I'd seen in that bomb-levelled Chinese capital—men about whom I hadn't written a word.

Nishikawa-san smiled pleasantly when he said to me, "You are a hate monger mistakingly arousing hate against a misunderstood Japan." He was "so sorry to have to talk like this on so pleasant a journey . . . but my duty to my country . . . you understand I am sure."

I could escape this little Jap "journalist" only by staying in my two-by-four cabin. There was so little deck space he always found me and continued to expound the theory of Japan's policy of Greater East Asia and the Co-Prosperity Sphere. The general theme of his sales talk was keynoted on the desire to keep America out of the coming Far East war—the war that was inevitable.

At that time (1940) the indication seemed to be that Britain would become involved because of Japanese invasion from French Indo-China into Thailand and perhaps into Northern Malaya. Following such action the guess was that Uncle Sam would come in quickly.

The day before the ship reached Amoy, Nishikawa cornered me at the rail. He had the real Los Angeles and Hawaii Tourist Bureau attitude that morning. He was honey and syrup and everything that was nice. He had, he said, something in his cabin that he must show me. Something of vital interest. We went to his cabin.

"Gunnison," he warned me, "it will be folly if, as you say, your President and the esteemed Mr. Hull permits your country to go to war with Japan. I can see you are not convinced that war between Japan and the United States can be avoided."

Now what?

He unlocked and fumbled in a black briefcase, from which he

pulled a six- or seven-page sheaf of papers and handed them to me. They were photostatic copies of something written in Japanese and German. There was a line down the middle. The Japanese on the left, the German on the right. Since I can read neither Japanese nor German this might have been a plan for the establishment of tiddly-winks as the national pastime of Japanese-occupied China, for all I knew.

"Will you translate this for me?" I asked him. He did falteringly.

What he read slowly unfolded as a plan agreed to between Germany and Japan to co-operate in stopping Britain and the Netherlands in the Pacific. Japan, it pointed out, must remain on a peace-time footing with Russia. The United States must be brought into the war quickly. Japan, the plan read, agreed "to strike surprising shat-tering blows" at the heart of United States defenses to cripple the United States before the fighting could get started. There was only one paragraph on that point, but I've often thought about it since.

Most of what Nishikawa read dealt with division of spoils in East Asia. The line of reasoning behind the idea—not so much the specific proposals—seemed most significant to me at the time, for underlying it was the desire to involve the United States in the Far East; to force Japan and the U.S.A. into war against each other in order to prevent the United States from continuing to send increasing aid to Britain in Europe.

The plan as he translated it was definitely German-inspired. It led with Japan's chin, and I told Nishikawa just that. He gave me that bland smile of his in answer. I asked him where he got this paper. He could not tell me . . . "so sorry." Would he let me have the document? "Oh, no . . . so sorry . . . this is impossible." Did he object to my copying it? This, too, he was sorry about; but it was also impossible.

As best I could remember Nishikawa's translation, there were ten points, most of them dealing with Japanese-Russian relations, and three points dealing with Japan's program for utilizing the raw-material resources of the Netherlands East Indies.

This was before Tokyo joined the Rome-Berlin Axis. This was prior to the threatening Japanese-Dutch oil talks when Prince Konoye sent trouble-shooter Kenkichi Yoshizawa to Batavia, Java. And this was almost nine months before Hitler attacked Soviet Russia.

The first section of Nishikawa's document pointed out that the United States was of more value to Britain out of the war than in. It argued that a fighting U.S.A. would not supply Britain with so many planes, ships, tanks, and guns.

"Britain is standing in the way of Japan's progress in East Asia. Britain is also an enemy of Europe. Britain must be eliminated," was one section of the translation.

As an ally of Britain's, the United States was also an enemy of Japan, the argument continued—thus the United States must be attacked.

Point two continued something like this, according to my notes: If the U.S.A. came into the war in the Far East after Britain had been attacked, such a war would become a "raider's war." The U.S.A. is in no position to carry the fight to Japan, it said. The Japanese, in the same position, would not carry the war to continental United States, or any of its near-by possessions.

Japan's strategy in such a case should be to return to its home bases and wait for an attack by the United States fleet—if the U.S. fleet had the audacity to come out and fight in the Pacific. The British fleet would be too busy in the Atlantic to fight Japan.

If the portion of the American fleet then in the Atlantic (September 1940) could be drawn out of the Atlantic and its potential of assistance in the Mediterranean eliminated, then Germany would have a better opportunity to deal a quick, finishing blow inside the Mediterranean, and to break the blockade in the North Atlantic.

Japan and Germany, the theme ran, must co-operate to split the forces that were working for Germany's and Japan's encirclement and defeat. Both Japan and Germany, it contended, were striving for a new world order—more efficient and profitable than the present world.

The third point seemed Japanese-inspired. It stressed the need for Japan and Soviet Russia to remain at peace, even though they never had been on good terms. Japan, it held, could win the fight against China if Russia would help—or rather if Russia would stop aiding China, and would withdraw its troops from the "Manchukuo" border. Obviously such a withdrawal would have permitted the Japanese troops held there to checkmate the Soviets, to move into action either in China or slip south to strike at Malaya. It was argued that even though Japan were weakened as a result of this struggle against Britain, America, and the Netherlands Indies, a victorious Germany could aid Japan economically and physically.

The other points came in quick succession.

Four: Germany would assist Japan to secure European economic profits—if Japan occupied French Indo-China, the Netherlands East Indies, Thailand, and Malaya. Germany apparently wanted French Indo-China and the Island of Java as out-and-out colonies. Japan was

promised Burma, Thailand, and the rest of the Netherlands East
Indies. (How this "big-hearted" Nazi approach must have ired the
Japanese militarists who disliked the German as a "white foreigner"
nearly as much as the Anglo-American-Dutch "interlopers" in East
Asia.)

Five: Once the war against Britain was won, Japan was promised
German aid against China. Russia, it was assumed, would not interfere since Germany would be victorious over the British and a new
pro-Nazi Soviet would be developed.

Six: Included in the new Russia, as bait for remaining peacefully
inclined toward Japan, would be the northern part of India—all the
mountain areas.

Seven: British-India was promised "independence." But this "independence" would be under Jappo-Nazi "protection."

Eight: Germany would aid Japan in engineering and financing the
cross-Thailand canal, to save rounding the Malay Peninsula past
Singapore.

Nine: If co-operative, Russia would be given Persia.

Ten: Russia was also promised Alaska, with special Japanese fishing rights permitted in Alaskan waters.

The three sections on the development of the Netherlands East
Indies dwelt on making (1) tin, (2) rubber, and (3) oil products
immediately available to Germany and perhaps to Russia in the fight
against Britain and the United States.

Nowhere in the translation did Nishikawa state that Russia was
expected to fight against either Britain or the United States, but
you'll note the Soviets were allegedly offered part of India and
Alaska.

I print this "plan" now because it is interestingly significant in the
light of what has happened. I wasn't at all sure of its authenticity
then, but it has interesting features historically. It shows what kind
of thinking was going on in the Jappo-Nazi chancelleries at that
time. It could have been an earlier draft of Japan's part of the soon-
to-be-signed Tokyo-Rome-Berlin Axis pact.

My fellow-passenger (Nishikawa) was too eager that I get the
story into print. He asked several times in as offhand a manner as
was possible, "You will have this printed in the United States, yes?"

I told him that the "proper persons" would be informed.

And once Nishikawa was convinced I would tell "the proper
persons"—he didn't ask who they were—he apparently felt his job
was done. He scarcely spoke to me again during the last day of the
trip into Amoy. I noticed that he was met by several Japanese Army

officers and was escorted off the ship the moment we pulled into quarantine. We in the "foreign ship" had to lie in quarantine for over five hours, while three small Japanese freighters came in past us and were checked over by the Japanese Port health authorities, although our "Tai Yuan" was at anchor long before the Japanese ships showed up.

The only excuse the Japanese doctors gave when they came aboard and then left immediately upon spotting the incoming Japanese freighters was, "Oh . . . so sorry . . . Japan ship must be inspected always first . . . so sorry. . . ."

III

I WAS called home shortly after this and flew back across the Central Pacific—Guam, Wake, Midway. But I had been home barely long enough to get up to Seattle to see my mother and ninety-three-year-old grandmother before I was sent back to Hawaii and the Southwest Pacific—New Zealand, Australia, Java, Sumatra, Singapore, Malaya, Siam, Burma, Free China-Chungking again, and to get the last Clipper out of Hong Kong for Manila and the war.

This time Marjorie went with me. We left San Francisco on January 3, 1941, and every mile of the entire trip, every interview, everything I saw headlined two facts: Our unpreparedness and imminent attack by Japan.

It's easy to look back and see what should have been done. But it's good to be able to look back at Hawaii and Australia especially and realize that in these two spots the Japanese overestimated our united strength, such as it was. If they had taped us correctly at Hawaii and at Australia, and had attempted what Lieutenant General Homma and other aggressive high-ranking staff officers strongly recommended —original attack and landings in these two places—the Pacific War would have been a longer, a much more serious affair.

John Curtin, who was to become Australia's Premier very shortly, told me he was genuinely concerned. He could get no indication of assurance from the United States that we would give priority to orders for fighter and bomber aircraft, ammunition, tanks, and motorized field artillery.

Almost everything furnished by the United States was being sent—

to England to forestall Hitler's invasion threat. Only a little was beginning to filter into the Middle East. And what's more, Australia was part of the Empire trading and supply setup which, even under the beginnings of Lend-Lease, made it very difficult to import much war materials from America.

Australia was wide open for invasion late in 1941. The Australian Staff and Government knew it, and were pale and trembling every time they switched on the wireless for fear they'd hear the Japanese had landed at or near Darwin. They'd been lucky to keep them out in peacetime. However, it wasn't all luck.

Australia has had an "All White Australia Policy" and has maintained it to the point where any Oriental has had great difficulty in getting into the country except on business trips or on pleasure trips. This policy is not stated as an "exclusion" policy but is just that in effect. Australia's attitude toward China after the war will be one to watch. The Australian has felt, and not without reason, that there were so few British and other Occidentals on his vast continent that an "open door" for immigration would lead to the entry of hundreds of thousands of Orientals and East Indian natives—an immigration movement that in time more than likely would swamp out the whites.

The Japanese, in particular, had been hard at it to get the Australian Government to ease off on the immigration restrictions. The Japs wanted to establish some good population bases on the rim of the central Australian desert—just as they did at Davao in the Philippines —as preparation for Invasion Day.

Only the Dutchman in the Netherlands East Indies was more Jap-conscious than the Australians. The English—including most of the high-ranking officers in Singapore, Malaya, and Burma—were typically old-school-tie; outwardly, at any rate, they were comfortably oblivious of the Japanese strength and menace.

In Java—seat of the Administration for the Netherlands East Indies—I found an awareness of the threat of Japan that led the fearful Dutch General Staff to advocate such "suicide" tactics as an all out swift naval attack, supported by landing parties, on central Japanese defense positions in the Caroline Islands.

And they weren't kidding. Admiral Helfrich, Commander-in-Chief of the small Dutch fleet, told me in his quarters at Surabaya one day that the only way to stop the Japanese from swallowing the Indies' rich resources of tin, rubber, oil, quinine, and other assets was "to attack quickly . . . before they attack us . . . which they will do any minute." This was in early September 1941. General

Berenschott, the N.E.A.'s Army Chief who was killed in an accidental air crash before I left Java, had told me several times that he knew the only action he could fight was "a retiring action; a final one of scuttling the Indies since we cannot get help from America."

I had my talk with Admiral Helfrich the day after I had made a "routine" patrol flight in an old Dornier flying boat; a flight that hadn't turned out to be so routine. We had sighted a small motor craft below on the deep blue surface of the Java Sea not far south of Bawean Island, part way from Surabaya Naval Base to Borneo.

"It's not usual to see a motor craft in these waters," the pilot shouted across to me. I was in the co-pilot's seat. And it was the first we'd seen. All other craft were the slow-moving single-sailed Prahaus usually manned by the fishermen off Madura Island. So down we circled in a long glide. The gunner in the forward cockpit gave his guns a short burst to clear them. The rear gunner fixed his 30-caliber gun in place. I stepped down from the co-pilot's seat and stood watching across the dashboard.

We crossed the small boat head on. Native men in whites were rushing about the deck. The boat was a Diesel about the size of a U.S. West Coast Halibuteer.

The Dutch were excited. They shouted rapidly. But no shots were fired. The men on the boat changed course several times. We crossed and recrossed low over the single mast of the Diesel. The Eurasian radio operator on our plane began to send steadily. He finally got an answer.

"Ah—goodt!" was what I thought I heard the pilot say.

Obviously we'd run into something out of the ordinary. But I didn't ask any questions. The Dutch were too busy. Before fifteen minutes had passed I noticed a thin pencil line with a white streamer out behind it on the horizon, perhaps 12 miles away.

"Destroyer," nodded the pilot.

"What's the trouble?" I asked.

"Sorry," apologized the pilot. "I think this craft below is Japanese. He flies no flag. He doesn't answer radio signals. He doesn't signal from his deck. We heard a Japanese fishing boat was in these waters. But why fishing here?"

Fishing, indeed. This sounded to me like the kind of Jap fishing craft operating off the Australian Great Barrier Reef that were suspected of laying mines and servicing German raiders reported in Australian and New Zealand waters.

We didn't wait for the destroyer to get any closer. We skimmed the surface of the water just abeam of the Diesel, then climbed and went on with our patrol to Bawean south to Bali and back on the long leg of the triangle to the base at Surabaya.

When we returned I was cautioned by everybody from the Captain of the Yard on up and down not to mention the craft we had seen. "Yes, she was a Japanese craft. No, she was not *exactly* a fishing boat. Yes, this is the first one we have found this close to Java. . . ." That Japanese "fishing" boat never got back to Japan, I learned. But there was no chance to get the story out.

The Dutch had the Japs on Java pretty well lined up as to residence, occupation—spy or resident with a job to do after the Jap invasion. The Dutch had already had one experience with enemy aliens—the Nazis, of whom some seven thousand were picked up that hectic May 10, 1940. If the Japanese had struck that day, as many Dutch thought they would, in co-ordination with the Nazi invasion of Holland, they'd have picked off the Netherlands East Indies without more than a desultory protest or two.

I went up to Palembang where the two largest gasoline cracking plants in this part of the world are located; one was Standard Oil, the other Royal Dutch Shell. I saw how both were carefully mined for destruction.

It was amazing to me to find that there were only four old French 75's along the river in front of these two great oil refineries. The employees had some old duck guns and tiger guns, and one or two 30-caliber machine guns. But the Dutch Army just didn't have enough equipment to "scatter" it by sending any up to Sumatra for even an attempt to defend the oil refineries. The refineries were supplied with plenty of dynamite and fuses. There was only one thing to do.

A Standard Oil official I talked with out there said they'd considered sending home for a "private arsenal," but upon second thought, since the U.S.A. hadn't got around to granting priorities for the $500,000,000 for military, air, and naval supply orders for the Dutch, a few pop guns more or less wouldn't help save the Socony Vacuum's cracking plant.

"So to hell with it," he said. "We'll just blow the joint up and run for the jungles." I have seen Japanese newsreel photos of the oil fires started by the explosions that this man set off. I know what the oil fires were like around Manila. They burned for two weeks. But this must have been a roaring inferno, for there were some 6 square miles of gas and oil tanks between the two companies' plants.

So much damage was done in these original demolitions that it was not until the spring of 1944 that the Japanese were able to get some of the refinery machinery in operation again—just in time for Mountbatten's fliers to smash the preparatory moves toward reoccupation. Most of the oil from these Palembang oil fields and from the East Borneo fields at Tarakan and Balikpapen has been shipped back to Japan proper for refining. Guerrilla bands in the Sumatra hills have harassed the oil pumping appreciably, just as the Chinese-led guerrillas in Malaya have fought a nuisance-value battle against tin mining, rubber planting, and rail-line operation from Singapore to Thailand.

The two men responsible for the N.E.I.'s splendid showing against the Japs are Governor General van Starkenborgh Stachower and Dr. H. J. van Mook, Lieutenant Governor and Economics Minister. It was these two men who refused to be bluffed by Japan's needle-men, Kobayashi and Yoshizawa, the "Ike and Mike—they look alike" of the oil-deal team. These two insisted that Japan be given priority on all N.E.I. oil, tin, and rubber, and demanded that the Japs be accorded the right to keep a military mission in the Netherlands East Indies to inspect and earmark all raw materials needed by Japan.

One of the high Dutch officials was taken aside one day during the negotiations and it was indicated to him that it was "quite possible" the Japanese might see their way clear to by-pass the N.E.I. at the time of the invasion—if the Dutch gave in to Minister Kenkichi Yoshizawa. The crust! The confidence!

IV

I F THE Dutch were aware of the Japs' full intent to rush in and grab everything in sight, up at Singapore only a few hundred kilometers away we found a complacence that can only be described as "dopey."

Two incidents illustrate the Malayan situation right up to the arrival of General Wavell less than two months before Pearl Harbor. Even ex-Minister of Information Duff-Cooper seemed lulled into the British attitude that somehow the American fleet and the "sliding airforce" that Air Marshal Sir Robert Brooke-Popham kept talking about would mysteriously float in and save the day.

"The airforce will operate on a sliding basis from India and the

Middle East down to Burma, Singapore, and the Indies, immediately a Japanese attack begins," he said.

It was the typical British attitude that "we may lose the first battle, but the bloody little bawstards cawn't win the lawst one."

Marjorie and I were talking with Lieutenant General Sir Archibald Percival, Army and Singapore Commander-in-Chief, one October evening after we had attended an early movie. (It was he who later surrendered at the Ford Plant outside the City to Lieutenant General Yamashita). As usual the subject of the defenses of Singapore came up.

Percival was a quiet-spoken, serious man. I expressed the opinion that from what I had just seen on my trip inside Malaya, where I had visited the Indian, British, and Australian forces and some of the smaller satellite airdromes, he must consider himself in a rather precarious position, due to unpreparedness.

"We are not unprepared, you know," he said carefully. "But we don't have enough men, equipment, and aircraft to be *adequately* prepared."

"Then what *do* you intend to do when the Japanese attack?" Marjorie asked. I expected the usual answer from a high-ranking officer to such a straightforward question. But the General apparently spoke his mind.

"That's obvious," he replied. "We will execute a series of delaying actions—withdrawals, you know—down the [Malay] peninsula to Singapore, where we will wait for support by the fleet."

Marjorie kept pressing, "What fleet, General?"

He looked surprised. "Why, the American—and—and—units from the British fleet, of course."

There were a few British officers who vigorously disagreed with the planned "retreat and be saved by the fleet" tactics.

One of these officers, Australia's Major General Gordon Bennet, was the most alert member of the British Staff whom I met in all Malaya-Burma. As an Australian, he was considered "a Colonial" by the English staff officers, purely as a matter of policy. He took the attitude that he and his staff officers would know how they would order the retreat, "if and when it might be necessary in the face of overwhelming odds." But he also contended that the actual fighting men in the Malayan jungles should not be told that they were probably going to have to retreat . . . and be instructed in retreating methods. The purpose of fighting men—"expendables" if you will—is to attack; to have an aggressive attitude toward the enemy; an attitude of "come on you S.O.B.s! I'm as good if not better than you are! And I'll lick you where you stand!"

But General Bennet was overruled. I visited Bennet's headquarters in Johore Bharu, and several of the Australian beach and jungle defense sectors—spots where General Bennet and his staff believed the Japs would land first. The General, even in October, was expecting a surprise attack. He sent word to me in Java that if I wanted to be in on the attack I'd better get up to his headquarters by the 27th of September. When I got there early in October, he warned me not to get caught in Thailand, where I was headed en route to Burma and back into Free China—Kunming, Chengtu, and Chungking again.

Admiral Sir Geoffrey Layton out at the Singapore Naval Base was charged with somehow protecting the great dry dock that held the *Queen Mary* the first time I visited the base, and somehow operating against what he knew was a vastly superior Japanese airforce and fleet. It was he who told me British warships were moving to Ceylon to be ready to "come in when the balloon goes up . . . but we do wish your Navy Department could see the value of getting sufficient fleet units out this way to be of some value in the area. Once the Japanese strike, we have got to strike back hard and fast to prevent, if possible, large convoys of troops from being landed all along these coasts." Admiral Layton was more concerned with ships than aircraft.

Up in Thailand, at Bangkok, I found the war tempo speeded up to a fast pace. Everything was set to move right in as soon as the "pool" of Japanese armed forces in French Indo-China reached a sufficient high-level mark to insure three- and four-to-one superiority over the British in Malaya and Burma.

While I was visiting Major General (then Colonel) Chennault's A.V.G. squadron up at Toungoo—between Rangoon and Mandalay in Burma—we had a surprise visit from the Japs. Harvey Greenlaw, Chennault's executive operations officer, usually the most cheerful guy in the world, was actually depressed. The Japs had sent a flight high over the then secret American-Chinese Volunteer Toungoo base (supposedly British) early that morning and Colonel Chennault had whipped a flight right up into the pale blue Burma sky to chase them back into Thailand. The Japs were based 65 miles away across the Burma-Thai border and naturally knew all about the training base for the "Flying Tigers."

Colonel Chennault told me to be in Kunming on November 15. "War will break about that time," he predicted. "And I'll have my boys moved up there—if I can only get the field in shape and the gasoline, oil, and spare parts up there." On November 24 Colonel Chennault and I had lunch on the mid-Yangtze River airfield between the river bluffs below Chungking. I had just come from an interview with the Generalissimo, in which he suggested it would be wise for me to join my wife, if she and I were planning to be together when the war began.

This was too good a tip on "the shape of things to come" to overlook. I still had some people to see and a trip up to Chengtu—China's West Point and its large air-training field. I made this trip as short as possible, interviewing War Minister General Ho Ying-Ch'in and checking on the kind of officer training given China's officer material; officers who were going out into the field to lead the "6,000,000 troops and 300 divisions" General Ho described to me.

A week later I was in Manila where Marjorie joined me by what turned out to be the last KNILM (Dutch Royal Airmail Line) plane from Batavia. Ten days after that, "Pearl Harbor." And then we began to learn in earnest what the Japanese military machine and the Japanese character were like.

PART TWO

Manila: December 1941

V

THERE was no panic in the Philippines when we heard the news of the surprise blitz on Hawaii, and reports of the landing of Japanese forces on the island of Luzon. People went out into the streets at the regular time and headed for offices and their usual occupations. Everyone kept glancing skyward. It was Monday there, but a special saint's day for Catholics—which most Filipinos are—and many went to church. It was a typically hot, muggy Manila day. Traffic moved slowly, as usual. There was nothing to note out of the ordinary except the tense cries of newsboys and the underlying excitement of the people and the sound of loud-voiced radios delivering every bit of flash news.

But by noon of that first day there was a noticeable change in the city. Civilian Emergency Administration arm bands—purple with yellow letters—had appeared on several thousand air-raid wardens and civilian-protection officials. The city went under the order of martial law immediately. The Army commandeered all automobiles in show windows and garages as well as all taxicabs. Busses and trucks, regardless of who owned them or whether they were loaded or not, were requisitioned on the spot. The only means of transportation apart from private vehicles that had not been taken over by the Army and Navy were picturesque little two-wheeled horsecarts drawn by pint-sized horses.

Voluntary evacuation had begun immediately from major towns of the southern Philippines to Baguio, the mountain resort capital in north-central Luzon. The people of Manila were urged to leave the city calmly and quickly if they desired to go out to the provinces. Highways were needed for speedy transport of troops and equipment.

I checked the main roads leaving the city twice during that first day, and several times a day for the next four. Voluntary evacuees moved along in single file at the edge of the roads. Guards along the way kept the file constantly moving.

The civilian administrator had announced that it was planned to send 217,000 non-essentials, mostly women, children, and aged, out of the city. But before they had time to act officially on the planned evacuation of the suburbs and slum death-traps, more than 70,000 people had already left the city. They had hired tiny horsecarts. They had piled all their children, belongings, and food onto these rickety two-wheeled carts and had climbed in themselves. I saw one miniature horse actually lifted off the street when the weight of the load tipped the cart backward.

On that same hot first afternoon and all that night, people trudged, pushed baby carriages, pulled carts and wheelbarrows with their children and belongings. They were getting out of the city. It was a grim, silent procession. There was no excitement. Rather, there was an ominous calm—the atmosphere of smoldering anger. I talked with many of the evacuees.

"If the Japanese take this country we'll never be free," one woman muttered as, with her two-year-old athwart her, she shuffled along the hot pavement carrying a washpan full of clothes and goods on her head.

"The Japanese don't play fair," an old man leading two youngsters by the hand told me. "They tell us they our friends. Then they stab in back. My son's in the Army. He'll show the Japanese." With this his face lit up.

This feeling of confidence was well-nigh universal among the people of the Philippines. Didn't the Filipinos—nearly all of the island's seventeen million—know of the solid conviction of the commander of the United States forces in the Far East, General Douglas MacArthur, that "the Philippines can be defended from attack?"

The Filipinos had heard this conviction expressed from the valley Barrios to the high hill villages. They were determined to give every assistance to see that the MacArthur defense plan worked.

MacArthur saw that if the United States should turn the Philippines loose and keep no hawsers tied to the U.S. fleet or the U.S. Army and Air Corps, the Japanese would not only have an open season on Filipino trade and Filipino livelihood; they would finally just swallow up the islands regardless of any unorganized resistance that might be put up at the last minute. He saw the Far East falling under total Japanese aggression.

Thus MacArthur sold the idea of a strong Filipino defense force to his friend President Manuel Quezon in 1935. Whatever Quezon ordered before the war was carried out by his political organizers and naturally by the people themselves. Thus was born the Philippine Army.

The Philippines Force was supposed to reach a number between 300,000 and 400,000 trained fighting men over a ten-year period. Unfortunately the ten-year training period had just begun to function properly when war broke out. The plan was to train between 30,000 and 40,000 Filipino soldiers each year. When war broke a sufficient number of Filipino soldiers had been trained to form the nucleus of a fast, hard-hitting Filipino force. This was the outfit which took nearly all the advance action against the Japanese invading forces.

The average Filipino knew less about the strength of the United States Navy than he did about island defense plans. But he knew the Navy's reputation. He "knew" that the combined Anglo-Dutch-American fleets in the Pacific outnumbered the Japanese Navy. Instead of shaking his confidence, the announcement of a declaration of war by the Axis on the United States had only served to strengthen his determination to defend his present position and what he believed would be his future independence when Japan was defeated.

The defeat of Japan by the American and British forces meant but one thing to most Filipinos—sure independence by 1946. We heard it discussed in official Filipino quarters something like this: "If there had been no war the chances of our even wanting to accept independence by 1946 would have been doubtful. But now we are going to defeat Japan. We'll halt their aggression. Once Japan is haltered and tied we'll be free to accept independence."

I mention this now to illustrate what the average Filipino from the first days of the war felt he had at stake. His morale was good. His troops were armed. Even the civilian Filipino was armed. But that wasn't surprising, for during peacetime nearly every Filipino was a walking arsenal, and during the days of the campaign he carried with him his whole personal armament from homemade revolvers with barrels made of gaspipe, to his traditional keen-edged bolo in its collapsible scabbard. And the Filipino of the Jap occupation period didn't change. His arsenal may have been out of sight, but you could be sure of its availability.

It was a Filipino division that met and defeated the first Japanese force when they were trying to get a toehold on the beach at northern Lingayen Gulf during the first week of war. The official Army statement reported that Filipino troops "mopped up" the Japanese.

MacArthur told me a few hours after this report that "the Filipino Division behaved magnificently." And from what I learned from soldiers and civilians later, during a trip up toward Lingayen before the second drive hit its stride, the success of this first Filipino mop-up on the Japanese gave the original boost to the morale of the Filipino troops and made possible their splendid fight.

Once the Filipinos—the well-trained Filipino Scouts, the Constabulary, the regular Filipino Army, the young R.O.T.C. and newer volunteers—learned of this success; once they knew from their own people that the Japanese soldier was not as good a fighter, man for man, tank for tank, or plane for plane, there was no more apprehension as to the final outcome of the war. The only problem was how many men, and how many planes, and how many tanks we were going to be able to put up against them at that moment.

Until December 24, 1941, when MacArthur left his Manila headquarters within the walled city to go with the forward echelon of the United States armed forces in the Far East, I had full opportunity to watch him work at close quarters. I attended his press conferences. I talked with him off the record in his Oriental-decorated office. I watched his military cards being played. I went out from Manila into the provinces where his troops and planes were deployed and striking at the Japanese.

With the material at his command, MacArthur accomplished miracles. He didn't permit himself and his Filipino-American forces to be sucked in or drawn out and weakened by the Japanese landings and forays designed to pull him out and divide his forces, then cut them to bits. Had he done so there would have been no Bataan, no Corregidor. The Japs say officially it took "only 33,000 troops" to invade the Philippines. Actually they used two seasoned divisions aided by superior airforce to maneuver us into Bataan. After that these two divisions were sent to invade Java. They were replaced by greener troops. I believe history will tabulate no less than 150,000 Japanese troops in the invasion of the Philippines.

By maintaining his forces in readiness, by keeping strong Filipino and American patrols out in front in every sector, MacArthur kept the Japanese guessing as to the exact number of men and planes at his disposal. He had about 125,000 men—38,000 Americans and 87,000 Filipinos, many with less than two weeks' training—and some 200 planes of all types including trainers, antiquated pursuits and bombers. After the first four days of the war he had half that number of planes and from there on the Jap blitz was practically unobstructed.

Despite widespread espionage and fifth-column activity during the first two weeks of war, MacArthur, through pre-arranged communication systems and vigorous counter-espionage, was able to keep information leaks down to a minimum. Over at Army and Air headquarters no one wrote down on paper anything of vital importance. He just remembered it. No one talked on the phone about anything important. It was done in person.

MacArthur's G-2 (Army Intelligence) had been busy in the days prior to the war and had everyone of any kind of odd background pegged the minute he had landed in the Philippines. They and the Constabulary had the names and numbers of most of the pro-Japanese leaders among the Filipino groups. When war broke out, there was a four-day spy clean-up that showed the minute planning that had been done.

When the Japanese landed in the Philippines, the troops, the General Staff, and the population dug their toes and heels into the jungles of the rice paddies; they took positions in trees; new guerrilla fighters went into the enemy camps with hand grenades and sticks of dynamite; thousands of young Filipinos volunteered for service, and were accepted. The President of the United States had sent a message to the Philippines which had said that he was counting on "every Filipino—man, woman, and child—to do his duty."

Believe me, they did it!

Two days before MacArthur left for Corregidor I discussed the matter of propaganda with him at some length. He had just announced that Manila might be declared an open city. There had been adverse reports from several fronts for about two days. Manila was taking a terrific bombardment from the air. The population was getting a bit jittery.

"Why tell them this discouraging news and then say that you are considering declaring Manila an open city?" I asked. "Don't you think that will create a feeling of great helplessness?"

This tall, expressionless general—the only modern American Army officer ever to hold the post of a full four-star general twice in one career—this usually affable, now slow-spoken officer, took a long draw at his cigar.

"I want to be perfectly honest with these people," he said. "I want them to know nearly everything I know. I'm confident they can take it and come back for more. They realize I'll fight to the last. They realize I'll not take a run-out powder on them. If I give them the bad news along with the good when it comes, then they'll know I've never tried to trick them."

He paused in thought for a moment, then continued: "I don't believe in feeding the population of any country false information. If you build false confidence and you are not successful, you lose their trust forever. If you give the average civilian the truth, he can take a lot more than these propaganda artists tell you is possible. And then when you tell the public you are holding or you are doing better it gives them something to hang onto."

This was fine in theory. The only trouble was MacArthur was not able to give the public anything hopeful. He couldn't give them anything to hang onto. And when President Roosevelt's famous message came to the Philippines—his message that began, "You will be redeemed . . ." everything was so far gone that the statement was more discouraging than it was helpful. It was like telling a man who had fallen overboard from an ocean liner that you'd pick him up on the return trip.

VI

THE first raid came at exactly 3:10 in the morning. The warning siren was hitting its highest wail as Marjorie and I stepped out of the door of the hotel. Just then the first bombs hit Manila. A Japanese plane laid a stick of incendiary bombs across the runways and onto an empty hangar at Nichols Field. The whole deep-blue moonlit sky exploded into a flaming backdrop against which the nearer buildings were silhouetted.

We could hear a Japanese pilot cut in his motor to pull out from the tracer crisscross of red balls of fire from anti-aircraft guns. He had cut off the motor and quietly glided to his objective from a great height. Other bombs dropped and shook the earth. The concussions enveloped us like heavy, padded blows.

High above, a steady double hum of Japanese bombers was unmistakable. Before long a new sound—the whine of the American and Philippine Air Corps interceptors—joined the others. We couldn't see anything for the glare of fire. Straining our eyes to look into the star-spotted sky, all we could see was a blur of green, the color complement of the dazzling flame of explosion.

But we could hear fighters slashing through the night. We could tell that the bomber squadron had been broken up. The deep drone of the bombers and the higher whine of the pursuits filled the sky. The Japanese were driven off.

We saw people running for shelter. Every few feet they would hesitate and look back at the fires, then run on again. But there was no panic.

With the first daylight air raid, at high noon, there came the primary test of how the Filipinos would stand up under bombing. More than sixty-six planes—officially counted—bombed military installations for four hours.

I watched the Japanese bombers sweep across the sky in three perfect V's, to be met by anti-aircraft fire. They kept just above it. I saw the planes drive directly to their objectives. They were broken up by interceptor squadrons. Bombs were dropped, fires started and great pillars of black smoke curled up straight into the blue, windless sky.

Police whistles blew. Cars were ordered to the curb. A few provincial police became excited, cocked rifles and fired into the air at the Japanese planes 15,000 feet above. Anti-aircraft flak began to fall in the streets. Those who had remained on the sidewalks or in open lots or squares scattered quickly. Some were injured.

I watched a spinning, rolling, tightly maneuvered dogfight between three Japanese planes and one American pursuit plane. I saw one of the Jap planes dive and machine gun a crowd standing in an open park watching the fight. An American P-40 pilot saw it, too. He lit out for this one plane, but when he turned, the other two Japs high-tailed away. Those Japanese planes were officially recognized as adaptations of the Seversky single-seater models the Japanese got from us some time before the war.

Official Army reports denied that some of the original bombers and fighters were piloted by Germans, and that some of the planes that were shot down contained Germans. They said they had heard about this, but they would make no comment.

But in the Philippines they will tell you confidently another story. During the first days of the war Japanese twin-motored bomber squadrons came in first and second teams. Not all of the first team, the boys who struck the first lightning blows at the Philippines, had slant eyes. I heard talk at the fields from our fighter and bomber pilots of certain Japanese planes flown with a technique entirely different from that of the general-run Japanese pilot. I checked as closely as I could about Japanese planes shot down, and whether or not the crews were all Japanese. One operations officer I talked with told me he had heard directly from a salvage crew that the pilot of a plane they'd fished out of Manila Bay definitely was "a white man." He was young, with blue eyes and blond hair, I was told, but whether he was a German or of another nationality we'll never know. But the assumption that he was a Nazi can't be far wrong.

When the air experts of the United States Army forces of the Far East say that so far as they have been able to determine there have been no actually German-made planes used against us out there, they are doubtlessly within bounds. But pilots I knew who examined Japanese wrecks saw the Messerschmitt trade mark on parts and instruments. These could have been made in Japan of course, and no doubt were. I saw some of the first "belly tanks" dropped from the Jap fighter planes. Some of the release mechanisms on these extra gas tanks were obviously not of Japanese design.

It has been well established that Japan's airforce is a "bastard" airforce. Almost without exception Japanese planes are adaptations of German, Italian, and American aircraft. The Japs have picked up any number of innovations from American planes captured during the occupation of East Asia. I saw them flying a Flying Fortress (B-17) over Shanghai one day, and nearly had heart failure thinking for a wild moment that here at last Shanghai was going to be bombed. But the Fort was being escorted by Japanese fighters. The Japs were particularly intrigued with this four-engined bomber because they have not been successful—at least up to the time this was written—with any four-engined land bombers. Their only four-engined operational aircraft have been the slow, kite-like flying boats.

When the Pacific war opened, according to a Japanese source Japan was manufacturing from 35 to 37 variations of six fundamental types of aircraft. They were making adaptations of the American Lockheed 14 (Lockheed Hudsons), North American 16's, Severskys, Martins, and something that looks like a Douglas DC-2 and DC-3. Two types of Italian planes were being produced as well as adaptations of German Junkers, Heinkel 112's, and Dorniers.

In addition I know that some sixty Nazi pilots with mechanics and crews were in Japan when war broke. They had come across Siberia with something less than 100 Messerschmitts just before Hitler made his fatal mistake of trying to smash Stalin with a double-cross to the chin.

At the time war broke, we knew Japan had about 6000 aircraft, including some American Brewster Buffaloes and some Curtiss pursuits given them by the Germans—planes the Nazis captured in Norway and Belgium. Of these 6000 planes about 4500 were available for some kind of military and naval activity. Military and naval experts throughout the Far East stated knowingly that Japan would keep at least 2000 of these planes at home to protect the wide-open Japanese cities from enemy bombings.

About three weeks prior to Pearl Harbor I had it on what I considered the best available authority from inside Japan that the Japanese were manufacturing some 1000 aircraft each month. Without even trying the Japanese could put operational planes in the air anywhere in East Asia with a numerical superiority of at least two to one. And they did.

From what I was able to gather from Japanese publications and from Jap officers who questioned me, after the war began Japan held back on aircraft production until it was discovered what new types of planes the Americans were going to throw at them. By the end of 1943 the Japs had begun again to produce as many as 1200 planes each month, with Premier General Hideki Tojo demanding more and more from Mitsubishi and other aircraft producers.

Against this numerically superior Japanese airforce the United States Navy pilots fulfilled the tradition of the Navy in the way they handled the few planes they had—mostly PBYs (Consolidated Flying boats of the "Catalina" type).

How Admiral Thomas C. Hart of the U.S. Far East fleet at the last minute hid five flying boats in the marshes near Manila for the final "withdrawal" of his staff is one of the best illustrations of the Army-Navy helplessness in air defense.

After nearly all of our Army and Navy planes had been bombed and strafed on the ground and shot out of the air, Admiral Hart had no alternative but to hide the few bombers he had left. In the air they were nothing but setups for the speedy Zeros. Just as the Admiral was ready to send his staff out to the Netherlands East Indies in these planes, Japanese espionage found the secret hideout and a few Japanese fighters dropped down over the hideout and destroyed two of the five planes. The Admiral ordered his staff out in two remaining planes, requesting that the third stand by.

When finally the question arose as to whether Admiral Hart would go in the last plane, and after he virtually had decided to stay behind with the sinking Philippines, his staff officers told him they'd "Shanghai" him before they'd let him stay. But when the Admiral learned that the instrument board of the remaining PBY had been completely shot away, and that the plane would have to be flown by dead reckoning, he decided to go in the remaining submarine. Admiral Hart is an old-time submariner. But if he had any misgivings about the instrumentless PBY pilot and crew making the Netherlands Indies on dead reckoning, they were dispelled later, for the Catalina was resting at anchor in the Surabaya harbor several days before he arrived in his sub.

VII

THERE was no need to worry about Filipino morale from the first. Out in the provinces, when the first Japanese bombers went over, the Filipinos stood and watched. When the planes dropped bombs these provincial people stayed where they were and shook their fists skyward. In the city the people, watching the white anti-aircraft puffs, often placed bets on whether the bombs would hit their objectives.

Nor was there any need to worry about Filipino reactions to Japanese propaganda. Japanese planes slipped through some of the interceptor lines and dropped leaflets on small villages as well as on the major towns and Manila. Most of the leaflets were printed in the dialect of the province in which they were dropped. They appealed to the Filipinos to turn against the United States. One leaflet text I saw was in the English of a Japanese movie comic. It read:

"The way to permanent peace. Causing this conflict between the Japanese and the United States is a Roosevelt attempt to curve [sic] our independence. Our mission is to end this as fast as possible and in order to accept this aim we should co-operate with Japan whole."

The dialect leaflets made much more sense. But the Filipino wasn't ripe to accept this propaganda. It made most of them mad. The police gathered as many of the leaflets as possible. In the provinces the people themselves brought them in and showed them to the local police.

The first big problem which faced the Civilian Emergency Administration of the Philippines was that of fifth-column activities. While there was nothing like the situation in Norway, Holland, Greece, or Crete, official Army headquarters statements and eye-witness accounts of fifth-column work showed that during the first few invasion attempts enemy planes were led directly to their military objectives by flares and lights at night and by fires and arrows in the daytime.

Of the 27,000 Japanese who were in the 7,083 Philippine Islands at the beginning of the war, more than 17,000 of them were in the southern islands, with the greatest concentration at Davao on Mindanao, the second largest island.

The first reports I had from Army-Navy headquarters at Davao —a Navy aircraft tender was down there when the first surprise air attack came—was that alleged Japanese farmer-fishermen at Davao had organized to take over the community. The Japanese had planned to capture Davao and the small airfield there. This would have given them a base from which to operate out of their eastern mandated islands and also would cut off the Philippines from the south.

But despite a dawn bombing raid the first day of the war which caught two Navy PBY Catalinas on the water and resulted in the death of a Navy ensign, the Japanese didn't act quickly enough. Hero number one of the United States Philippine forces in the Far East was a Filipino soldier named Castillo. Acting on his own that morning he had sensed what was about to take place. He collected all the male Filipino residents he could find, armed them, and proceeded to assume official control of Davao. He rounded up Japanese leaders and generally took over, until Lieutenant Colonel Roger Hillsman and his forces in the vicinity got to the spot and relieved him. Castillo received the war's first high commendation from General MacArthur's headquarters.

Many other Filipinos distinguished themselves in defense of their islands. One of these, a lieutenant in the Air Corps, who had had the least number of flying hours in his pursuit interceptor squadron, knocked out the first Japanese plane known to be shot down by a Filipino. That was the first plane reported at headquarters as "officially down." Then a Philippine division at Lingayen Gulf and at the town of Lingayen itself was the first force to block and drive off primary Japanese landing units. That was during the first week of the war.

The way the Filipinos reacted during this period definitely shows that American colonial administration during forty-two years in the Philippines was, at least, partially successful. The Filipino was of greater aid to our forces than the natives of any other Far Eastern colonial empire were to the forces of their mother country. The way he reacted under fire, and the way he reacted when later the Jap occupied his islands should be indicative of what he's going to do when the American returns.

VIII

WHILE the war was still new I drove out one morning through the peaceful Philippine farm country at dawn, just in time to hear the crowing of awakening roosters drowned in the roar of airplane motors . . . just in time to catch a glimpse of swift pursuit planes with pointed noses streaking over the rice paddies and angling skyward into the sunrise. They were headed on a special mission over the Japanese invasion position to the north.

Out at a country interceptor base I soon caught in full the pace of the Far East war. It was a 400-mile-an-hour pace. The quiet countryside was only a camouflage. I realized it was there with all its verdancy, its gray water carabao, its muddy rice paddies, its slow-moving Filipino farmer. But it seemed unreal. It seemed a hazy backdrop for the droning, bullet-scarred planes and sweating, wisecracking pilots who whipped down out of the blue sky with stories of death —terse, straightforward official reports of missions accomplished, comrades lost, Japanese stupidity and smashing, brilliant Japanese-German strategy and aerial combat tactics.

Here it was that the first lessons were learned on how the Pacific war was going to be fought. From this base came the reports of the first island landings. Here it was that our air strategists got their first hints on how they would have to come back, as they did later at Guadalcanal, and the Gilberts, and the Marshalls, and as they finally will in the Philippines.

An interceptor base in the Far East was no place for anyone with a weak heart. There were no warning devices for attacks by enemy planes. And if the enemy attacked there was no defense against it except a few 30-caliber machine guns on the ground. The Japs had nearly everything their own way. That is what got everybody. What I saw at Clarke Field of destruction of United States planes and constant surprise attacks would make any aircraft defense production worker weep.

The first time I went up to Fort Stotsenberg and Clarke Field I arrived only shortly after the surprise bombing that destroyed most of our B-17 Flying Fortresses of the 19th Bombardment Group on the ground. The pilots and crews were still groggy from having lost so many planes and crew members without having lifted the ships off the field. What hurt them so much was to have flown these planes all the way out to the Far East planning to bomb Formosa and the Hainan Islands "if and when" war broke. And then, due to some stupid technicality, they were cheated out of the first and only chance to crack at the Japs. And on top of that to lose the planes and their crews!

The next time I stopped there was about a week later, when Jack Percival, aviation editor of the *Sydney* (Australia) *Morning Herald*, and I were hurrying back to Manila after nearly being caught by a Japanese patrol which had slipped behind our irregular northern jungle line. Or perhaps we had got out ahead of our withdrawing forces. I never knew which. We'd been up a narrow mountain road in a jeep, looking for one of General Wainwright's Filipino battalions. Our driver Sancho began to get fidgety and wanted to go back. "I think there are no soldiers up this far," he kept saying.

It did seem strange that we hadn't run into any Filipinos along the two-rut single-track road. And besides I had come to have a great deal of respect for Sancho's knowledge and judgment. (Sancho, of course, is not his real name, for he did not get out.) He was the Filipino driver who had come with the car which I had rented, and more than once he had given me valuable advice in his unobtrusive manner. So we turned back. About a mile along the return trail the road took a series of meandering turns as it dropped down to the swampy plain. I'll never know why—and I don't think he will either —but just as we got down the valley to the last turn Sancho stopped. He ran the jeep over the edge of the road, and got out.

"I think I take a look around this turning, Seer," he said. He walked about 100 feet. Suddenly he stood still and motioned downward with his hands behind his back.

"Into the ditch," Percival warned. It's lucky for us we moved as quickly as we did.

In what seemed less than a minute I could see shadowy figures emerging from the jungle on our side of the road. Sancho just stood watching them.

"Japs . . ." whispered Jack.

If he said anything else I couldn't have heard it. My heart was thumping too hard! Here was our first close-up of the enemy.

Fortunately Sancho was not in his driver's uniform. He wore old greasy pants and a torn short-sleeved polo shirt. We'd been wading in the mud earlier in the day. And Sancho looked like any other Filipino who might have been walking along the road.

The Japs had on camouflaged jungle uniforms. In the fishnet over their helmets they had fastened green twigs and bamboo leaves. Their rifles were slung over their shoulders and each one of them carried a long *machete* or *bolo* that looked like an executioner's blade. But it had a peculiar sharp hook at the head. These Japs moved almost noiselessly out of the jungle. The leader raised his hand. He spoke to Sancho. Sancho just bowed slightly and shrugged his shoulders. The Jap turned his back.

Then was when my heart really pounded. Which way were the Japs going to turn? Would they turn up the road? If they did they couldn't miss the jeep just over the edge. And they couldn't miss us. But this patrol wasn't using roads. The leader hit off across jungle again. We counted as fifty-two shadows moved across the road . . . each with its razor-edged *bolo*. When the last one had crossed, we continued to lie low for another twenty minutes until Sancho again appeared from around the bend.

Not one of us said a word. We pushed the jeep back up on the road and then pushed it for about half a mile more before starting the engine.

"What did he say to you, Sancho?" Jack and I asked the question almost in the same breath after we had started the jeep up again.

"I do not know, Seer. But he was trying to speak Tagalog. If I had tried to answer, he perhaps take me with him for a guide."

"But, Sancho," I pressed, "how did you happen to stop back there to go and see what was around the bend in the road?"

"There is no way to tell, Seer, but I have just a feeling in my stomach, like once before when my house was burned down and I did not go to look. This time I say to myself, 'Sancho, you had better take one look.' "

Thus it was we stopped at Stotsenberg to report what we'd seen. And while we were so close to Clarke Field where a few of the Flying Forts were still operating we thought we'd see how the "truck drivers," as this 19th Bombardment gang called themselves, were getting along.

The war up to then had been such a whirlwind of activity with pursuit pilots doing most of the early fighting, by intercepting the Jap bombers, that Jack and I wanted to get some stories on what our bomber crews—or what was left of them—were doing.

We'd exchanged the jeep we'd borrowed for our own car and had just driven up to the hangar that was serving as the field control tower, when a coverall-clad figure waved frantically from the top of the hangar, and began to shinny and slide down a series of ladders to the ground.

"Bombing attack . . . bombing attack . . ." he shouted.

I looked around the horizon and listened for the hum of the Japanese engines, but instead of a hum there suddenly came a roar. The twin-engined light bombers were coming in fast and very low in a surprise attack.

"Pick a hole near the target . . . that's the safest place," shouted the man in coveralls, and dove under an unfinished concrete hangar foundation, part of the building program scheduled to get the Philippines ready to defend themselves against the Japs in 1942. I followed quickly, with Jack right behind me.

There were only nine of these bombers. They unloaded everything right down the middle of the runway and across what was left of two hangars at the far end of the field. Then they came back and strafed everything, setting fire to four bamboo dummy Flying Forts that had been parked in the cane fields to draw off Japanese fire.

The British had used clever Chinese bamboo workers down in Singapore for the same purpose—to deceive anyone from a distance as to the number of aircraft actually at the base. When I'd examined the bamboo planes at Singapore only three months before I had been astounded at their likeness to the actual planes they represented.

Some enlisted men ran out of hangars with 30-caliber machine guns and fired at the bombers, but no luck that afternoon, except that none of our men were killed and not one of the few precious planes we had hid on the cane field on the opposite end from the bamboo planes was hit. Of course the field itself was in pretty bad shape. But the boys were out with tractors and bulldozers almost before the Japs had lined away toward the coast.

We climbed out from under the cement foundation and found Sancho inching out from beneath the car. I'd told him a hundred times not to hide under the car when we were being bombed or strafed. But he always tried to explain that he had to be on hand to protect it if it caught on fire. Lieutenant Sam Maddux from Oklahoma, who'd been under the foundation with us, was getting a laugh out of Sancho's explanation when a captain came up.

"Where are those duds?" he asked the Lieutenant.

"Oh, the duds, Captain," replied Maddux as though he had mislaid his cigarette. "Oh, they're right here."

He walked about 20 feet to the place where we had been standing looking at the Japanese bombers as they hedge-hopped away. I knew that a percentage of Japanese bombs don't go off, but it gave me a funny feeling to realize I'd been standing practically on top of one of them.

In one area we found more than thirty duds, some from previous bombings. According to the ordnance experts these bombs were poorly constructed, but deadly stuff when they exploded. They had three rows of three-quarter-inch rivets that shot out like bullets. These bombs weighing 30 to 50 and 100 to 500 pounds were double-purpose missiles: to destroy the physical objective and "counter personnel" anyone within range.

The ground crews in the Philippines worked twenty-four hours a day with no protection, no proper tools, and in dirty field tents or bamboo machine shops where grit covered every part taken out of a plane. They were the real heroes of the 19th Bombardment gang, the 31st Pursuit, and all the others. Since we had only a dwindling number of serviceable planes, it was these ground crews who miraculously kept as many planes in the air as there were. Less determined men would have said, "The hell with it, we're not going to get any replacements. Why fix 'em up with bailing wire. They just fall apart and will kill the pilot anyway." But you never heard a word like that. You did, though, hear plenty of plain and fancy talk about the Congressmen and Senators and Isolationists and Pacifists at home who tied up armament appropriations, and who bucked arming the Philippines, Guam, and the rest of the Far East.

IX

I PICK the afternoon of December 24, 1941, as the beginning of the end in the Philippines because it was that afternoon, following a particularly heavy noonday bombing, that President Manuel Quezon was sent out to Corregidor. Within a few hours both Francis B. Sayre, High Commissioner to the Philippines, and General Douglas MacArthur followed Quezon.

The full Quezon-Sayre-MacArthur families went along, taking with them a small, picked coterie of friends whom these officials didn't want to leave at the mercy of the occupying Japanese.

The aerial bombardment that noon was a careful, unhurried placement of bombs across the port area and over Nichols Field. Silver

Japanese twin-engined planes floated in unobstructed. A few low-caliber anti-aircraft guns coughed at the planes and the black flak explosions showed harmlessly beneath their targets. It is history that after the first few days we had nothing left in the way of interceptor aircraft that could even touch the Japanese, and the only anti-craft that could get up anywhere near the enemy were at Corregidor, 30 miles away.

No sooner had the planes droned away in perfect formation than Marjorie noticed several trucks and a large limousine pull up before a landing float next to the Manila Hotel. We hustled down to the float. There was the Quezon family. President Quezon was in a USAFFE (United States Armed Forces Far East) uniform with a helmet slanted on the back of his head. Servants hurried to and from the float carrying family belongings—even a parrot went along with them.

Jorge Vargas, Quezon's executive secretary and righthand man, was there to bid his chief *adios*. Marjorie and I were the only non-Filipinos present. Quezon was nervous, and when he's nervous he shouts. He shouted his farewells to a few Filipino USAFFE officers who remained on shore and walked slowly with Vargas to his private speedboat.

Quezon talked incessantly. He was at his most eloquent peak during those final Manila moments. He didn't want to leave. Yet he was convinced it was the right thing to do. He didn't want to walk out on his colleagues or his countrymen. Yet like heads of European states who were faced with the same problem before him, he felt he was compelled to go. He still had a job to do as President. Someone had to go to help prepare the way overseas for the return of a free government.

A brief handshake, the roar of the speedboat's engine and President Manuel Quezon, the Philippines' most influential citizen, was gone for the duration. Vargas watched for a minute, then slowly walked back up the gangway to the shore. A few USAFFE officers and weeping Quezon family servants stood around not knowing what to do.

"Well, what's next?" I asked Vargas.

"I wish I knew," he replied. "But whatever it is, it looks like it's going to be for a long time." He shook his head slowly. "I suppose you'll be going out there soon?" He nodded toward Corregidor.

"I don't know," I told him. "Certainly not as long as communications hold out."

"Well, some of us have to stay," he noted a little bitterly. "I've got more to do now than I know how." He paused. "I guess I'll be seeing you—some time."

"The ship's beginning to go down," Marjorie said to me as we walked back to the hotel. But neither one of us voiced what each knew the other was thinking. Would we get away? And if not—what then? What was going to happen to us?

When the American Government—General MacArthur in particular—saw that the Philippines couldn't be defended against the growing sweep of the early Japanese military wave, an effort was made to leave the political-civilian situation in a position that would not bring harm to thousands of defenseless Filipinos. In effect, General MacArthur and President Quezon told Jorge Vargas and other Filipino leaders left behind:

"Go ahead. Do the best you can. Make what bargains you have to with these people. Try to keep the Philippines (17,000,000 people) together in one piece. Try to protect the people from Japanese brutality and avarice. You'll have some tough decisions to make. But the job must be done. Do it for the future Philippines."

Vargas became Mayor of Greater Manila and finally was appointed by the Japanese as Chairman of the Philippines Executive Commission. This Commission was liaison between the Japanese military occupational forces and the Filipino people.

To the best of my knowledge, as the Commision's Chairman Vargas did everything possible to cushion the blows struck at the Filipinos by the arrogant Japanese military. Vargas made many speeches. He was forced to. They sounded pro-Japanese. They had to.

As I interpreted Vargas' position, someone had to be chairman of the commission. That someone might just as well have been Vargas instead of another Filipino who was openly pro-Japanese—for instance, José Laurel. The fact that Laurel, not Vargas, was chosen by the Japanese military as the "President" of the puppet Jap-Filipino "independent" state indicates that Vargas was not a Japanese choice. Vargas was not even Chairman of the "Independence Constitutional Convention"—the Filipino group backed by the Japanese and maneuvered into signing what was merely a dictated, camouflaged constitution.

The fact that Vargas was picked by the Japanese as the first Filipino Ambassador to Japan is also in Vargas' favor. Why did they want him in Japan if it were not that they did not trust him and wanted him out of the Philippines where his influence was felt?

Before taking him to Japan the Japanese "invited" two of Vargas' sons to study in Japan, taking them along with a group of other Filipino boys. Neither the boys nor their parents had any choice in this matter.

To my way of thinking, all this is circumstantial evidence in Vargas' favor. What Vargas has done for the Philippines of his own free will and what he has been forced into doing by the Japanese Military Administration of course will always be a question in the minds of millions of Filipinos and Americans. The same goes for others on the Executive Commission and Independence Preparatory Commission. That José Laurel, "New Philippines" Japanese-picked President, and Benigno Aquino, head of the Kalibapi, Jap-Filipino co-operation political group, are Quislings, there seems little doubt in anyone's mind. These two became marked men the moment they began to play openly with the Japs.

X

LATE that same afternoon on returning from watching the Quezon departure for Corregidor I went over to Cavite to see Admiral Rockwell, who had just come out before the fighting started to take over the 16th Naval District. I wanted to see if the Japanese had done any severe damage in their morning bombing.

The Admiral was in khaki, wearing a tin helmet. His single star was the only thing that marked him from the hundreds of other unshaved, dust-covered men at the Navy Yard. We found a spot under a tree near a shallow drainage ditch which would make a fair foxhole in case the Japs came back for another surprise raid, as they often did. We were almost directly beneath the huge radio towers—a favorite Japanese target.

The Admiral told me, off the record, about the naval situation. It was pretty gloomy in the air and on the water.

"I'm moving the station to Olongapo, up the Bataan coast," he told me.

Everything was moving. He didn't need to tell me that. I knew from the questions asked by the officers who hurried informally past and by the orders given. The general activity in the yard showed that a move was imminent.

The Japanese were landing just down the Batangas coast on the west side of Luzon. The line around Manila Bay was tightening; the fight for Manila was just about over. No one would admit it; no one did. But when you looked at it carefully, there it was. One hundred and twenty-five thousand men, mostly untrained Filipinos, scattered from Luzon to Mindanao; less than 50 aircraft left that could be used even for spare parts; a few ancient destroyers; a couple of mother ships and enough arms and ammunition to put up a pretty fair fight at Bataan and Corregidor, and the rock-island Fort Drum (Battleship Rock).

Mulling this over as Sancho careened back to the city to catch MacArthur's late afternoon press conference at Fort Santiago USAFFE headquarters, it looked pretty black. I knew now that MacArthur's steady assertion that somehow, some way, reinforcements—especially air reinforcements—could be got into the Philippines was merely public eyewash.

Previously I had gone over to Air Corps headquarters at Fort McKinley and helped to plot out a ferry route for aircraft—from Australia to Mindanao across southern New Guinea and the fringe of the Netherlands East Indies, as well as a second and longer route through Java and Borneo to Del Monte, the central Mindanao field. I had been across sections of the route before, and Jack Percival, who went with me to headquarters, knew most of the fields, their condition, length, and radio facilities. Jack and I had both been in and out of the Indies for the past two years, and Jack had been particularly close to the Dutch Royal Airmail Line organization.

Both Jack and I were amazed at the necessity of our being called on for such information because we had seen the United States mission in Java, the mission which was sent out for the express purpose of mapping these air routes to Australia. This mission, which included Colonel Les Maitland, the well-known Hawaii flier, should have returned to Manila from the Indies with definite information on each base. It certainly seemed to Pervical and me that if we, as civilians, knew what we did about the Netherlands East Indies bases, these American Army men who were in the Indies on a special mission should have known more.

Colonel George, later General, who was killed in an air accident with Mel Jacoby in Australia, was furious over the lack of knowledge of these routes by his own officers. Colonel George even invited Percival to make the first reconnaissance flight to Australia and to return when the first aircraft were brought back. But Jack refused. He and I both knew there weren't any aircraft available in

Australia for the Philippines. And Colonel George never sent the flight because we lost most of our airplanes on the ground due to some sort of bungling between MacArthur's headquarters at Fort Santiago and the operational fields.

Not only was there no aircraft available in Australia to send to the Philippines, but there was not even enough to help Singapore or the Indies themselves. Air Marshal Brooke-Popham's sliding airforce just didn't slide, because the airforce consisted of less than 1200 fighting planes of every description in the entire Far East. What's more, there were no planes available from the Middle East where Rommel was keeping us busy. Tojo had us outnumbered in the air at least three to one.

When I arrived at MacArthur's press conference Major Le Grand Diller, the press relations officer, was reading a list of names. Major Carlos Romulo, editor of the *Manila Herald* and Filipino press officer, was there talking to Marjorie. "Diller's called your name with four others," she told me. "He wants to see you privately in the next room. This is it."

The thirty-odd Filipino and local Manila reporters stood around waiting to see what was going to happen. The four others whom Diller had asked for were already in the next room—Hammond of Reuter's, Frank Hewlett of UP, Ray Cronin of AP, and Mel Jacoby of *Time* and *Life*. We all knew what was coming. Diller was brief.

"The General is leaving for the forward echelon just before six o'clock tonight. The time has come to leave Manila. The General has asked the five of you accredited correspondents to accompany him. What about it?"

"What's the forward echelon—Corregidor?" Jacoby asked.

"Never mind. Do you want to go?"

"What will our filing facilities be?" I asked.

"The General won't guarantee any filing facilities, but he'll do his best to help you all he can."

There were other questions. We tried to find out just how serious the situation was in Manila at the moment; when the Japanese were expected and whether we could get out to Corregidor later if we waited until the local communications facilities failed. Diller was uncommunicative and in a hurry. We all decided to pass up the invitation for the moment, but told him we wanted a raincheck for transportation across with the last officers who would leave the city, whenever that might be.

Actually it turned out to be one week later when communications facilities were demolished by our own forces. A Reuter's man, not

Hammond, and Hewlett were the only ones who were able to take advantage of the Army transport offer. Clark Lee went for the Associated Press and the Jacobys went with him on the night of December 31. My plans misfired.

XI

CHRISTMAS EVE at the Manila Hotel in the air-conditioned Winter Garden dining room was a pretty glum affair. The room was sandbagged, of course, and smelled heavily of damp sand. A Filipino orchestra grimly played gay music alongside a gigantic Christmas tree which had been brought down from Baguio for the celebration.

Marjorie and I came down late and sat at a table with some PBY pilots who had just delivered a squadron of Catalinas to the Netherlands Indies and were waiting for a clipper to ferry them home when war broke. Most of them had been ferrying across the Atlantic and some had delivered planes to Australia. Now it looked as though they were caught. The Army didn't want them; the Navy said they couldn't take them as the boys were civilians.

No one had much appetite in Manila on that Christmas Eve of 1941. When the newspapers and local radio announcements revealed the official transfer of headquarters to "the forward echelon"—obviously the depths of Corregidor—many a Christmas Eve dinner was left untouched. Then suddenly had come President Roosevelt's promise "to redeem the Philippines," before the average Filipino knew that he had lost anything, or the average American guessed that things were nearly so bad as that. Marjorie and I ate little, and went up to bed. But our rest was fitful for we were routed out several times during the night by bombings—Christmas presents from the Japs.

When the American woke up the next morning to the fact that he might need some money in the future, and finally got down to the bank to get it, he found all the banks were closed "for the holiday season." And they never reopened. The money went out to Corregidor for transfer by submarines to the United States.

Christmas Day we took what was probably the worst bombing the Japanese laid on the city. They plastered a small projection into the harbor called Engineer's Island, and they roared in and out with more than 100 planes of all descriptions (even four-engined seaplanes). At that stage 100 aircraft were a lot of planes to use in a single Far East operation.

During part of that bombardment Marjorie and I were on our stomachs on the floor in the office of Dr. Heunder, Netherlands Consul General. He had been depending upon us for some of the latest news developments and we had been hoping he'd be able to tell us before it was too late that the Dutch were sending a plane after him and we would be able to get seats. Whenever we went to see him his office boy would hand each of us a tin helmet which we kept at our elbow for any emergency, as the Manila air-raid warning system was a total failure. More often than not the planes would be overhead dropping bombs before the sirens sounded.

On our return that day we expected to find the Manila Hotel a shambles, but the Japs were extremely accurate in their bombings. They wanted to take the city as intact as possible. They bombed all along the port area, hitting their objectives pretty successfully. There was no indiscriminate bombing of the city despite that erroneous impression. The Santo Domingo Church and walled city sectors that were hit, along with other residential areas which caught the brunt of the destruction, were adjacent to military objectives.

Back in the Manila Hotel we tried to get something to eat. Eating was a growing problem in Manila at that time. Everything was closed except a couple of small restaurants and the dining rooms of the Manila and Bayview Hotels. Many Manila residents, anticipating food shortages and the siege of the city by the Japs, moved into the hotels. Hundreds of people moved into the city and the hotels from the outlying mining country—many with exciting stories of close escapes.

The Manila Hotel management and the Filipino boys there carried on calmly, despite some hysteria on the part of a few of the guests. The Manila Hotel had the only cellar which might even be termed an air-raid shelter in all of Manila. You could always get something to munch on and take it down to the shelter with you if necessary.

That noon, during what turned out to be only a breather between heavy raids, we went into the open dining room facing onto the bay. Admiral Thomas C. Hart walked in with us. We kidded about our Christmas dinner of a cheese sandwich and a glass of milk.

We no sooner had our sandwiches in hand than Whump! Whump! Whump!—six heavy explosions spouted water all over the open side of the hotel and shook the place like a toy blockhouse. It seemed as if the whole building were coming down. Glass broke, guests were thrown off their feet, and general confusion reigned. As a human-reaction peculiarity under stress, I saw one guest run across the dance floor headed for the air-raid shelter carefully carrying a glass of water in each hand.

Marjorie, the Admiral, and I raced across the floor. We've had some argument since about who ran the fastest. The Admiral insists Marjorie was waiting for us pressed tightly against the cement wall by the main staircase when he and I finally got through the dining-room door. Perhaps so, but as I remember it the Admiral was a pretty fair sprinter himself and was not far behind.

The three of us stood there together during the rest of the raid, the Admiral in his crisp whites with his gold-encrusted cap under his arm. His face became livid. He was mad clear through because he didn't have any aircraft, any guns, anything he could throw against the Japs. What he said is unprintable, but it was the feeling all of us had—frustration.

During the week between Christmas and New Year's Day, the Army was concerned with snapping the tail of its southern tangent up through Manila and around to the north of Manila Bay into Bataan, meantime holding off the northern Japanese forces outside San Fernando where Clarke Field and Fort Stotsenberg were located, about 65 kilometers north of Manila. I went north and south that week. It was rearguard action all the way. Army engineers, mining engineers, in fact anyone who could plant a stick of dynamite or light a fuse was commandeered to delay the enemy.

Navy censorship was a continual nightmare. They were operating on rules from the last war. I was shown by Lieutenant Fritz Worcester regulations out of a Navy book dated 1918. My first broadcast under the new censorship was heartbreaking. Lieutenant Green monitored the broadcast—that is, he followed the script after speaking a key word to the Navy censor in the control room of a receiving station in the United States. At the slightest deviation from the script he was under orders to flip a key which would take me off the air immediately. All broadcasts were under the same regulations.

No sooner had the broadcast started than an air-raid siren screamed. However, air raids were not official until announced by Army communiqué. I glanced out of the window and I could see Japanese planes already overhead. This was early in the fighting and we still had interceptor aircraft.

The P-40's were up among bombers and Zeros. Anti-aircraft

bursts were everywhere. Bombs came down into near-by gasoline dumps with terrific whumps. What a perfect setup for an ad-lib broadcast! I looked at Lieutenant Green and eyebrowed toward the air fight. He shook his head and pointed to the copy. I was to finish the written script or be cut off the air.

All I could do was pause now and then when there was a particularly heavy bomb explosion or when some of the planes roared a few hundred feet over the studio roof in low level attacks. I cursed my luck. If this had only been the day before.

This broadcasting studio in the penthouse of the Life Theater Building finally got too uncomfortable for continual use. There was too much air activity near by, and a couple of times during broadcasts, bombings, falling plaster, and other disturbances, including the roof being strafed, made me feel that the better part of valor was to move. I talked it over with Tom Worthen, a local Manilan who was broadcasting for CBS over the same outlet (KZRM), and we decided to move Mutual and Columbia over to the Wilson Building, where Navy Censorship had established its office, deep in the basement. The best place in town. The building was of reinforced concrete. We couldn't get a spot in the basement, but the building management found us a small room on the sixth floor. Bert Silen, local KZRH (NBC) manager, had already moved over.

What we did was to move out of the strafing area right into the middle of the bombing area. The Japanese soon began to bomb some inter-island steamers tied up to the shore quays along the Passig River, just opposite and about half a block from us.

I got the last broadcast out of Manila from the little room in the Wilson Building. By this time—December 31—all the Army and Navy people had left the city. As far as we were officially concerned Manila was an open city. As far as we civilians were concerned it was wide open. The Japs were only a few miles out.

The last three broadcasts I made were virtually uncensored. The people the regular Navy left inside the city were given their "honorable discharge" from the Navy. They were the civilians who had been reserve officers, or they had enlisted to help in censorship or communications at the outbreak. Most of them were sore at being left behind. They all wanted to go out to Corregidor. But space was limited on Corregidor and only trained fighting men were wanted. It seemed ironic, at the moment, to see these men who had been so intent in their war activity in uniform one day, and at the end lolling around nervously wondering just what attitude the incoming Japs would take toward their "honorable discharge" papers.

These were the men who half-heartedly went over my last script. The man who monitored the last broadcast almost held up the script at the last minute because he wasn't sure it was all right to mention the fact that Hong Kong had fallen. But after much argument I convinced him the world knew about the fall of Hong Kong—and especially the Japanese, to whom he was sure this information would give comfort.

Then during the broadcast, the city was bombed. The men at the RCA transmitter on the outskirts of the city left the transmitter and ran for their shelters. The section of the city where the ships were moored near the Wilson Building caught it again. The lights in the small studio room went out, but somehow the other electric connections held. I had to ad lib part of the broadcast in the dark, with the building shaking from the bombs dropping about a block away. That was the last one. Within a short time the U.S. Army special demolition crew dynamited all radio transmitters, and cut the cable connections with the outside. Manila was finished.

XII

LAW and order in Manila during the days preceding the occupation was sporadic and phenomenal. One minute looting was permitted by the authorities; the next minute anyone with a parcel under his arm was suspect.

Manila had been declared an open city, but no unified plan of action had actually been agreed upon. If it were an open city, as the Army alleged but the Japanese refused to admit, then there was no need for a blackout. Half the city was blazing with lights; the other half was black. Filipino policemen and armed, self-appointed air-raid wardens went around shooting at windows showing lights or at anyone who lighted a cigarette on the street. Actually your life wasn't worth a paper peso if you were outside at night.

But Marjorie and I had to go out, for I had nightly broadcasts. One night on our way to the studio, bullets ricocheted off the pavement under the car as we skidded to a stop and waited for a policeman to examine our credentials. Our driver never batted an eye. He bawled out the policeman in Tagalog, the policeman apologized, and we drove on through the darkened streets waiting for the next "halt" and accompanying shots.

"What did you tell that policeman?" I asked Sancho.

"I tell him, Seer, he should be ashamed to stopping anyone so important as us. I tell him you are making the radio talk to people in the United States. I tell him you going to get help to drive Japanese out. He say he very sorry, Seer."

The atmosphere in Manila these last days was as heavy as the oppressive, muggy heat. This ominous sluggishness was cleared only momentarily by such electric movements as great mobs suddenly scenting loot, or the milling street crowds scattering to escape low-level bombing attacks.

There was no business going on. All stores were boarded up. The people wandered about visiting their friends, packing their belongings, starting to move out of the city, then changing their minds and coming back. Thousands just sat on their doorsteps or along the bay parkways on their heels, stoically waiting. Their ancestors had watched Spanish *conquistadores*, their fathers had seen Americans invade their islands, and now—*quién sabe?*—they were waiting for the next invader—the Jap.

The ominous feeling was accentuated by the dark smoke pall from great oil and gasoline fires. At least five great swirling smoke plumes rose from the scuttled oil reservoirs and streamed toward Corregidor where they were joined by the larger pillar from the Cavite fire. Marjorie and I had watched this fire—caused by the ignition of gasoline drums—send great arms of flame into the night sky the evening of December 26 when it had begun with a terrific explosion. We had stood in the driveway of the Manila Hotel and looked across the bay over 12 miles of water. We could hear explosion after explosion. The great pillar of flame lighted the whole city of Manila. That was a week past. The smoke from this fire and from others that were set at about the same time enveloped the city for more than two weeks. The sun was completely blotted out, and the heat from the rising fires created an atmospheric condition that often brought a gentle rain drizzle. This accentuated the smell of burning oil and through it all filtered fine oil-saturated raindrops that covered us with tiny grease spots. Everything we touched was smeared with oil.

Japanese bombers roared down low through the smoke and Zeros skimmed over the rooftops, sometimes firing short, clearing bursts from their guns—warnings of what would happen if anyone fired at them. The Japs sought to put the fear of Hirohito into the hearts of Manila residents. It wasn't so much fear of Hirohito as it was waiting for the Japanese to come into the city and take over. That got you. And among the women there was a constant question in back of their minds: "Will it be a second rape of Nanking?"

During this period I rid myself of all incriminating evidence that could be used against me by the Japs, knowing full well that as a correspondent I would be particularly suspect. So Marjorie and I had our own private "demolition." We had our own little bonfire in the wash basin and toilet bowl in our bathroom at the Manila Hotel. Among the material we burned was a complete book manuscript. I had been working on it for the six months past, all around the circuit from Australia and the South Pacific up through the Netherlands East Indies, Malaya, Burma, Free China, and finally I had put the finishing touches to it in the Philippines. It was about the Japanese attitude toward the white man, about Japanese plans for supremacy in the Pacific, and it had the same title as this: *So Sorry, No Peace*.

It took three days to burn my manuscript. We burned and burned until the porcelain bowls cracked with the heat and the room boys came in to see where all the smoke in the hall was coming from. We would wait for the bowls to cool, then would start over again.

Why didn't we use the hotel incinerator? War was on and anyone who was seen trying to burn papers or records was immediately under suspicion as an enemy agent. A friend of ours had decided to get rid of his social security card and a few other documents he felt it not wise for the Japs to find on him. He went out in back of the hotel and had no sooner struck a match than two Filipino constables jumped on him. He spent the greater part of three hours trying to get out of jail where he had been taken on an espionage charge.

The morning of January 1 I heard of the open looting down at the port area where the bonded warehouse and other sheds were thrown open to the Filipinos by the police. Carl Mydans, photographer for *Time* and *Life*, Jack Percival, and I went down to the piers with Sancho. We knew before we were within a quarter of a mile that the looting was being done on a big scale, for thousands of Filipinos were streaming toward the docks, and other thousands in laden horsecarts or pulling small overloaded wooden wheelbarrows were hurrying away to dump their loot and return for more.

More than 40,000 Filipinos, most of them small shopkeepers and average citizens, pulled off the best organized major looting job in history!

Thousands were inside the sheds handing out loot which included everything from airplane gas tanks, boxes of spooled thread, unexposed moving picture film, talcum powder, and metal files containing ten years' back correspondence, to sulphuric acid boxes and "Superman" colored crayon cartoon booklets. There was anything and everything you could name. There were bolts of cloth from blue denim to silks and laces. There were new automobiles, motorcycles, and radios. Since there was no gasoline the Filipinos banded together and pushed the cars away.

Most of these people had no idea what they were getting. Many took articles merely for their bright colors. However, a few did believe things were going to be tough, and they carefully picked out cloth, automobiles, rubber tires, lumber, gasoline tins, and medicines.

There was no grabbing, no pulling and hauling. All was order, and quiet, beaverlike activity. Everyone seemed most polite and intent on helping the fellow next to him.

I noticed a little man in a bright blue cotton shirt, and a very bright green pair of slacks. He was sitting in the midst of a pile of straw hats that completely encircled him and came almost up to his waist.

"You've got a lot of hats there," I commented.

"You like them, Seer?" His smile was as brilliant as his clothes.

"They're very fine straw," I said, picking one up from the pile.

"You like, you take, Seer. Here." He picked up a pile that must have had a couple of dozen hats piled on top of each other, and thrust them toward me. I protested vigorously but he continued:

"You take, Seer. Plenty hats. Plenty for you. Plenty for me. Plenty for everyone. I can get plenty more. You take these. I get more." He put the hats down and turned to leave.

"You better not go away and leave these here," I warned him. "Someone is likely to take them. You better hang onto what you've got."

"Oh, but these will be here when I come back, Seer. This is my pile. No one will touch. See, there are other piles. When we take something out of the box and put here outside that means this something belongs to somebody."

I looked around and sure enough there were piles of all sizes containing all kinds of articles. No one seemed to be disturbing the piles. From time to time a Filipino would hustle up to one of the piles, lay something down and go off to hunt more loot. These were goods that had already been taken and were earmarked. Now and then a Filipino would gather up one of the piles and start for home, satisfied for the moment.

The warehouses and sheds were opened to the public bit by bit by the police in order to let them have these goods rather than leave them for the invading Japanese. Many old-time Manilans regarded this as a "scandalous procedure." But this was war—as they were to learn a few days later—and the enemy was a tough, greedy customer. It was much better to let the Filipinos get all they could, while they could. Why leave everything for the Japanese so that they could send it back to Japan?

Shortly before noon we heard the sound of sharp police whistles above the chatter of voices. A group of civilians from the High Commissioner's office appeared on the scene, as Police Chief Torres had said he was afraid to clear the looters out of the port area. With whistles and a little verbal persuasion the forty thousand-odd Filipinos left in as orderly a manner as they had come, and not a club or a firearm was in sight.

XIII

"STOP them! Stop them by any means you can. Sure, shoot if you have to."

Mydans, Percival, and I had gone directly to the High Commissioner's office from the port area looting, and had found Claude Buss in the midst of a most exciting telephone conversation.

"A group of self-appointed vigilantes have taken it upon themselves to blow up or somehow scuttle the Manila waterworks system and the light and power company," Claude told us after he had hung up. "They're a group of stupid, super patriots. They take the attitude: 'We'll be damned if we'll let the Japanese get hold of the water system or use electricity in Manila. We'll make it tough on the yellow bastards.'"

Obviously this group had gone off half-cocked, failing to take into consideration that 400,000 Filipinos would be streaming back into the city after the occupation. They had given no thought to what a city with no water would mean. They had not considered the danger of plague. Naturally they had to be stopped. A counter-vigilante group was formed and they were stopped—fortunately with no casualties.

Carl, Jack, and I had gone to see Claude to discuss with him some of the problems of internment such as food and sanitation, and what could be done before the Japs came into the city to prepare, through the media of the Red Cross, certain stores for use of the Americans, British, Dutch, and others. It was pretty evident that everyone was going to be interned. There had been a couple of very ragged meetings at the High Commissioner's office during the week. Certain old Manilans had wanted to be chairmen. There was no leadership at all. Claude did the best he could. He was executive assistant to Mr. Sayre and worked closely with Jorge Vargas.

It was also evident that the Japanese whom we had interned at the beginning of the war would have to be released. The roundup of these Japanese had begun immediately with the first airplane attack. Those who were known to be dangerous characters were bundled into trucks the first day and transported to internment camps. Those not so dangerous, and others who were felt to be pro-American, were put under house detention. Violence was not used except in instances where resistance to arrest had been encountered.

The Japanese who were in the Islands when war began had fully expected to be interned since they had been left there by their government for a purpose. This purpose had been to take over, occupy, and operate from the civilian side immediately upon the occupation by the military. Those who were not needed for use after occupation had been removed by special Japanese ships sent to Far Eastern ports in August and September 1941.

Those who were left behind were well treated when the time for their internment came. In all cases the Japanese women were offered a choice. They could remain in their homes, or they could accompany their men to camps. Most of the families went along with the men. A few schools had been used as places of internment, as was the Nippon Club with its green lawns and tennis courts. The internees were allowed to send some of their people out each day to the markets to buy the kind of food they particularly liked to be paid for by us.

When the time came to release the Japanese the questions to be answered were, "when and how?"—particularly in the light of the hatred of civilian Filipinos for the Japs. If the Japanese internees were held too long, however, it might lead to sharp retaliation against the Americans, British, and Dutch when counter-internment took place.

The interned Japanese counted on retaliation being meted out by their Army after the occupation. I happened to be at the Nippon Club the day the Japanese were released. One Jap said to me, "We expected our troops in one week earlier. It has been a long time. But your time will be longer. You cannot expect any help, any reinforcements from your government. It's too far away. It's too bad for you." He smiled. "So sorry—but now you will have your turn. You will have to suffer."

The problem which faced Buss and Vargas should have been made simpler by the Japanese Consul, Niro, with whom they conferred constantly that final week before the Japanese Army staffs preceded their troops into the city. But so far as I could ascertain very little progress was made through Niro. His attitude was typically Japanese. As a consular officer, naturally he could make no commitment for the incoming Army chiefs. He could, he said, "make suggestions" regarding the treatment of civilians to the occupying general, General Homma. But any suggestions made by a mere consular officer to a conquering general of the self-impressed, anti-foreign type represented by General Homma were of no value at all.

The best that could be done was to survey several likely areas for the concentration of nearly four thousand Americans, British, and Dutch, and submit this to the military administration through Niro. This, Buss told us, he had done. He had suggested Santo Tomás University as the place thought to be most suitable. However, knowing Japanese psychology, Buss had also submitted some other definitely unsuitable spots such as Rizal (open) Stadium and the Philippine University. But Buss knew the Japanese would want to use these places for themselves, which would leave Santo Tomás as their third choice, although unknown to them it was our first choice.

Another idea that Buss presented to the Japanese was that the Anglo-Americans be registered and then released within an area inside the city—a ghetto. If this was unsuitable to them he suggested (you always suggest, never recommend, to these arrogant officials) that the women, children, and aged be released and either allowed to return to their homes or be placed in some restricted area.

While the negotiations were going on prior to the occupation of Manila, Buss was at a great disadvantage for he was without any real authority. Also he was negotiating through a Japanese consular officer. He never knew whether Niro actually presented the plans to the military authority or not. And before any negotiations could be carried on with the military Buss and the other officials from the High Commissioner's office had been locked up under special house arrest, separated from the other civilians.

About the only success Buss could be said to have had in these negotiations was that his suggestion, that Santo Tomás University be used, bore fruit. Since the Catholic fathers accepted the idea and told the Japanese they were agreeable to the plan of using their university as a concentration center, the Japanese obviously used the line of least resistance.

XIV

"I CAN take you to the general, Seer."

"What general, Sancho?" I asked him, wondering for a moment if perhaps MacArthur had returned to the city. Major Diller, MacArthur's aide-de-camp, had come back on December 29 for a short time. Perhaps MacArthur was doing the same thing.

It was January 2 in the early afternoon. The Japanese still had not entered the city although our troops had been gone for more than a week. The reason Manila was not occupied earlier was because the Japanese High Command suspected a trap. I found this out from Japanese officers who interrogated me after my capture.

The people were on edge—just waiting, waiting. Rumors were plentiful. "The Japs will bayonet us; the Japs will rape; the Japs will torture." Both the Filipinos and Anglo-Americans were bewildered and fearful.

"I can take you to the general, Seer."

"What general, Sancho?"

"Why the Japanese general, Seer. He is in a schoolhouse. It is not far."

"But there is no more telegraph, Sancho. Everything has been blown up. I can't send a story. There is no need to see the general."

"My people are afraid, Seer. Perhaps if you see the general he will tell you what the Japanese will do to my people. Perhaps you can help my people."

"Okay, Sancho. Let's go."

My car had several official signs on it as well as a special police flag which had been issued to all the correspondents by Police Chief Torres as protection against overzealous local policemen. We were stopped twice by sentries. Sancho pointed to the Japanese characters that were pasted on our windshield. What they said and where he got them I didn't know. But we were passed through. Once we had to thread our way through a squadron of small yellow-green, 3-ton tanks apparently awaiting the order to move toward the city.

Finally we pulled up in front of a schoolhouse on a muddy cross-roads just outside the city. How Sancho knew where the headquarters building was I never found out. During the past month he had led me to many a good story. He was a good newsman, and like a good newsman he always protected his source.

At the steps of the little schoolhouse lounged several mud-spattered Japanese soldiers. Two of them stood on guard.

"This is it, Seer. The general, he is inside."

This was it, all right. And I wasn't liking the idea a little bit. Perhaps I could help his people? Well, perhaps I could. But perhaps I could get my neck in a noose, too. I had certainly stuck it out far enough. Well, there was nothing to do now but bluff it out. There was no turning back.

I had sense enough to bow to the sentries. I had learned that much in China. You always bow to the uniform of the Emperor. The sentries clomped to attention and bellowed something, but I paid no attention and kept right on going. As I stepped onto the porch a young Japanese officer stepped out of the door and in perfect American asked, "What are *you* doing here?"

Meantime the two sentries pulled up so close behind me I could feel their breath on the back of my neck and smell the three weeks' campaign sweat encasing them. I talked fast. I had to. Here I was. A civilian with no standing. Perhaps they would take me for a spy. I don't know why I hadn't thought of that before.

"I'm a newspaper correspondent," I said. "I want to find out from the general how the entry into Manila is going to be made, how the people can expect to be treated, and what the attitude of your occupying general is going to be toward the American, British, and Dutch civilians. I think there are about four thousand of them in the city."

The young officer, slight of build, mud-smeared and weary, studied me for a few seconds. "Wait here," he ordered.

Fortunately for me I had run into a propaganda corps officer whose reaction was that of a person who was used to Americans. He had lived in America. If he had been one of the local boys who had had no experience with Americans his reaction would likely have been to clout me across the face or knock me down the steps. I didn't know this at the time. But I learned. I had two years of daily lessons.

I waited on the porch for about fifteen minutes, although it seemed hours. The two ugly-looking guards with fixed bayonets eyed me fixedly. I had a feeling that if I moved suddenly they would jump on me.

I was just about ready to try to saunter past the guards to the car, for I had done a thorough job of convincing myself that I ought to get out of there, and quickly, when the young propaganda corps officer stepped onto the porch from the darkened doorway. I wiped the perspiration off my hands onto my trousers and followed him inside upon his order. Seated behind a desk was a man considerably beyond middle age, heavy set, with bull neck and shaven head. Like all the others, his uniform was muddy and bedraggled.

"This is the general commanding the southern army," the young officer informed me. "Bow to him in recognition of his rank."

I had already nodded, which seemed adequate, but now I bowed. "What's his name?"

"Never mind name," the general barked for himself and in good English. "You've come to find out about treatment of your countrymen? Is that right?"

"Yes," I answered. "And about the Filipinos . . ."

The general cut me short. "It's none of your business."

"I realize it's none of my business. But I ask you because I thought perhaps it might not only help the Filipinos and my own people, but it might also help you. That is, if you told me how you plan to enter the city and what the people might expect."

"How help *me?*" The general eyed me suspiciously but there was curiosity in his voice. The Japanese are a very curious people.

"It might help you if you could know, for instance, that the people in Manila would stay off the streets. If the people were told that you—the commanding general—ordered them to remain in their homes when your troops enter the city, that might be of help to you. It would aid your *orderly* entry." I stressed the word orderly, and waited.

"So-oo-oo-diska!" The general didn't take his eyes off of me. I was beginning to get a very uncomfortable feeling, when he suddenly pounded his fist on the desk.

"I order you to tell the people to stay off the streets when I make the entry."

He looked around the room as he continued to talk.

"The entry will be orderly. The Filipinos will come to no harm. They are our brothers. We have come to free them. We will treat your people according to international law. If your people do not resist they need expect no harm. You must all be registered and placed in concentration centers. That will take time. But tell your people to stay indoors. You will receive instructions through the newspaper. We will treat you in accord with our spirit of *bushido*. We are an honorable people."

(This was the first and last time I heard any Japanese speak of international law without spitting, without angrily saying, "Never mind the international law. We make the international law.")

The general stood up and turned his back on me. The young officer nodded toward the door and I followed him outside.

"You speak excellent English," I commented.

"Yes. I went to Stanford University," he told me, and the tone of his voice implied, "Yeah, and how do you like that!"

"Your car is ready." He waved me into it and I didn't bother to bow to him. He sent a guard along who hung onto the running board and stayed with Sancho and me until we had passed the tank squadron.

That was to be the beginning of nearly two years of daily contact with Japanese officialdom. The statement made by this general (who was not General Homma, but whose name I never learned) was a fitting introduction.

I reported my conversation at the High Commissioner's office, and Sancho spread the word among his people. It probably didn't help very much, but Sancho was happy, which was enough for me.

XV

LATE on the afternoon of January 2, I received a telephone call from someone who refused to identify himself—a not unusual procedure those days. He insisted that I come immediately to Fort Santiago to MacArthur's headquarters as he had news of great importance for me. I tried to get more information over the telephone, but the voice at the other end refused to say anything else.

"I'll be along in about ten minutes," I told him before I hung up.

This seemed a most peculiar request to me since MacArthur had left the city and there shouldn't have been anyone at his headquarters. I knew one of the first places the Japs would undoubtedly go to would be MacArthur's office in Fort Santiago. And I knew the

Japs were just outside the city. I'd just been out there—to the general's headquarters. Was this some kind of a trap?

Marjorie insisted on going with me. We didn't want to be separated any more than was necessary.

When we arrived at Fort Santiago there was no one around, not even a Filipino street urchin. We went into the radio operating room. Everything was in perfect order. Chairs were pushed back. There was the smell of cigarette smoke in the room. A half-empty glass of beer was on the table, and behind it a cigarette stub just burning out. The radio tubes were warm to my touch. Strange, I thought, that they hadn't been smashed.

"Where is everyone?" Marjorie wanted to know in a hushed voice.

"Let's look upstairs," I suggested.

We went up the winding, wooden stairs to find the same eerie atmosphere we had encountered below. It gave me a queer feeling, as though someone just behind the curtain was watching us.

Again the chairs were pushed back from the tables; more beer glasses were partially empty, the smell of smoke was in the air. The slow whirling of the electric fans overhead whumped through the still air. We had the impression that the phone had just rung, and everyone had run out to answer it. Obviously something had jarred someone loose from this place. And not many minutes before. It was not more than fifteen minutes since I had received the telephone call at the hotel.

We turned into MacArthur's office. It was cleared out. Not a thing was left of all the Oriental trappings and finery he always kept around him. The "V for Victory" Blue Eagle poster was all that was left. "Keep 'em Flying," the poster blazoned. It was the first thing you saw when you entered the office.

I couldn't resist the temptation to sit down in the General's squeaky desk chair, the one he had told me his father had used as general in the early days. I placed my arms on the desk and looked around the room where we'd had our daily press conferences, and where I had interviewed the General the year before. He had carefully explained to me then, on wall maps that weren't there now, just how the Japs would be repelled. The only thing that still held was what he'd told me, off the record, about Bataan and Corregidor.

"Come on," Marjorie urged. "Let's get out of here. It gives me the creeps. I expect to find a Jap behind me any moment. If the G-2 boys aren't around, there must be a reason, and it won't do us any good to get caught here."

We got out. Within the hour the Japanese advance guard was in. I never did find out who called, nor what was wanted. I have often puzzled over what that important news could have been. This final visit to USAFFE headquarters in the open city of Manila was one of the eeriest experiences I've ever had.

The occupation itself began late that afternoon. When it started, at the suggestion of Claude Buss most of us correspondents rounded up as many other loose-end Americans as we could find and went down into the walled city and along the downtown business sections to warn Filipino looters. This looting had swelled to open breaking and stealing. The Chinese shops were gutted.

Hundreds of Filipinos were breaking into the tiny shops in the deep narrow streets. It was nearly sunset. Smoke from the burning oil and from some of the buildings at the north end of the walled city was fanned low into these dark streets. People were mere fleeting forms and shadows.

We drove very slowly calling: "Go home! Go home! The Japanese are coming. Don't be caught looting. Go home!"

We stopped hundreds of these Filipinos who were operating individually or in gangs. But nowhere did we run into any nasty situations, although several of the younger ones showed sharp, long-bladed, snap knives. "We weel sleet the throat of any Japanese who try stop us, Seer. Do not be afraid," they'd say, and would slash the imaginary throat of a Japanese soldier. These were undoubtedly some of the Filipinos who, during the first part of the occupation, actually did murder a number of Japanese soldiers who decided to go sightseeing while off duty.

As soon as it became dark we returned to the Bayview. Marjorie and I decided to go over to the Manila Hotel to have our last good meal. We met C. C. Chapman ("Chappie") of International Telephone and Telegraph, who had helped us speed our communications several times through his contact with Mackay Radio. There was no electricity in the city that evening, due to partial sabotage by the vigilantes. We dined by candlelight in the almost empty dining room.

Just as we were finishing, our former room boy came to the table. He was considerably upset. "The Japs are coming. They are here, Seer. I think maybe they come into your room. I pack all the things you have leave, Seer. I hide them for you."

This boy packed everything we had left in boxes and kept them for us. Eight and a half months later a delegation from our camp was allowed to go to the Manila Hotel and gather up any belongings that had been left behind by internees. These goods had been pretty thoroughly gone over by the Japanese and what they had wanted, they had taken. I was a member of the delegation from the camp and I found that there was not very much left. But our room boy, true to his promise, had packed our things and kept them safely for us. Even Marjorie's hairpins that had been on the dressing table were carefully placed in the boxes.

This boy's concern for us, and his act of saving our few possessions, is just one of the hundreds of examples of the Filipino's friendliness and loyalty which we Americans in the Philippines experienced.

"I guess you've heard this story about the world's greatest optimist," Chappie said, "but it certainly is to the point."

He told us the old one about the two Christians who were to be thrown to the lions in the Roman days. One of them was telling the other about a sex-ridden dream which he had had the night before. Just at the crucial moment in the story the gates of the stadium were thrown open and the two men were pushed into the arena.

"But how did the dream end?" asked the first Christian.

"I'll tell you later," replied the second, "but right now here come the lions."

With that we pushed back our chairs and walked out into the Palm Lobby, right into the middle of the arrival of the commanding Japanese general.

PART THREE

Manila: January 1942

XVI

THE Japanese general was pudgy. His dirty, bilious-green uniform jacket carried three campaign ribbons. An ordinary safety pin held a five-pointed gold-braid star to his left sleeve. That meant staff. He tugged at his brown, hard leather gloves as he stomped up the three steps from the driveway into the long lobby of the Manila Hotel. The general's dust-encrusted staff climbed heavily from their mud-spattered, camouflaged cars, dragging their long, leather-cased swords behind them like tails.

This was the first official party of His Imperial Japanese Majesty's Officers to enter the City of Manila. I glanced at my watch. It was 7:30 P.M. (January 2, 1942). Marjorie, C. C. Chapman, and I arrived at the reception desk from our dining-room table just as the general elbowed his way through a group of unaware hotel guests, who jumped as though a whip had snapped when they suddenly recognized his uniform.

"It's the Japanese. The Japs are here!"

This electric news crackled around the hotel. Curious crowds began peering down the palm-lined lobby, and stood in "nonchalant" poses near the elevators to watch what was going to happen.

But it had already happened.

The general was halted momentarily on his way toward the reception desk by a tall, heavy-set, pink-cheeked American dressed in a neatly pressed white sharkskin suit, who towered above the squat Japanese.

"Sir!" he declaimed in a deep, demanding voice. "Sir, I expect your treatment of me will be exactly the same as yours would be if I were in your position."

63

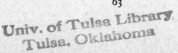

The general still tugged at his gloves. He was growing impatient. He was tired. He was busy. But—he was polite. Those had been his orders: ". . . an orderly occupation." He looked up at the American.

"Are you the manager of this hotel?" he asked.

"No."

The general, by this time flanked by his burly staff officers, moved straight ahead to the reception desk without another word. The American had to step back quickly to keep from being trampled.

The Japanese had taken over.

"What do we do now?" Marjorie asked.

Sancho answered that question for us. "I belieeb, Seer," he whispered as he carefully watched the Japanese officers at the hotel desk, "we may be able to escape through the southern route. We might get around to Cavite and across to Corregidor."

I just nodded toward the outside entrance. Chappie, who had lived for years in Japan, decided to stay.

"If you're going to try to make a run for it, I guess I'll take over your air-conditioned room for the night and try to get as much sleep as I can before they march us all out somewhere to live behind barbed wire," he said. So we left him at the hotel.

For two hours and twenty minutes Sancho drove us around the city of Manila, from one exit road to another. This was our third attempt to escape—our third try at reaching Corregidor. But no luck.

I turned to Marjorie. "Are you sorry about not accepting MacArthur's invitation last week?" I asked.

She just squeezed my hand.

It all seemed very unreal as we drove through the half-darkened Manila streets that night. Long columns stomped and limped in across the Passig River bridges. Oddly enough they came in on the righthand side of the street, although traffic normally moves on the left in Manila, just as in Tokyo.

As we drove past these columns we didn't know when we'd be stopped. All traffic had been ordered off the street. But we flew a special white police flag that I'd persuaded Police Chief Torres to give me a few days before when all his constables were shooting at automobiles moving around town at night.

We crossed and recrossed the Passig River. Japanese Diesel sampans—just like those you used to see in Hawaii—were chugging up and down the river, loaded with troops. They must have come from the marshes at the north of the bay. We drove out the North Road. We passed Bilibid Prison and headed northeast past what—

although we didn't know it then—was going to be our prison for the next eight and one-half months—Santo Tomás University campus. We inched south along toward Nichols Field, past tanks and trucks rolling down Dewey Boulevard. Sancho drove up to the south end of a dirt runway at Nichols where we saw Jap bombers and Zeros being refitted and refueled under high-rigged swinging lights, for which the power was generated by field gas engines. The Japanese thought of everything. Their invasion force brought everything; everything except the ability to win over the Filipino.

Surprisingly enough no one seemed to notice us. No one challenged us except at the city's outskirts—where tanks akimbo across the road and Japs with automatic rifles turned us back. Everywhere there were Japs, Japs; marching, marching. Their clothes were torn and dirty. They hadn't had any walkover, despite the speed of their occupation. Some of them sang marching songs, while others counted step. Some outfits just stumbled along.

Germans and Italians, including some Nazi Party leaders, drove about in large limousines, sounding their horns constantly, triumphantly.

Truck after truck, loaded with supplies, rumbled into the city from all the outlying roads. The Philippines had never seen such a display of military might. Tanks and staff cars moved around the grassy Lunetta. At first the Staff made its headquarters at the Manila Hotel. Why shouldn't the commanding officer of the occupying army afford himself the same air-conditioned privilege as had General MacArthur, and live in MacArthur's penthouse atop the Manila Hotel?

I called Carl Mydans, who was at the Bayview with his wife Shelley. Carl had said he thought he could get a room for us. He did. We took the Jacobys' room. Mel Jacoby, of *Time* and *Life*, and his wife got away at the same time Clark Lee of the AP and one or two of the others made their way to Corregidor.

At the moment when Sancho dropped us at the entrance to the Bayview, a truckload of Japs pulled up behind us and a young Japanese propaganda officer grabbed me by the shoulder and spun me around just as I was helping Majorie out of the car.

"Here we go," I thought. But I said, "May I be of any assistance to you?" He was nonplussed. He'd expected me to push him away. But since I was equally nonplussed we just stood there looking at each other measuringly for a few seconds. It seemed like a long time to me. Finally I heard myself saying, "This is my wife."

Marjorie nodded. Again, this kind of reaction from the captured enemy baffled the propagandist. But what was more astounding was the fact that he touched his finger to his cap, bowed slightly, and in very clear English replied, "How do you do."

Obviously his automatic reaction came only after long practice among Westerners. Psychologically I had the upper hand—for the moment. The other Japs crowded around to get their first good look at a captured American man and woman. Some of them—bandaged —had been wounded. None of them had had a chance to wash. We knew that without being told.

"You are newspaperman—journalist?" the propaganda corps officer asked, pointing to the press police flag on the car. "All journalist are arrested . . ." he continued. But I cut in on him. I knew if I were picked up here, it could mean almost anything. There was no military organization in the city. Because all Japanese correspondents are trained as espionage agents, the Japanese consider all American correspondents as spies. If I were taken off anything could happen, from being shot right then and there to being dropped for the duration in one of Fort Santiago's deep dungeons, formerly of the Spanish Inquisition.

"Yes, I am a journalist," I replied quickly. "I live here at this hotel with other journalists. This is our headquarters. If your superior officers wish to contact us, they will find us here." Without waiting for him to answer, I took Marjorie by the arm and hustled her into the hotel and into the open elevator at the front of the lobby. It was just like walking through a graveyard on a dark night when you were a kid. I waited for the shout behind me; the heavy hand on my shoulder. But none came. When we were in the elevator and it was actually on its way up I mopped the perspiration from my face— and it wasn't from the stifling heat.

XVII

THE Japanese officially took over the Bayview Hotel on the night of January 2-3, 1942, and it was quite a ceremony. Everything with the Japs is a ceremony.

The occupying forces distributed to their advance parties badly mimeographed maps of the city with lettering in both Japanese and English. These parties, in trucks, were to proceed immediately to key points and take them over in the name of Hirohito. Somehow that first night, while they had set up their machine-gun nest on the Bayview's front stoop, they had missed the official adoption ceremony.

The ceremony took place at 1:00 A.M. while I was on duty in the lobby with about twelve other men. We had arranged our own night-watch system since there was still plenty of robbery going on in the city, and we wanted someone on hand for just such an occurrence as this first official visit.

Fifty men from the Army-Navy YMCA were asleep on the floor and in chairs in the lobby. Twelve of our men were busy making their rounds. I happened to be in charge during this particular watch, so I was sitting behind the manager's desk when the take-over squad burst in, led by a squat, bull-necked, noncommissioned officer. His uniform was a disgrace to his Emperor. There were holes at the knees and a tear from cheek to cheek across his seat. He hadn't shaved for a long time. He was one of the toughest; the kind you read about.

No sooner had he stepped through the double door than he pointed his finger at me and bellowed like an enraged bull. I had been dozing, waiting for the men making the rounds of the floors to check in. By the time his bellow ceased echoing throughout the lobby my heart was trying to get out of my throat. I watched ten soldiers, a Filipino interpreter, a Filipino policeman, and what turned out to be an army propaganda corps and intelligence officer all file through the doorway.

"He orders you to get everybody in this hotel out for inspection immediately," the interpreter told me, pointing to the officer. The fifty YMCA men were stirring uneasily on their chairs and couches in the darkened rear of the lobby. Intelligently they didn't come out to see what was happening.

"Will you please tell him that this hotel is full of women, children, and very old people?" I urged the interpreter. "Tell him it would frighten the children to get them out of bed at this time of night. I know he wouldn't want to do that."

There was considerable walla-walla between the noncom and the propaganda officer. Finally the latter said through the interpreter: "All right. All of you here line up for inspection and questioning."

The other men had come downstairs from their rounds. I sent one of them to get Don Kneedler, the owner's son. We lined up and the pugnacious noncom strutted down the line, jamming his ugly face within a few inches of each man's nose. "You will give your name and occupation when you are ordered to," the interpreter said, and added under his breath, "Stick to your story once you give it. Think carefully what you're going to say. Make no mistakes."

The man on my right was a Pan American Airways technician, and on my left was a tall, heavy-set, well-known Manila gambler who had been with the armed forces as a civilian and then had been left behind.

"What am I going to tell this guy?" he murmured. "I can't tell him I've been out at Nichols Field running a machine gun and helping fix up airplanes."

"Tell him you're a night-club dancer," I said offhand. I was trying hard to figure out my own story.

The interrogation was quick until my turn came. "Salesman, bank manager, radio operator, Pan American Airways . . . journalist."

"Ah, *ha!*" The noncom dragged the "ha" out as though he'd really discovered something. "What do you write?"

"I don't write."

'Why not?"

"Communications have been blown up."

"Who blew them up?"

"The United States."

"Why?"

"So your army couldn't use them."

"Ah, so!" A new tack. "What kind of articles did you write?"

"I wrote stories from the official communiqués."

"Were you with the Army?"

Here was my first lie. I wasn't going to tell this punk I had been in both the North and South fronts and out on airforce bases only to be thrown into some prison with no appeal. If the Japs took me for questioning it would be later when some officer was present.

"No," I lied, "I wasn't with the Army. I never even saw the Army. I've been in Manila all the time. I wrote stories from the official communiqués. I didn't see anything of the war. I lived in the hotel."

Anything I could do to keep out of this boy's hands would increase the length of my life. I was sure of that. At this point the propaganda corps man pulled me out of the line and began questioning me more thoroughly about what I knew of the last days of the Army in Manila. He didn't need an interpreter. He spoke English as well as I did. I could see I was going to have an embarrassing time of it if something wasn't done. So I used that old one: "My, what perfect English you speak."

"I ought to," he came back. "I was born in Seattle and went to the University of Washington."

"Well, well, so did I. Do you remember Dean Condon, the dean of men?"

He did. We never got back to the subject of war correspondents because the noncom suddenly decided he'd done enough for that hour of the night. "Stop," he bellowed twice officially and once un-officially to his men, saluted smartly with his ham hand and clanked out into the street.

Everyone breathed again. We'd just relaxed when the bellowing started all over again. Everyone jumped to his feet. A soldier had returned and slapped a mimeographed sticker on the marble pillar by the door. He presented arms twice, bowed twice, screeched at the top of his lungs, faced us, pointed to the sticker and left.

We crowded around the pillar sticker and read: "This premises has been officially occupied by His Imperial Japanese Majesty's Army and is officially under Army control. All former ownership now passes into the hands of His Imperial Japanese Majesty."

There went old Doc Kneedler's hotel, his home, his life earnings. Don Kneedler came out of the hotel office and reported that the Japs had sealed the safe, filing cabinets, and all desk drawers, and told him they'd shoot him if anything was disturbed.

Just as I started to climb upstairs to call Carl Mydans who was in charge of the next two-hour watch, the gambler who had been standing next to me when the questioning started, stopped me.

"That was a good idea of yours, that night-club dancer gag," he said. "The guy asked me just one question."

"Yes? What was it?" I asked.

"Well, he asked me what kind of dancing I did—*sumo?*"

The noncom had a sense of humor after all. *Sumo* is Japan's heavyweight wrestling profession.

The next morning Jack Percival, whose room was just down the hall from ours, came in to see if we had any ideas regarding how to get his wife, Joy, out of the Manila British Club and over to the Bayview. Joy had been staying at the Club just prior to the occupa-tion and had gone back there early in the evening of the 2nd in order to get a few things she had left behind. It had proved to be just the wrong moment, for suddenly the Japanese were "in" and she was not allowed to return to the Bayview. Jack had not gone with her because he was checking on a final lead he thought they had for escape to Corregidor.

Joy was pregnant and Jack was greatly concerned about her.

When he had returned to the Bayview after his fruitless attempt to find an out for both of them, he was nearly frantic to find that Joy was not there and that he couldn't get out of the hotel again. He had tried for hours to get through to her by telephone.

While we were talking with Jack a knock came on our door. No one budged for a second. We weren't eager to find out what might be on the other side of that door. Every knock brought the same picture to mind—Japs.

Marjorie was nearest. As she opened the door I heard a squeal of sheer delight. There was Sancho grinning from ear to ear, his arms filled with packages. We rushed him in and shut the door quickly, pulled up the best chair for him, and while he sat, the three of us stood around him plying him with questions.

"How did you do it, Sancho?"

"How did you get by the Japs?"

"How did you know what room we're in?"

"Are you all right?"

Sancho carefully laid down his packages and started fishing in his pockets. Finally he pulled out a small slip of paper that was covered with Japanese characters.

"I have the pass, Seer. It gives me the freedom for the whole city."

"Where'd you get it?"

"Once there was a Japanese man I used to drive from his home to his business each day. Now he is a big man. Now he is important official." Sancho paused a second.

"Yes, yes, Sancho. But how did you get the pass?" Marjorie prompted.

"I am telling you, Mum. I saw the Japanese man today. Now he is a big man. I drive him to the Manila Hotel."

"And he gave you the pass?" I asked, trying to hurry things along a bit.

"Yes, that is so, Seer. I tell him how difficult is everything. Always the Japanese guards they stop me. I tell this important man I need a pass so the guards will not stop me. He give me this and he say, 'This will give you the freedom of the city.' He is a big man. Now I have no more trouble."

"But how did you get into the hotel?" Jack asked.

"Oh, that is easy, Seer. This pass is very good. I just show it to the guard at the door and I bow. I can go anywhere now. I bring you a little food."

Sancho picked up the packages and handed them to us one by

one. He had bought bread and a little fruit. We had known him for exactly one month. He owed us nothing. And yet he had come to us with food and with words of encouragement. Just before he left us he turned back for a moment and said: "Don't you worry, Mum. Never you mind, Seer. No matter where they take you I will find you. Do not fear. I will take care of you."

XVIII

WHEN we stepped into the Bayview Hotel our freedom was ended for nearly two years. I'm glad we didn't know how long it was going to be. It was better taking it bit by bit.

For three days we were confined in our quarters inside the Bayview. We were free to wander around the hotel. Japs would stalk in and snoop about, but as far as I heard they stole nothing; they harmed no one.

From our windows on the sixth floor and from the Mydans' room on the fifth floor front we watched the occupation activity. Since the rooms were on the front looking directly down on the modern newly built home and office of the United States High Commissioner, as well as giving us a view up and down Dewey Boulevard right along the waterfront, there was plenty to look at.

Lieutenant General M. Homma, bald-headed commanding general of all Japanese forces in the Philippines, made a pompous entry, with all the drab Japanese military ceremony that could be mustered. We watched it all. The Japanese staff took over the air-conditioned office of the High Commissioner in this ceremony, which included lowering the American flag and hoisting in its place the Japanese "Fried Egg"—as we called their flag.

The Japanese placed a few small cannon, which looked like Navy sunset guns, out in front of the High Commissioner's office. What appeared to be two companies of marines and one company of soldiers formed ragged lines on either side of the wide doorway and just at the head of the long driveway up from the high iron gates at Dewey Boulevard. The flag pole was right in the middle.

Marjorie and I watched this "ceremony" with mixed feelings. The city was burning behind us. Explosions were still rending the air with tremendous concussions. These were gas-tank explosions. The Japs couldn't get close enough to the flaming gasoline and oil tanks to extinguish the fires at Cavite across the lagoon, or at Pandacan behind the city. Long plumes of oil smoke waved 40 miles out across the harbor past low-lying Corregidor and on out to Bataan and to the horizon.

To us at that moment the lowering of the American. flag seemed like the end of everything. Other such moments will remain in the minds of those who saw the Nazis march into Oslo, Warsaw, Paris. Marjorie couldn't keep back the tears. We vowed we'd do everything possible to be back there when the American flag was raised again on this very flagstaff.

As the flag fluttered down there was much shouting and cannon firing from the pint-sized sunset guns. No one caught the American flag. It fell to the ground. A Japanese marine unhooked it from the rope and attached a brand new, red-centered Japanese flag. As it went up the band played the Japanese national anthem, which sounds weird enough anyway, and created an unreal atmosphere in the already eerie smoky sunset glow.

The marine stood with one foot on the American flag as he slowly hauled the Japanese flag to the top of the pole. During these few moments there was much bowing, cannon firing, rifle saluting, and more bowing toward the Imperial Japanese Palace and "Presence" at Tokyo.

I was conscious of all this, all right, but the dull feeling in the middle of my stomach seemed to spread throughout my whole body. I felt cold and rigid, although it was a sticky, hot afternoon. Both Marjorie and I stood at the window motionless until the quick darkness dropped over the city. That was the last American flag we saw until we reached Port Elizabeth, South Africa, on the *Gripsholm* twenty-two months later.

There were nearly four thousand United Nations civilians caught in Manila. Japanese Army headquarters chuckled tolerantly at the pleas from civilian Japanese to permit them to do the interning. Hadn't the Americans interned them? Then why shouldn't they, the Japanese civilians, be given the chance they'd been waiting for? They would show the arrogant superior white race who was who in East Asia.

The argument suited anti-foreign, Oxford-educated Lieutenant General Homma. And civilians, under careless military supervision, went to work on the Americans, British, and Dutch. The first night of occupation three hundred men were ordered out of their homes, leaving their wives and families behind them. To what?

The men were not allowed to take anything with them. They had what they stood in; in most instances open shirts and shorts. Their families were told that they probably wouldn't see their menfolk again. Yet the Japanese at that moment had no place to intern them. They had no idea what to do with them, or even how to register them.

But they had their fun. They marched the men through the streets for hours before the sullen-eyed Filipinos who recognized many of them as their former employers and benefactors. Finally the Japanese just stopped where they were and ordered their prisoners to sleep on the cement sidewalks or on grass parkways. But as soon as any of the men fell asleep their captors would swat them across the feet with swords or long sticks—just to keep them from forgetting that there was a New Order in East Asia.

The next day a general clearing out of enemy alien-occupied dwellings began. The first groups together with the men who had been marched off that first night were taken to Rizal Stadium where some of them were registered. Others were jammed into uncovered trucks and driven hit or miss around the city streets under a blazing tropical sun. The idea seemed to be to show the man on the street who was boss. Thousands of Filipinos merely turned their backs when the trucks rolled by, which made the Japanese madder and madder.

Some of these people were finally taken back to Rizal Stadium, while others were driven to Villamor Hall, a public recital hall of the University of the Philippines that was supposed to hold between five and six hundred. But there were eight hundred men, women, and children crowded into this space. They were not allowed to leave their seats—seats that had been built for small Filipinos. For three days and for three nights they sat there. They were given no food and but very little water. The two small toilets in the washroom were soon clogged and the filth was indescribable.

The only time these people were allowed to move around was during roll call when the men were ordered to line up on one side of the room and the women on the other, which in itself was a physical impossibility in the limited space available. The Japanese could never count accurately and usually gave up in disgust. That was one thing I found consistent about the Japanese throughout the whole two-year period. They could not count. Roll calls in the Manila and Shanghai camps were universally off unless the prisoners made the count themselves.

A few of the civilian Japanese became frightened at the terrible situation at Villamor Hall and finally decided to go to a Japanese staff

officer. What this officer saw and smelled in this room brought immediate action. British men were lined up, counted, and taken away.
Where, no one knew. Wives and families were left behind. A little
later American men were taken off in the same manner. In parting
the husbands and wives had little hope that they would ever be together again.

The men were trucked to Santo Tomás University, where on the
night of January 4, 1942, 350 began their camp life. This was the
opening of the Santo Tomás concentration camp. The next day
those who had been left at Villamor Hall were also transferred to
Santo Tomás. We discovered later that we had escaped the Villamor
Hall experience only because there were not enough trucks available to commence clearing the Bayview Hotel at that time.

The method the Japanese used in collecting enemy aliens clearly
indicated to us that registration and segregation, perhaps separation
of families, was imminent. Even at this early stage we had heard the
rumors, later substantiated, that at Baguio families had been separated. This was the last thing we wanted to have happen, but I must
say that Shelley Mydans, Barbara Brines, wife of Russ Brines of the
Associated Press, and Marjorie took this rumor like troopers. They
never batted an eye when they heard it.

The Filipinos were left pretty much alone. Many Americans
turned over their houses completely to their Filipino servants or
friends. It was better to do that than have everything lost, burned,
or looted. If the Filipinos could get some use out of these things,
so much the better.

General orders and proclamations came out in rapid-fire sequence
in the daily papers, now taken over by the army propaganda corps
and a Domei news agency staff. The most important first proclama-
tion ordered death to anyone or any group of people who "by word
or deed" so much as indicated opposition to the administration of
His Imperial Japanese Majesty's armed forces—now the complete
and "friendly administrators" of the Islands. That was interpreted to
mean anyone who harbored or gave succor to Americans, British,
or Dutch.

We were told by the papers that it was but a matter of a few days
before Bataan and Corregidor would capitulate, and that both spots
were being heavily bombed by the Japanese "war eagles." We could
see that much through the smoky haze from the burning city behind us. Planes would take off from near-by Nichols, Zablan, and
Nielson Fields, gain altitude as they rumbled low over the city,
make a wide sweep out across the bay to drop their bombs, and then

slide back in. We spent a lot of time counting the number of planes that went out and came back. We never counted the same number returning. But of what significance were one or two lost Japanese planes at this stage? However, it did make us feel better to know that the Japs weren't having it *quite* all their own way.

We didn't think much of the Japanese propaganda which claimed that Bataan and Corregidor would fall. In fact, we were surprised when they did fall four and five months later.

Life in the hotel was full of rumors. Most of them we traced to fear and hysteria among the guests. We began our long experience of tracing rumors right here at the Bayview. The internment camp rumor is a much more vicious thing than the small town rumor, because as a prisoner it's virtually impossible to trace the source, and there's no way to combat a rumor except by counter-rumor—a dangerous business.

At the Bayview also we began our long experience with food lines. Old Dr. Kneedler, owner of the hotel, couldn't keep his Filipino servants, largely because a vitriolic housekeeper thought war was a temporary imposition—like a hot Sunday afternoon—and made all sorts of impossible demands on the servants and guests alike.

Before long we were doing all our own work. We stood in line for everything. Food ran short and we had two meals a day—at 6:00 A.M. and at 5:00 P.M. Most people had a little something in the way of crackers or cookies to help fill the crevices. The fare was not plentiful for we didn't know how long we might be kept there. No one was permitted to go out to purchase any food, and even if we could have gone out it would have been extremely difficult, because the Japanese had commandeered all the city's food supplies. They had announced that they would set the prices, and they would tell the people how much food they could have.

That was the Filipino's introduction to the East Asia Co-Prosperity Sphere.

XIX

THOSE three days of house arrest in Room 620 at the Bayview Hotel provided a much-needed opportunity, an opportunity to organize my thinking, for I knew I must be able to answer intelligently—to my own advantage—the hundreds of questions the Japs would soon be throwing at me. How fortunate we were to be there instead of in a private dwelling or at Villamor Hall we learned only later when we began to get stories of mass looting, rape, and torture. For the "orderly" occupation in which the Japanese had been instructed soon turned into the revels of barbarian conquest.

One man told me how a civilian Jap and a gang of these loot-minded soldiers broke into his apartment. They tied him to a kitchen chair. They told his wife to sit in a chair across the kitchen. Then they ransacked the apartment. They found almost nothing they wanted, except some silver picture frames. Frustrated, the sergeant came out into the kitchen and gave some order to the wife. Of course she didn't understand and started into the other section of the apartment to find the civilian Japanese who spoke English. The sergeant followed her, bellowing. The civilian Japanese laughed. "Go to bedroom. Take off your clothes . . ." he ordered.

She screamed and tried to run back to the kitchen where her husband was still bound to a chair. The sergeant grabbed her and tore her dress at the top. Seeking the next best "out" she rushed into the bedroom, slammed and locked the door. By this time she was hysterical and was screaming for help.

Manila apartment doors aren't much protection. The burly sergeant aided by the others broke the door down immediately. The others stood around shouting encouragement—like a crowd shouting directions to a fighter—as the sergeant took off his clothes. The woman, horrified, tried to shut herself in the closet.

The other men broke open the closet door for the sergeant and he pulled her out and to the bed. The great commotion brought people down from upstairs. They were driven out. A squad of Japanese military police arrived from outside where a crowd had gathered. And they came just in time.

Why they stopped it the husband told me he'll never know. But his wife, a rather pretty woman, had never recovered from the terror of the experience.

In another instance, civilian Japs led a gang of soldiers to the home of a partially paralyzed American. He was over sixty and his entire family including some baby grandchildren were all gathered here, in order to face whatever they had to face together, as a family.

The Japs entered the house, breaking all the glassware and furniture with rifle butts.

"You get out," the civilian Jap ordered. "You be out in ten minutes."

The mother pled for extra time because of the father's condition and the babies.

All she got in reply was a blow across the face. "Get out."

They scrambled to jam a few things into suitcases. By the time they got the old father, the babies, and the near-hysterical mother out into the yard, the soldiers were throwing furniture out of the windows. The family—eight adults and four babies—were lined up in front of the house. The civilian Japs—there were two of them—brandished large revolvers.

"If you move I will shoot you," the nastiest yelled, red-faced. And he shot twice into the ground near the father's feet to emphasize what he said.

Systematically the Japs went from person to person taking money, rings, everything of value. About this time, the "sporting" soldiers lighted a bonfire of the furniture they had thrown out the windows. They had decided they liked the house, and that they would live here. They didn't like the "foreign" furniture and the only way to get rid of it was to burn it.

A truck came by and was hailed by the civilian Japs. They hoisted and shoved the family onto the truck. In the last view this frantic family had of their home was this bunch of ugly looters virtually doing a war dance around their burning furniture.

"We show you who is strongest man in the world. We show you who is master out here . . ." was the parting cry from the squat Jap civilian leader waving his revolver in the face of the paralytic father.

This sort of thing went on sporadically throughout the city over the first week of occupation, during the rounding up of the Americans, British, and Dutch and the carting them off to camp.

This is the way the "polite" little Japanese civilian, who always bowed and was so pleasant at the silk store, or the barber shop, fought the war against the "white man" he'd been trained from childhood to hate. This was "victory" the Japanese way!

There were other incidents of finished rape. There were atrocities of every kind imaginable, from snatching away children's dolls and breaking the dolls' heads to such mass terror as the Villamor Hall affair.

This was the Japanese conqueror's manner of showing his inferiority-complexed "superiority" over the "foreigner." The Jap understands only one thing. That is force. He uses brutal force in its most sadistic forms to make his point. That to him is winning the war. That is what must be beaten out of him. After he's defeated in battle it will take generations to do it through enforced education by the conquering United Nations, or he'll be, "So sorry"—and attack us again.

XX

IT WAS about six in the morning, January 5, 1942, when the Japanese finally ordered us to vacate the Bayview Hotel. We had waited for this order for three days and three nights.

Marjorie and I had a quick breakfast of bread, coffee, some papaya, and dry cereal—there was no milk. That was the last we ate until we split a can of spaghetti with the two Mydans and three Brines late that night inside the camp.

The Japs told us to be ready for an inspection at any moment. Once inspected by the gendarmerie we would be permitted to take with us whatever we could manage to carry. We were told to take food for three days and a mosquito net. Marjorie and I were not so much concerned about the matter of food as we were about the possibility of being separated. I asked the officer who gave the order whether there would be segregation of the men and women. He wouldn't say.

"By noon Japanese Army take over hotel," he told us. "No more Americans; no more British—now finish." And he laughed as he drew his finger across his throat in a typical gesture.

We were out and sweating on the street shortly before noon. We had to carry what baggage we had down the six flights of stairs, for we were not permitted to use the elevator. It was a Herculean job. Once in the street we began a long, six-hour wait atop our two suitcases.

We were briefly amused by a Britisher who was being helped out of the hotel by his American friend who was trying to steer him straight, at the same time getting luggage out for both of them. "Want any help?" I asked, realizing the Britisher was a total loss as far as carting baggage was concerned.

"No. But thanks just the same. Say, do you know that guy"—he pointed to the Britisher—"just can't get it through his head that there's a war going on. He don't know what's hit him."

He dropped the suitcase he was carrying, pulled out a handkerchief and mopped the perspiration from his forehead.

"My name's Joe," he told us, "and that"—again pointing at the Britisher—"that's m' friend John."

John wasn't paying any attention. He had sat himself down on the curb and was holding his head between his hands, his long legs sprawling.

Joe was short, red-headed and blue-eyed. Marjorie and I liked him at once. I never did learn his last name.

"Your friend looks a bit unhappy, Joe."

"He just don't know what it's all about," Joe told us. "He's been drunk ever since this war started. Yesterday he run out of liquor. This morning I goes into his room to tell him to get his stuff packed. 'John,' I says, 'you better get your stuff packed 'cuz we gotta get outta this joint.' And he says to me, 'What for? I ain't goin' anywhere. Get me some whisky, will ya?'

"Well, of course I tells him to quit his kiddin' and get a move on 'cuz the Japs want the hotel and we have to get out, or else. His voice, John's I mean, gets all squeaky. Really, I wouldn't of knew it was him, his voice was so high and funny like.

" 'The which?' he says.

" 'The Japs,' I tell him. 'You know, them bandy-legged little yellow bastards.' But he didn't get it. Then all of a sudden it dawns on me. This guy has been *so* drunk ever since the war started he really don't know what's been goin' on. So I explains it to him. And then I tells him that the Japs are in and that we're goin' out, so to get goin' and pack up. And would you believe it. He gives me one more squeak that sounds like, 'My God. Japs,' and he passes out cold. Faints dead away."

"He sure looks unhappy," I said.

"Well, I better go back and get the rest of the stuff. Keep an eye on John, will ya?" he asked. "See that John don't get into any trouble."

Joe crossed the street and disappeared inside the hotel. John proved to be no trouble. He just sat on the curb still holding his head as though he were afraid it might come off. A couple of hours later I helped Joe get him and their baggage onto a bus.

Marjorie and I were jammed into the last bus, after sitting in the street for six hours in the penetrating sun. Jap trucks and tanks had rumbled past all day. Some fleets of trucks carried small, Fordlike cars, and these were often followed by several gasoline trucks. When we stopped to think that the Japs had landed all this equipment, and more, on small docks and beaches of northern and southern Luzon, in the face of a pretty persistent if not sufficient opposition, we caught a glimpse of how well Tojo's boys had prepared and how long and carefully they had planned it all.

The sun was setting as we were finally jammed into the bus that had been commandeered from the Convent of the Immaculate Conception. Somehow this last group of seventeen got in with all the luggage. There was not a square inch of space to move in. Marjorie sat with her knees right under her chin. Of course we had to be counted and recounted before the bus could move. We sat there for twenty minutes before we woke up to the fact that we would have to count ourselves if we ever expected to start. After we had counted to seventeen enough times to convince the Japanese guards that there was no one missing we started off. How the Japs could have known whether anyone was missing when they never knew how many there were supposed to be in the first place was slightly puzzling, but we soon became used to this sort of thing.

"I don't believe it," Marjorie suddenly stated flatly. "I simply don't believe it." And a little later as we dragged from room to room in the great Santo Tomás University building trying to find space to squeeze into she said it again. "I don't believe it." And I knew exactly what she was trying to say, for I felt that way too. Here we were, hot, tired, dirty, with no food and no beds, people milling all around, Japanese guards everywhere clomping along in heavy boots, grinning, grinning. Yes, we were prisoners. But we just couldn't grasp it. "It can't happen to me!" That was the general feeling, and it took days, weeks, even months before anyone of us could actually take in the fact that "It *has* happened to *me*."

Mydans, Brines, and I finally worked as a unit in trying to find space in that steaming bedlam of distraught Manilans. We hunted and reported back to a designated spot. We hunted some more until through all the confusion we finally squeezed our wives together in one of the schoolrooms which we thought would be airy, but which turned out to be directly over the hot and smelly camp kitchen. Marjorie went to bed many a night during the next eight and a half months with a perfumed handkerchief spread over her face to counteract the smell of greasy, stale food.

Russ, Carl, and I found a very special spot out on a small balcony off of what had been the university's zoological museum. We had just managed to get our mosquito nets all strung up when a roving

Japanese policeman told us we could get our nets unstrung, and quickly. Russ tried to talk him out of it. Carl and I were quite impressed with all this walla-walla in Japanese until Russ turned to us and said, "The answer is no." Carl and I decided that the two years Russ had spent in Japan with the Associated Press were a total loss.

We pushed our way down the crowded hallway to a room next to the one in which we had placed our wives. The door of this room was closed and it had Japanese characters scratched on it. We pushed the door open to find an empty room except for a Japanese Red Cross chest and half a dozen tall school laboratory tables. "This is it," I said. "Let's get settled." We spotted Sam Gaches, one of Manila's oldest residents, who was looking pretty forlorn, but as usual talking himself into high spirits. We invited him to come in with us, but shut the door to keep others out. We were quickly learning to keep what we could get and say as little about it as possible.

We restrung our nets and were just going in to tell our wives where we were located when the door burst open and several nasty-looking Japs strutted in. They were unanimous that we couldn't stay. The door was plainly marked Red Cross. Couldn't we read? There were loud guffaws.

"Are you Red Cross?" one of them asked.

"Not especially," I said. "But I am member," I added suddenly, deciding to try to bluff them. I pulled a card out of my pocket that I had received in Honolulu during a Red Cross membership drive. "See, this shows that I am Red Cross member."

The Japs looked uncertain. Before we had finished we talked them right out of the room. "You can stay one night," the leader of the group told us after he had gone into a huddle with his three friends. "One night. That's all. Tomorrow you move. You get out."

We stayed permanently. This became the famous "Room 26." Here thirty-two of us—Carl, Russ, and I were the only non-Manilans —lived mattress to mattress, mosquito net to mosquito net. Here were twenty-nine of Manila's most solid, conservative old-timers. Carl, Russ, and I were rank outsiders and were tolerated only because we had found the room first, and they couldn't very well throw us out.

That first night next door in "Room 27" where we had hung our wives' mosquito nets from schoolroom chairs piled on top of each other, they had as many visits from the curious Japanese guards as we did. There were already some twenty out of the eventual thirty-two women in Marjorie's room and it seemed overcrowded then. All the women slept on the cement floor, although a few had mattresses. Marjorie had only one blanket under her.

It was ten o'clock before we finally opened a can of spaghetti and carefully split it seven ways on plates we had brought from the Bayview Hotel kitchen. It was twelve o'clock before we settled down to try to get some sleep. "Try" was a good word. We tried but there wasn't much sleep. There was still a terrific clamor in the halls. People milled back and forth all night. They'd burst into the room loaded with bundles, dragging crying children, pleading for space, no matter how small.

All night long groups of gendarmes or Japanese civilians wandered through the great building shoving in and out of rooms, counting and recounting, or just staring, laughing and gloating. It was great sport. This was their day. And did they enjoy it!

About three in the morning the gendarmes went into Marjorie's room and ordered all the women to get up off the floor. "Any ladies here from Bayview Hotel?" one Jap asked.

Several women indicated they were from the Bayview. "Get dressed and come out in hall," was the order. In the process of getting dressed the women found the gendarmes all back in the room watching the dressing bug-eyed and with wide Tojo-toothed grins. Barbara Brines, who had picked up some Jap colloquialisms fitting for the moment, let a few fly and the Japs, word-slapped, quickly filed out.

The women eventually went out into the hall. Marjorie told me that they merely stood there for several minutes, the Japs just staring at them. Finally one of them grinned. "Sleepy? Huh?" he asked. He looked at the other gendarmes and they all giggled the typical embarrassed Japanese cover-up—their defense when they don't know what to say next.

Another long pause. One of the gendarmes finally handed each woman a mimeographed questionnaire, the first of almost daily forms on every imaginable subject which we had to fill out.

"You fill out. You hand it in tomorrow morning by eight o'clock." He turned to go. The women still stood. "Now you go to bed," and he and his "Yes-men" went laughing down the hall.

In my room, next door, we had several visits during the night. We were all dead tired after days of strain and pressure resulting from our capture and pre-camp treatment. The oppressing, ever-humid heat of the Philippines added to our discomfort. Each time we would doze off into a fitful sleep the door would burst open and the brilliant ceiling light would flood the room. Finally, after the fifth or sixth time, the officer in charge shouted, "There are one man not enough in this room. Who is missing?"

A deep, sleepy voice from the far corner yelled, "That's Uncle Sam. But he'll be back. And sooner than you think."

PART FOUR

Internment at Santo Tomás

XXI

WE WERE up early the next morning. We were hungry and we were anxious to see what kind of a place this was that we had been thrown into.

We were particularly worried about Joy Percival, who as far as we knew was still at the Manila Club. As it turned out, before she and Jack got together again—ten days later when Joy was thrown into camp with the rest of us—she had a pretty rough time of it as an Australian in an English Pukka Sahib, an old school-tie-crowd. She and some other women slept on the floor of the women's washroom while the regular men residents of the club remained in their own upstairs apartments.

The British had hoped that they would be able to remain at the Manila Club, but the Japanese propaganda corps wanted the club for its own headquarters and moved the British, who eventually numbered eight hundred, to Santo Tomás. The British were much more forehanded than the Americans and had the Red Cross beat as far as preparedness was concerned, for they had quite a good supply of food stuffs which they took into camp with them, and doled out to their own people as long as it lasted.

The very first night of our internment I talked with Charles Forster, the American Red Cross representative in the Philippines, about getting some kind of an organization functioning. Forster's answer was, "But how can I do anything? I don't know what to do."

The Red Cross representative may not have known what to do, but one American Red Cross nurse not only knew what to do but she went ahead and did it, with half a dozen Filipino assistants, regardless of the great personal danger to which she exposed herself.

This nurse went to a large Red Cross warehouse filled with medical supplies and some food stuffs. She posted Red Cross flags on the doors and sides of the building, and then placed her Filipino guards in front with Red Cross arm bands. She wore a Red Cross nurse's uniform. They awaited the arrival of the Japanese, and when they came she pointed to the Red Cross flag and posters and said, "No. This belong Red Cross. You cannot touch!" It is uncertain whether they understood her words, but they did understand the meaning of the Red Cross and her gestures. She did this time after time during the first night of the Japanese entry into Manila. Finally she got a Japanese officer to write a sign in Japanese and post it on the door of the warehouse stating that this was Red Cross property and should not be touched by the army or the navy. Some of these supplies found their way into Santo Tomás, and others were used by the Philippine Red Cross in helping the Filipinos outside.

The first emergency which we encountered in Santo Tomás was caused by hunger, for we soon discovered that the Japanese had no intention of feeding us. It was the gambling element that saved us. A few gamblers together with some of the businessmen representing large firms, both of which groups had good contacts, provided credit with the Filipinos on the outside to purchase and bring food into the camp.

When Marjorie and I went onto the compound that first morning, we gravitated toward the gate along with the other two thousand internees. Along the entire street-length of Santo Tomás University compound there runs a 7-foot-high iron picket fence. We saw an amazing sight. Along most of this fence were crowded several thousand Filipinos—some just curious, but most of them friends and servants of the newly interned Americans. And most of them had food with them—bread, jugs of coffee, papaya, pineapple, eggs.

This was the beginning of what still exists at Santo Tomás—"the fence." Nearly a thousand Filipinos, Chinese, and some neutrals bring daily food parcels to internee friends or former employers. It's this fence line from nine to ten each morning that keeps a good one-third of the internees in a fair state of health.

The first day the Japanese watched this demonstration very carefully. They saw the food coming in. That was fine because they didn't want to feed us. But what they didn't like was the obvious loyalty of so many Filipinos. The double width roadway in front of the camp became blocked to all traffic. Then the soldiers drove off the Filipinos in large numbers. But in a few hours they were back. We organized our side of the fence system designating thirty men to hand the parcels to the recipients, and the Japs seemed satisfied.

As Marjorie and I watched the milling throngs both inside and outside the fence we noticed a cardboard sign being held up above the heads of the crowd. Suddenly Marjorie shouted, "Why, that's our name!" We squeezed our way through the jam and finally managed to get up close to the fence. And there with his face pressed between the bars was Sancho. He had placed a large piece of cardboard on top of a long stick. He had written GUNNISON on the cardboard and was holding it as high above his head as possible.

"I knew I mebbie would not find you if I did not do something, Seer," he said. "You have seen the name, and you come straight to me. I knew it would be like that."

"You are wonderful, Sancho," Marjorie told him smiling, but with tears in her eyes.

"You are all right, Mum? And you are all right, Seer? They have not harm you?"

"We are all right, Sancho. But you must be careful. Perhaps it is not good for you to come to us like this. The Japanese might not like it."

"Oh, never mind the Japanese, Seer. I will come to you every day while we are in this trouble. See, I have brought you something to eat."

At his feet were some bundles that were being carefully guarded by a little boy of perhaps twelve years of age. "This is my son," Sancho told us proudly. "He is Ike."

"Ike?" I asked in amazement.

"His name is Pedro, Seer. But he likes to be Ike, like one friend he work for. So I call him Ike."

Sancho lifted Ike up so that he could hand the bundles over the top of the fence. There was bread and papaya and a can of beans.

"It is not much, Seer. But I will come every day, and I will bring more next time. You meet me here this same place. What time, Seer?"

We decided that Sancho should come every day at three. Later, of course, he brought the packages in through the regular line, passed the Japanese guards for inspection and left them for us. For three months Sancho never saw either Marjorie or me because we were not allowed down near the fence when the Filipinos came in with the packages. The internees had to wait until after they had all gone before going down to pick up these bundles of food.

But Sancho came every single day with food and other necessities. He came every single day for eight and a half months until he bade us good-by before we boarded the troop transport on which we were transferred to Shanghai. For three months of this period I could give him no money with which to buy us food, but there was no break in the packages received. Later, when I was able to get money through a loan, I tried to make Sancho take some to use for his own needs. At that time I was working at the fence myself so I saw him every day. Sancho would always answer, "Oh, no, Seer. I cannot take the money while we are in this trouble."

And Sancho was only one of thousands in the Philippines who showed their friendliness to America and Americans in countless, unmistakable ways—ways that made the Japanese furious. They call them "unenlightened ways" and try to "educate" the Filipinos out of them. But, knowing only one method, they have made the mistake of using force in the attempted "education," and thus have only increased the Filipinos' friendship for Americans.

XXII

WHEN we first found ourselves herded into Santo Tomás camp with no food, no beds, no medicines, with inadequate clothing and with an overbearing non-English-speaking colonel as Camp Commandant, it became immediately evident that we must either take care of ourselves quickly, or face starvation and sure, slow death. That meant organization.

In Manila we had to start from scratch—and scratch we did. It was the Manila internee organization pattern that was later adopted by most of the North and Central China camps, a pattern developed in Manila purely from a trial-and-error operation.

By the third night in the confused Manila camp the commandant had appointed an internee "chairman" to act as go-between for him in issuing his orders to the increasing numbers of Americans, British, and Dutch being dumped out of trucks on the great asphalt apron in front of the main building and told to "go find a place to sleep."

This first chairman was Earl Carroll, a young, quiet, soft-spoken and level-headed insurance executive. He was one of the first to arrive in the camp and was picked almost at random by the Japanese. Carroll knew from the first that he faced a tremendous job, and one for which he would get no thanks. I walked around with him looking over the tumbledown university with its 52-odd acres, its tremendous main school building that soon held two thousand people, the smaller education building and the large gymnasium.

We noted the two annex sheds behind the main building. We waded through dirt and an utter confusion of litter wherever we went. How the Japanese were going to crowd the more than 4000 civilians then in Manila into this place was hard for us to visualize. We figured approximately 1000 could be placed in the main building and 400 in the gymnasium. If the Catholic sisters were moved outside the compound from the education building perhaps 250 or 300 could be housed in the classrooms there—a total of perhaps 1800 people.

The annexes in back could be used for the kitchen and the hospital, with staffs living there. But we didn't figure on Japanese standards; especially for enemy prisoners. Actually the Japanese put 3300 into this space at first—later 3900. That's one way in which they fought the war against civilians.

Before three weeks had passed the commandant ordered us to take down our mosquito nets and give up what few beds were available "to make room for more people." Here was the first test between internees and Japanese authority. "Body space plenty space for prisoners," the commandant said.

"To take away mosquito nets and beds from the internees and to crowd them further will cause widespread illness," Carroll told him, and he refused to comply with the request, stating that the commandant would have to go into the rooms, tear down the mosquito nets, and take out the few beds himself if he wanted this done. Carroll added that the commandant might very well have to face an investigation by the military administration of the Philippines if there were widespread illness among the internees as the result of such overcrowding. Here he was, of course, taking a long chance and bluff-guessing. But some feature of his refusal argument worked, for the matter ended then and there and no action was taken by the Japanese.

From here on our camp internee organization took hold with a bit more confidence. I sat in with the original planning group that organized what we called at the time "a small municipality with no assets except manpower and a few people with ideas."

We had to envision a pioneer community. We had every type of person from parson to prostitute and virgin to venereal, from great-grandparents to week-old babies.

"I agree temporarily," the commandant said when we presented our prisoner municipality plan—an internee organization that would run itself under the General Japanese Military regulations. This plan outlined departments for sanitation and health, education, work assignment, entertainment, purchasing, and even our own police department.

The commandant's eyes were thin slits as he spoke in precise staccato Nipponese. "I agree. But be sure you make no mistakes or you will be punished according to the full extent of Imperial Military Law."

That means death. But there was no alternative. It was a case of accept his deal or continue the confusion resulting from the lack of any organization. Confusion which could only mean slow death from filth and starvation.

"We accept," Earl Carroll told the interpreter. "Tell the colonel that we will co-operate with him only so far as we have to in order to insure the best conditions possible for the prisoners. Tell him, too, that we feel the Japanese have certain responsibilities for the care and health of these people. Try to get a favorable answer from him."

We were not at all certain of the "loyalty" of our interpreter, a man who claimed to be a missionary from Japan, but who bridled when asked what mission he represented; a man who took an officious attitude with other internees as though he were the final authority. That's why Carroll told him to "try to get a favorable answer."

There was a flurry of conversation between the interpreter and the colonel. The colonel made a sign with his hand that he was through talking. He motioned us to the door.

"What did he say?" I asked the interpreter.

"Nothing, nothing; nothing at all!" The interpreter shooed us before him to the door.

I was the last one out. Just as I left the room I heard the colonel retch some kind of a command. But I'd learned never to turn around unless I was sure I was the one being called. I closed the door. The interpreter reopened it. "The commandant wants to talk to you, Gunnison."

Now what? I stood before his desk and bowed, slightly.

He made quite a speech.

"You are a journalist?" the interpreter translated.

"Yes."

"You are a spy."

"No."

"The commandant says you are," insisted the interpreter.

"I don't care what he says. You tell him that because all Japanese newspapermen are trained espionage agents, that does not make all foreign journalists spies . . . and you be certain you tell it to him in just that way, too."

There were a few seconds of rapid-fire Japanese between them.

"The commandant says he believes you are a spy. But he says if you behave yourself in here and cause no trouble, you may not be sent outside to prison for questioning."

There was no use arguing with this man. Maybe a little soft soap was in order. "Tell him I appreciate his attitude toward me . . . that he may be assured that I have no choice in here but to behave myself."

The commandant made another speech.

"The commandant says to tell you he knows that it is the practice of journalists to influence public opinion. He wants you to know there can be no complaints in this camp about conditions, food [that was a joke for they weren't providing us with any] or treatment by the Japanese. If there are any public demonstrations, he says, you will be held to blame for inciting the prisoners to demonstrate. If there is any trouble—you will be shot!"

"Is that exactly what he told you?" I asked the interpreter.

"Exactly. Word for word."

"Tell him this." My voice trembled I was so mad. I took a deep breath. "Tell him I haven't enough influence to make 3500 people revolt without weapons. Tell him also that he is mistaken if he thinks I would jeopardize the lives of women, children, the sick and aged in this camp by stirring up a demonstration against the Japanese authority. Tell him I recognize superior strength, and that I will not serve in any capacity on any committee in this camp or act in any way that will give him occasion to think I'm stirring up trouble."

"A-a-a-ah, so!" the commandant snorted. He waved me out of the office.

But that wasn't the last I had to do with him. I turned out to be an "Exhibit A." Whenever there were any English-speaking admirals or generals or Japanese journalists in camp on inspection tours I would be called down to the office as a rarity among those captured. They'd usually ask me an assortment of questions from, "How do you like it in here?" (this from naïve embarrassment over not knowing what to say) to "Now don't you see what great mistake America made by starting this war?"

Once this questioning resulted indirectly in our being permitted to stay out on the compound an hour longer at night. The rule was that we had to be inside the stifling hot buildings at dark. There was no public room space and the dimmed out halls at night were jammed with steaming, restless humanity.

In reply to a question from the visiting general the interpreter told me that the commandant said, "But the committee makes its own rules about when the internees must come in off the compound to roll call at night." That gave me the lead I needed. I went to Chairman Carroll. He brought the problem to the commandant and the hour for returning to quarters was extended.

Until Bataan fell (April 9, 1942) and Corregidor surrendered (May 5) there was an unsettled feeling around camp. As each week had dragged on it had become clearer and clearer that no help was coming; that no help would be able to get to the Philippines. And we could note the growing strength of the Japanese forces. One morning I counted 264 planes take off from the three military fields near the camp and head for Bataan and Corregidor in one attack formation. Tanks rumbled by the camp day and night; and thousands of troops marched in and out of the city—right past the camp gate. The Japanese were planning to finish off Bataan and Corregidor. Of that there was no doubt. How long it would take them was the question most argued in camp.

And until they did fall in April and May many internee prisoners refused to take the long-range view of their imprisonment. The committee took the attitude that since things looked pretty black we had to take the long view and prepare for the worst. And before long we had a fairly smooth-functioning organization from an office staff and an elected executive committee to a large sanitation department of over seven hundred internees; a camp hospital, a baby-diet kitchen, and of course the regular camp kitchen. What we cooked in those kitchens we had to get for ourselves since the Japs supplied us with no food for six months.

We supplied ourselves. This was done through representatives of such concerns as Libby McNeal and Libby, General Foods, and also the Rockefeller Foundation. Representatives of the firms secured credit on the outside to purchase whatever foods and medicines we could get; subsistence rations that kept us barely alive on two meals, or rather "feedings," daily. For breakfast we had cracked wheat without milk but with plenty of worms. The second meal of the day, at 4:30 P.M., usually consisted of a watery, greasy stew of bloated buffalo, gluey rice, and sometimes pechay, a kind of spinach.

Because of the lack of food, and its poor quality plus the increased amount of physical labor required, the camp hospital was soon overcrowded with exhausted men and women. And here our troubles began.

Fortunately for the internees, Dr. C. N. Leach and Dr. Frank Whitacre, doctors attached to the Rockefeller Foundation, and a missionary, Dr. Robinson, had been caught in Manila en route home. It was tough on this team, but a blessing for the internees. Dr. Leach headed the camp medical unit. He and his organization of local doctors and nurses, later augmented by imprisoned U.S. Navy nurses, and finally the Bataan and Corregidor U.S. Army nurses, did an "impossible" job of keeping the 3500 internees from just completely folding under. It was a twenty-four-hour-a-day job. But there were few complaints from the staff. If the nurses got tired out or balky, as a few did, they were relieved temporarily.

We made a complete personnel survey of everyone in camp as to his work abilities, hobbies, entertainment ability, and likes and dislikes. These reports were studied by a work assignment committee, made up of some social workers and headed by an executive committee member. It was estimated that if everyone in camp did two hours' work each day, no one would have to volunteer for the extra jobs that were always coming up, such as clogged plumbing, garbage disposal gangs, and late night police watch. We had trouble with drunken Japanese guards returning from a night out and deciding to have fun with the internees. One night a friend of mine was routed out of bed, and made to bow before the guards until he wondered if he weren't doing setting-up exercises. They finished up by making him run up and down the hall, smacking his behind with drawn sword blades. This sort of thing and the possible molesting of women in the halls late at night was what caused us to set up the night watch. The boys on this watch drew the attention of the Japs to themselves and away from the other prisoners. While they sometimes got into jams, they were younger, and they could take it better than the older people and the women.

Melancholia became as great a problem as enteritis (food poisoning) or dysentery. Dr. Leach—and the other doctors confirmed his observations—said it was the greatest camp disease. "It's a creeping disease," he said. "At first you simply don't remember things. Then you begin to get morose and before you know it you are a patient."

The attitude of the internee in hundreds of cases becomes warped by the long period of imprisonment. He tends to become bitter even though his nature may be just the opposite. Although his physical suffering may be acute, actually it can't compare with the mental suffering. He becomes irritable, sometimes vicious. He's aggressive and antagonistic toward anyone who crosses him or doesn't hold the same point of view. There is nothing new to talk about except the Japanese propaganda or rumors which come in over the fence. But there's always the committee to criticize. There's always the fellow who sleeps in the next cot to swear at. Probably he has moved over into your 2 inches of allotted space, and a half-inch space—your only home being some 6 feet long and 2½ feet wide—is worth fighting for.

These internees can be divided into three groups. The first consisted of those who were always thinking of getting out, of what was happening on the outside, and of the future. Some of these people were the rumor mongers, but many of the others were just commonsense thinkers who were trying to keep alert and who tried to sift truth from rumor.

The next group included those who accepted internment as a necessary evil which they couldn't do anything about, but they did everything possible to keep their minds clear and their bodies in as good physical condition as they could.

The third group were those who seemed to give up and fall into the rut of camp routine along the lines of least resistance. The heat, the lack of anything to do except the hard labor necessary for mere existence, and in leisure hours playing cards and reading trashy detective novels was too much for them. They became lethargic. You would see them with the camp stoop, going about their camp work glassy-eyed, washing clothes, cleaning rooms, carrying garbage, standing in food lines, toilet lines, shower lines, but obviously in a mental fog. They weren't energetic enough to attend the adult education classes or get a group of their friends together for two or three discussion periods each week on some specific topic. These were the internees who were stupefied as the result of their imprisonment, and it was from this group that the greater percentage of the sick came.

But it wasn't all sordidness. In spite of our environment and the fact that we didn't know what would happen from one day to the next, there was a great deal of good-natured give and take. There were birthday parties and grammar and high school graduations; the weekly amateur nights and later the twice monthly shows produced by master of ceremonies Dave Harvey and specialty dancers Billy and Chita Carroll. One of the most popular songs, verses sung by Harvey and chorus by the audience, was entitled "Cheer Up, Everything's Going to Be Lousy." Fun was poked at everything from the food to the executive committee. It was an ironic kind of humor, but it gave the internees an opportunity to let off steam. The words for each show were written by Dave Harvey and Bert Covit, a United Press correspondent.

Sports events in the camp brought the only open international rivalry, especially the soccer-football matches between the British and Americans. These matches were usually held once each week, late in the evening, just before sunset. And they were well attended. Even the Japs came. They did here what they did at our camp theatricals and "Footlight Camp Revues." They elbowed their way through the crowd to the best spots and ordered the prisoners away.

One night when there was a particularly large crowd down at the field watching the Americans, for once, leading the British "footballers," the Japs lost face—plenty of it.

At the height of this game we suddenly heard some highly retched Japanese orders. The crowd at one end of the field fell back. Three platoons of Japanese soldiers, minus packs and rifles, marched bowlegged and droopy out onto the field.

The players halted momentarily. But not for long. Despite the marching Japs the boys kept on booting the ball around the open end of the field. The Japanese officer marched his company to the far end of the field, gave them a belch that obviously meant "to the rear . . . march!" and back they came. At this point the playing and the marching became intermeshed. The ball got under the feet of the Japs in the third platoon just as the officer gave "to the rear . . ." again. Some of the Japs missed the order. The collisions resulted in several Japanese helmets falling to the ground. You couldn't tell which were helmets and which the soccer ball. Inadvertently, the enemy had been routed with a soccer ball in the midst of carrying out its nuisance-value duty. Although there might have been heavy repercussions, there were some pretty loud snickers from the spectators as they walked away from the field. The game ended there. On the sports bulletin board the captain of the American team, which was leading when the marching began, "forfeited" the game to the British, saying "the British know why."

The British team took a lot of good-natured razzing that week. The Americans kidded them about arranging with the Japanese commandant to "march in ringers" at any time the Americans were ahead in a soccer game."

Anything like that, which furnished stimulation to an honest, heartfelt laugh, was like a gift from heaven to us.

There was another day when an elderly gentleman with an umbrella gave us one of the best shows of our entire internment period.

I was down at the gate that morning when I heard the commotion begin.

"Lemme in. Lemme in," I heard someone shouting. "I'm an American, and I'm comin' in."

I saw an old, white-bearded man brandishing an umbrella and carrying a small black suitcase. He was banging on the gate with the umbrella. The guards who didn't understand English just blinked at him. Obviously they didn't know quite what to make of the scene. A civilian Japanese who was on duty motioned to the guards to bring the old man to his desk. Tall and very erect, he glared down at the little Jap.

"What do I want? I'm an American, Goddammit. And nobody's come to pick me up and bring me into camp. I've been awaitin' for more than a month."

It was perfectly obvious that the old man was a bit deaf.

"But you don't have to come into camp if no one has sent for you," the Jap told him.

"What's that you say?"

The Jap explained again in as loud a voice as he could command. The old man finally understood.

"But I'm an American," he protested, "and you can't leave me out. I'm going to be with the other Americans. I'm just as good an American as any of them."

The Japanese civilian began all over again explaining the best he could that the old man didn't have to be interned.

"Now look here, young feller," the American shouted, rapping on the desk with his umbrella. "I'm an American and I'm comin' in, so you better make room for me. Now you pick up my bag and help me git up to the buildin'."

And the Jap did pick up his bag and carry it all the way up to the main building for him.

Because you never knew when a Jap or two might come round a corner or out from behind a bush or tree about the time you were venting your feelings on the Japanese in general or anyone in particular, we had to have some kind of a warning signal.

It was euphonious to shout "Jiggers the Japs!" but more than often not the wisest thing to do since no Jap likes to be called a "Jap." And you never knew which of them understood. So we fell back on the story of the Chicago gangster who, going to England to "get some culture," couldn't contain his excitement while fox-hunting and, instead of crying "Tallyho!" when he saw the fox, shouted, "There goes the son-of-a-bitch!"

Soon throughout the camp the cry of "Tallyho!" heralded any Jap prysters.

The Japs, finding they were unable to overhear much—or enough to give them material for a "third degree"—planted spies among the internee-prisoners. These spies came into camp ostensibly as prisoners, at the time other Americans, British, or Dutch were rounded up. We knew who many of them were. You could spot them occasionally. For the most part they were mestizas or Germans.

I remember one day standing in one of the large patios when a Japanese twin-engine plane, patterned after the American Lockheed, roared in for a landing at one of the near-by fields.

"There goes a Lockheed!" one of the men standing near me said.

That started a discussion of how the United States and British governments, over a period of years before Pearl Harbor, permitted Japan to secure everything from scrap iron and airplane spare parts to actual design of aircraft and aircraft motors.

The next day the internee who had expressed himself most strongly was called before the commandant. His conversation was repeated to him nearly verbatim. He was put through some very uncomfortable hours "for expressing a point of view which is contrary to the best interests of His Imperial Japanese Majesty in establishing the Greater East Asia Co-Prosperity Sphere."

It wasn't very hard to decide who had repeated the conversation to the commandant. But we had to be careful in punishing such people.

One morning in passing the bunk of a man whom we all suspected, a friend of mine brushed some sheets of paper to the floor. His first instinct was to pick them up. He did, and in replacing them on the bunk couldn't help but see that they were personnel dossiers of certain internees. They even told of pre-war connections, and gave alleged anti-Jap activities.

The word was passed. We had suspected this man for some time, especially since he had come into camp with a group that had been picked up in southern Luzon while hiding in the hills. These people had suspected him of turning them in, but had no proof. But here it was. We had a "vigilante" group that took care of the fellow who, I still believe, was a German. He was given no trial beyond being confronted with the evidence. He merely shrugged his shoulders. Externally he wasn't hurt at all. But he was so broken up internally that the Japs had to rush him to an outside hospital to save his life. No retaliation from the commandant was possible for a thing like this, for if he admitted this was one of his men, he would be admitting what he denied to our committee, that he had others. The next commandant we had openly admitted he had spies planted among the internees and even used to joke about it.

The first commandant showed puzzlement over the relationship of husbands and wives who lived in separate rooms in Santo Tomás. This situation actually bothered the Japanese authorities. They watched couples reading or talking, stretched out on blankets or mats under what shade trees there were. The commandant shook his head. There is nothing wrong with such a situation from our point of view, but to a Japanese any public indication of affection is definitely taboo.

We were ordered not to kiss our wives good night in front of the main building (many husbands lived in the adjoining education building or gymnasium). Such an exhibition was "bad for the morals of the soldiers and guards." However, we were told we could kiss our wives good night out in back of the building.

A further concession was offered us. As a solution to the problem of split families, the commandant one day called together the members of the executive committee. After a formal cup of tea and many preliminaries, he made the suggestion that the committee take the big tent which formerly housed a circus side show and was now used for an eating tent, and "arrange for husbands and wives to meet each other there in privacy."

At the same time the commandant denied the committee's request for an extension of the period allowing the internees to remain outside the buildings in the evening. At this time we had to be inside the hot stuffy buildings by 7:30.

The commandant was nonplussed when the committee thanked him for his thoughtfulness on behalf of the husbands and wives but said they felt it would be impossible to accept his offer. He shrugged his shoulders and walked out. His suggestion made sense to him from the point of view of Japanese custom.

"The love-tent line forms on the right," became a Santo Tomás catchphrase.

Later when the third commandant took over, the attitude toward the internees was completely changed, and any intimacy between husbands and wives was expressly forbidden. When the birthrate continued regardless, the Japanese became furious and ordered that all "pregnant fathers" be sent to jail for thirty days. For this purpose a jail was established on the grounds of the compound.

XXIII

IN THE camps in which only men were held the problem of morale—the job of keeping spirits up—was admittedly harder than in the camps imprisoning both men and women. The men in the co-ed camps shaved more often, even though razor blades were scarce, and they washed their clothes more often; and changed them more often.

On the other hand, they felt the responsibility for their women keenly. When Commandant Colonel Tomoyashu at Santo Tomás ordered women to come to his office to polish his boots, and other Jap officers ordered our women into their quarters to scrub the floors, we men refused to let the women go.

We sent a delegation, including the internee chairman, to the colonel's office. We told the colonel that in America we respected our women. We showed him that even in camp women did not do manual labor such as sweeping halls, carrying garbage, or cleaning the men's rooms. We flatly told him—taking quite a chance on reprisals—that we had arranged for a squad of men to come to polish his boots and police the other officers' quarters. And because the men's squad was already at work when the delegation called on the colonel and because his face was saved in that way, he agreed temporarily to excuse the women. They were never ordered to do this work again in Santo Tomás.

Because the woman's point of view in these concentration camps was so important to the camp life, I've asked Marjorie to write a chapter emphasizing how the women reacted to their life behind barbed wire.

BY MARJORIE HATHAWAY GUNNISON

I played at keeping house during the months I was imprisoned in Santo Tomás concentration camp, as did the hundreds of other women prisoners there, Americans, British, Dutch, and Belgians. I say "played" at keeping house because although I had no house to keep I had to go through all the motions—cooking over hot stoves, cleaning overripe fish and rotting vegetables, washing grimy clothes you couldn't get clean in cold water—which was all we had—mending, scrubbing floors, and helping to look after squalling children, even though they weren't my own.

Our sanitary equipment was totally inadequate. Oh, yes, there were toilets. Five of them for all the women on the second floor. Five flush-with-a-bucket toilets for five hundred women. Of course occasionally the bucket wasn't needed, and you never failed to express astonishment when that happened. That was a matter of conversation for the rest of the day. "My dear—just imagine. It actually *flushed* by itself, without the bucket."

There were showers and there were washbowls. Three showers and three washbowls for five hundred women. Cold water only, but water, which was the important thing. Of course you always had to share the shower with from two to six or eight other women. A ruling for their use was made the very first thing. A ruling to the effect that each woman could have a shower every other day. I appreciated the seeming necessity for making such an order but I knew that it would be impossible to enforce it and I, for one, didn't intend to adhere to it. The building was filthy in the first place, the weather terrifically hot, and water was the only enjoyable phase of a most uncomfortable and annoying existence. As it turned out, the sanitation and health department didn't have to enforce such a ruling for, although the showers were always crowded, with a little patience and standing in line it was possible to get wet almost as often as you wished. The trouble was we all lived together, the washed and unwashed alike, and in that tropical climate the intimate proximity was pretty hard to take.

One duty at which nearly every woman in camp took her turn for a period of half an hour or an hour two or three times weekly was "issue tissue" duty. A really responsible position because toilet paper was precious, very precious, and had to be doled out carefully. I used to sit on a high stool just inside the washroom door and issue four sheets—four sheets at the most; it finally got down to two sheets—to each one who came to stand in the ever-waiting line.

How to get hair washed was always a problem. We were not allowed to wash it under the showers because the drains were ancient, and hair stopped them up. Finally a cracked, rusty bathtub (where it came from I never did find out) was set up in back of the large main building. Here hair was washed. Here the vegetables were cleaned. Unsanitary, yes, but the lack of equipment gave us no choice.

Those first days in the Santo Tomás concentration camp in

Manila were probably the hardest. The period of readjustment was difficult. From a luxury hotel to the primitive, filthy, crowded life we lived in the camp was not an easy thing to which to accustom ourselves, and we tried to spend as much time as possible outdoors on the compound. We were one of the first to start building a "shack." A grass mat for the roof nailed on top of four posts which Royal, Jack, and Harold Bayley scrounged somewhere on the compound. The shack grew, others sprang up alongside it and all over the camp until there were more than five hundred "Hooverville" shacks in groups which acquired such names as "Shanty Town," "East Shanty Town," "Frog Bottom," and "Glamourville."

Eight and a half months later when we left Santo Tomás to be transferred to Shanghai our shack had become a rambling "country house." The grass mat had been replaced by a real roof made of boards and papered with tar paper for waterproofing. The dirt floor had become a board floor. A 10 x 5 kitchen annex had been added onto the original one open room, a long counter made for dish washing and clothes washing, a small round table made by using the wheel from a caribou cart on top of a post that was sunk into the ground. The floor had to be laid around this table. Stools had been made by Harold and Royal and a couple of chairs brought out from the main building. They were regulation schoolroom chairs each with a wide wooden arm, cafeteria style.

We were homesteading in true pioneer fashion. We couldn't sleep in the shacks. The Japanese wouldn't permit it. That would have made life "too comfortable" they said. It wasn't until after we had left the camp that this ban was removed. But it did help to have a place to sit during the day, a place where we could eat and talk and play bridge, where we could cook on our native stove with charcoal when we were lucky enough to get it, or with twigs picked up on the grounds.

The lumber for the shack we bought from the camp construction and repair departments lumber yard which was established soon after the camp had started. The native stove was sent in to us by Sancho.

Each morning we went to the shack. Here in 5-gallon gasoline cans stolen from the guards Royal carried water for me so that I could wash clothes in our one tin washbasin. Here I made jam from the fruit which Sancho sent in to us. Here I fried the rice for our dinner, and when we could get one, added an onion to make it palatable. Rice was the mainstay of our diet. We seldom ate the greasy caribou stew or the hard boiled beans which was most often the main dish in the dinner line. Despite our constant hunger, it was awfully hard to get down. And after I had suffered from enteritis and spent some time in the makeshift camp hospital, the seldom became never. So we lived on the rice from the camp kitchen, and on the fruit, the occasional bread, the few eggs which Sancho was able to send us. And even on this starchy diet we steadily lost weight.

Like all good housekeepers I stayed "at home" while my three men went to work, Royal, Jack, and Harold. Harold Bayley was a commercial test pilot for Brewster. Jack had a roving assignment in camp, for he was a room monitor and his duties were more or less of an executive nature. Harold kept regular business hours—8:30 to 12:00 and 1:30 to 5:00—as the number two in the camp lumber yard. Royal worked every morning down at the fence on the package line, and in the afternoon he cleaned one of the women's washrooms.

While they were gone I washed the breakfast dishes, swept the floor, sometimes mopped it, did our laundry—Royal's and mine—and perhaps darned socks, sewed on buttons for my three men, or cut off the sleeves and tails of their good shirts to make them more comfortable for camp wear. Finally the day came when I had to begin patching clothes, here, there, and everywhere.

Once a week was jam-making day; twice a week came school days and I had to hurry through the morning routine to be ready at 11:00 for my Spanish class. The camp educational system was an excellent one. Of course all the school teachers from nursery school up through the university were interned and they established a regular school including excellent adult classes in almost anything you could think of studying.

My own housekeeping routine was also broken into with regular camp duties—vegetable cleaning, "issue tissue," and the weekly general cleaning of sleeping quarters, when everything had to come off the floor for thorough scrubbing and dusting down of walls and ceiling.

My three men were always on hand at lunchtime. We had to figure that meal out ourselves for there was no food served to the camp at noontime. The two meals a day came at 7:30 and at 4:30. Our lunch was usually bread, jam and peanut butter, and fruit. It seldom varied. That was the trouble with everything you had and everything you did in camp. It seldom varied. Monotonous was the word.

Of course we did go visiting occasionally. These visits in this camp city of 3500 were planned and looked forward to just as eagerly as to a dinner or party back home. In spite of the crowded living conditions, contact with your friends was not much different from what it was in normal living days. We tried to keep it that way. Nearly everyone became a member of a so-called family circle. A routine was established and usually followed rather closely. Days might pass before you'd even lay eyes on a friend unless you met by appointment. When you invited someone to dinner, naturally you expected him to bring his own "eating irons," and to go through the camp food line to get his own food. The occasion of the visit would usually mean there was some delicacy which you, as hostess, would furnish—a cherished tin of corned beef, French toast, cookies.

After lunch Harold went back to the lumber yard, and Jack would usually absent himself. Royal and I would have an hour or two alone before his three o'clock toilet-cleaning duty. We would read and talk, discussing the problems of the day: ". . . The new stove already had a crack in it, couldn't it be wired together somehow so it wouldn't fall apart; what could we do about socks, the darns were practically the entire sock, so perhaps to go barefoot was the answer; how about finances; were we going to get the new loan, or weren't we; and what interest would we have to pay this time—50 per cent! my God! Isn't that awful? But we have to have it, so I suppose we should be grateful we can get it and not fuss about a mere percentage. What about changing jobs for a bit, it's getting darned monotonous; have you heard that Bob is adding a room to his shack? How does he get the money? Barbara's black cat had three kittens. . . ."

Royal and I always changed for dinner. White or black tie? Hardly. But a shower, then fresh shorts, and for me a clean cotton dress. It always made us feel a bit better. Then back to the shack for our early 4:30 dinner, to remain until the 7:00 P.M. roll call, when we had to go inside to report. A stroll around the grounds in the front of the main building in a Japanese restricted area, which was designated as within bounds, after roll call, until 9:00 P.M. when everyone had to be inside the buildings, although "lights out" did not come until 11:00. Music was broadcast from a loudspeaker system during this early evening period.

We women in Santo Tomás tried to prevent any relationship between soldier-guards and the children, especially after experiencing a situation which backfired against the Japs, and nearly brought heavy repercussions on all of us.

The Japanese are lovers of children—at least of Japanese children. The guards who patrolled our compound apparently weren't quite sure whether they were going to like white children or not. It was their first contact with them. Perhaps they thought—or were told to think—they could make friends with these white children and through them impress the parents with the strength of the Japanese forces that controlled Greater East Asia. At any rate, it became evident the soldiers were making a play for the hundreds of children that ran around the compound with little or no organized activities. Everyone was too busy to organize anything for the children.

I remember one day looking out across an open field waist-high with tall grass and hearing a series of blood-curdling shouts from a gang of small boys. What I saw made me blink and look twice. Two Japanese soldiers were training these twenty to thirty youngsters in open order infantry attack tactics. They'd wriggle through the grass on their stomachs, then rise to their feet with a shrill cry of "*Banzai*," and with their stick rifles at bayonet charge, rush ahead in attack. Although these Jap soldiers spoke no English they had no difficulty in transmitting their instructions to these boys. These were boys from, say, eight through thirteen or fourteen years old.

I told Royal and Harold about it at noon. They had seen the same thing with other guards and boys. Of course this developed, as was natural, into "armies." There were two large boys' camp armies. They fought from the time school was out until dusk with all the technique they could learn from the Japs. This went on for perhaps two weeks.

One afternoon Royal and I happened to be out near the front gate. A caravan of shiny, black official cars turned in at the gate—cars that had doubtlessly belonged to prisoners in our camp. Everyone usually turned to watch these official inspection parties roll up the long driveway to the main building. This driveway was raised about 2 feet from the rest of the compound level to keep cars out of water in flood times.

The cars full of highest ranking Japanese Army and Naval officers began to move slowly up the drive. The officers stuck their heads out of the windows, gawking at their white prisoners working in the terrible heat or trying to get some rest under the few shade trees. Suddenly from behind these trees popped the combined "kid armies"—about one hundred screaming youngsters. Just as the Japanese soldiers had taught them to do, they charged across the open space toward the official caravan. They all had stick rifles. Some even wore U.S. Army cartridge belts found in the camp gym. But they weren't shouting "*Banzai!*" They were yelling, "Down with the Japs. . . ."

They flopped down on their bellies along the driveway embankment making an assortment of noises only boys can make—sounding for all the world like a machine-gun attack; all stick rifles pointed at the surprised faces of the spick and span Japanese admirals and generals gawking from the car windows.

The situation resulting from this "sixty-second attack" was tense. Potentiality of reprisal was high. The Japanese commandant made inquiries into who had organized the "kid armies," charging parents or ex-U.S. Army men with making anti-Japanese demonstrations. This was punishable by death. For several days things were difficult. The "kid generals" were subdued, but proud of their victory. The commandant was informed that his own guards had taught the boys the attack technique. There was an investigation. The "kid generals" told the commandant what had happened. The commandant had to save face for his guards. Yet, he had to save his own face for the indignity to his superiors. It was a compromise. No more "kid armies." We were forbidden to walk along the road. But everyone breathed more easily again.

One of the interned women's earliest and most constant fears was just what the relationship was going to be between Japanese soldiers and themselves. We all knew of the horrible treatment Chinese and some white women had received at the hands of the Japs in North and Central China. We had heard through the underground of the rape and rough handling of white women during the occupation of Hong Kong, and we knew what had happened to a few of our own women before being interned in Santo Tomás. It wasn't a pretty picture to contemplate. No one spoke about it much. But we and our husbands did plenty of thinking about it.

When we were thrown into Santo Tomás that first night everyone was nervous. Some of the civilian Japs, who had been interned by our people and only recently released, were pretty ugly. They pushed the women around, rifled their purses, and slapped their faces. But no one was harmed.

The Japanese commandant in the Philippines stressed to the internee committeemen the need to keep women "covered." No abbreviated shorts and bra-tops. The commandant spoke of having "to keep the morals of our troops on a high level." As long as they kept their morals on any level, and didn't bother us, we were relieved. I'm sorry to say, however, there were some of our women, believe it or not, who gave the old "come on" to some of the Japs in expectation of some added favors and perhaps release. Most of these were Eurasians. But generally speaking, the Japanese paid little attention to us. This we feel was due in the main to the precedent which our own men early established with the commandant, obtaining from him an order to his guards which was posted in Japanese. This order stated that there should be no relationship between Japanese guards and women internees. The twist the commandant gave it was that "Japanese man should not soil himself by contact with hated foreign white women."

My day in the Santo Tomás concentration camp was pretty much like the day of the thousands of other women interned in camps throughout the Far East, with perhaps a few variations.

Playing at keeping house? Well, I've heard Royal use different words—but I won't put them down here.

(End of Marjorie Gunnison's story of Santo Tomás)

XXIV

DURING the eight and a half months of internment in Santo Tomás I was often questioned, as were the other newspapermen, by the consular officers and gendarmerie. Their main purpose at first was to try to get me to write stories or make definite statements that they could use for propaganda purposes.

They wanted stories especially about the camp life, telling the native populations how well we internees were being treated by the Japanese, and expressing our gratitude to them for their magnanimous treatment. This not only would be good propaganda for the native populations in the occupied areas but for Japanese home consumption, as well as for foreign consumption to be put out over Radio Tokyo.

The Japanese psychology does not permit him flagrantly to make up such stories or statements. He must have some basis for his propaganda statements allegedly made by foreigners. Once he has a story, then he will use it as he sees fit, cutting to suit his best needs, or twisting the meaning to indicate what he wishes regardless of what the original thought of the writer may have been. The Japanese Army Press Corps and the Propaganda Bureau tried constantly to get statements they could expand. There were several categories of persons whom they wanted to quote. First, the women and children whom they would permit to send messages to families at home to be read over Radio Tokyo. The Jap usually let it be known that the messages would go definitely if gratitude were expressed to the Japanese Government for the kind treatment being received and the privilege of sending the message. Many women flatly refused, fearful of how their message might be twisted. Others who were offered a chance to do voice broadcasts that were recorded, took the opportunity, hoping that by voice inflection they could indicate the type of treatment they were receiving.

A second type of prisoner sought by the Jap to be interviewed was the well-known local businessman. If this man could be maneuvered into an answer of any kind that indicated he was being well treated—in other words if he permitted himself to be quoted by even answering the Japanese questioner—the Jap would quote the businessman as "grateful" for Japanese kindness. This was used in two ways. First, as local propaganda among native peoples to prove that the Americans and British were "better off inside the camps," as the Japanese said they were. Secondly, this was used over Radio Tokyo to the United States via short wave to counteract U.S. Department of State protests at abridgement of Geneva Convention regulations. The Japanese had signed but not ratified this convention for humane treatment of prisoners of war. And that lack of ratification gave them just the "out" they thought they needed.

The third type of prisoner especially desirable for quoting was the high-ranking U.S. or British Army or Navy officer and the American or British foreign correspondent. Japanese reasoning was something like this: "If we get one of these officers or correspondents to say something, no matter what, he with his peculiar sense of honor will never deny that he made a statement, and his government will always be in doubt as to whether he did or did not make the statement we quote from him." (This was explained to me by a Japanese newsman in Shanghai, who was after a statement from me.)

The Japs wanted stories and broadcasts from me; they wanted Carl Mydans to take pictures, and repeatedly approached us. Finally, unknown to each other, Carl and I hit on the same answer. And it worked.

One day after a particularly insistent propaganda corps officer flanked by two gendarmes offered every inducement including a room at the Manila Hotel, and then every threat hinting at a cell in Fort Santiago, a very simple idea occurred to me.

"Let me give you my point of view," I interrupted when the going was getting a bit hot. The propaganda corps officer said nothing, but he waited for me to continue.

"Suppose you were in my place, and I were in your place," I said. "Suppose you were interned in the United States and I came to you and asked you to write stories for American newspapers."

The Japanese officer stiffened in his chair, but he still said nothing.

"Suppose you said, 'yes,' that you would write stories for the American newspapers."

The officer said something in Japanese to the two gendarmes but I went right on.

"Then suppose you were repatriated," I continued. "Or perhaps you went home to Tokyo after the war ended. What do you think your people would say about the stories you had written for the enemy? What do you think your family would say, and what would your Emperor say?"

It all sounded a bit thin to my ears. But either he would see the point, or he wouldn't. Of course, even if he did get the point, it might not make any difference anyway. I waited while the propaganda corps officer carried on a very pebble-throated conversation with the gendarmes. Evidently they all agreed, for suddenly he turned to me and his only words were, "You may go now."

I went through further questioning periods, the toughest concerning what I knew about guerrilla activities. How were the guerrillas being financed? How were they organized? Who in camp was connected with this activity? Where were the guerrilla headquarters? At one time the military administration was obsessed with the idea that someone in Santo Tomás was the "brains" behind the guerrilla activity and was financing it as well. But on investigation nothing was found to substantiate this and Commandant Tsurumi told me "there has been great mistake."

However, in proving that there had been a great mistake to the entire satisfaction of the Japanese, a few internees had some pretty bad moments. We always had the feeling that the Japanese could and very well might trump up some charge, regardless of facts, and all our protesting wouldn't do a bit of good.

We saw in Manila the daily Japanese propaganda newspaper published in English by the Nichi Nichi Company. They took over the *Manila Tribune*, and continued to publish its English edition as well as its Spanish and Tagalog editions.

Reading this daily paper was more heartening than otherwise although we became very tired of reading that Americans were "barbarians, beasts, greedy aggressors, exploiters, two-faced materialists, and imperialists." However, the paper often provided the necessary daily laugh.

We learned to read between the lines. One friend of mine used to say, "The only thing you have to do to get a true picture of the war is to read the daily Japanese *Shimbun*, divide all figures quoted by 2, add 10 and subtract 5, shake well, and digest slowly."

But it was a little easier than that. What was not printed was often more significant than what we read. Naturally there were rumors from the outside as to what our forces were doing and were not doing. These were of course distorted and untrustworthy, but there was some basis of truth in most of them, and the daily paper sometimes unwittingly confirmed these rumors, as in the case of the reports of the Doolittle raid on Tokyo.

It was about five days after the raid that we first began to get rumors. But since it was so close to the Emperor's birthday, in April, we discounted the reports as wishful thinking. However, there was much subversive but real celebration within the camp on the day the Japanese *Shimbun* inadvertently admitted that Tokyo had been bombed by American fliers. What was printed was tucked away in a small item on an inside page. This item stated that the Japanese had done a wonderful job "in putting out the big fires caused by the inhuman bombing of Tokyo's schools and hospitals by American bombers."

The point the Japanese made was that the city of Tokyo was so constructed that after enemy bombings "buildings burned very quickly. But in America when there are such bombings it is much more disastrous because there the buildings are concrete, steel, and brick, and the fires will burn for hours, for days."

This story not only provided us with a laugh but it was a morale builder for weeks after, especially since it came in between the surrenders of Bataan and Corregidor. This bombing made us expect that there would be continued steady bombings of Japan because few believed the United States would try a mere stunt raid. The general impression was that there would be no raids on Japan proper until we were ready to do it in earnest.

After my transfer to Shanghai where I talked with people who had been in Tokyo during the raid, I found that its effect had been devastating on the Japanese public morale. However, the bombings also resulted in a complete reorganization of the air-raid defense of the city of Tokyo and other Japanese cities. This took three forms. First, military anti-aircraft defense—changing of positions of balloon defense. Second, construction of underground air-raid shelters where before a type of Anderson shelter and open ditches were provided. Third, a more practical education of the people regarding what to do and where to go during air raids, for even well-trained Japanese mobs become confused when surprised.

XXV

AFTER several successful internee-prisoner escapes from the Santo Tomás concentration camp the guards at the gate picked a Filipino at random one day—a Filipino who hadn't bowed low enough in passing through the gate. Who's to say how low you should bow to a guard? The decision is only a whim of the moment.

The guards pounced on this hapless Filipino with much shouting. He was to be used as an object lesson. But they'd have fun doing it! The shouting brought several hundred internee-prisoners down toward the gate to see what was up. That's exactly what the Japanese wanted. What the internee-prisoners saw made some of them so nauseated they vomited. Young girls twelve to fourteen years of age screamed hysterically and ran sobbing away from the scene.

I watched the guards strip the Filipino and truss him to a crisscrossed bamboo scaffolding after one of the most brutal beatings a human being could go through and still live. Once the body was strung up by the wrists and neck—tied by bamboo thongs—the guards began a bouncing, prancing, bayonet practice. They used all the tricks known against all vital parts of the human body. They yelled, retched, and howled at the top of their voices.

The Filipino at first tried to keep his poise. Finally he called in desperation to the crowd of internee-prisoners—menaced some 200 feet away by other guards with rifles.

"Help me—oh, please help me. I have done nothing. Please tell them I have done nothing. . . ."

The bayonets slipped in and out of his naked body. It was too late to do anything, even if we had been able to. A member of the camp internee committee ran breathless to the office of the commandant and the captain of the guard. But they professed ignorance of the episode. "Probably the Filipino was to blame for what he received in the way of punishment," was the only answer.

The guards at the gate would have been pleased had any internee-prisoner made a move to protect the dying Filipino. There was no alternative. Your heart, your head thumped with blind rage. But actually what could you do in a moment like that to prevent such an atrocity? The answer is nothing.

The entire camp of 3500 rumbled for several days with unrest over the incident. The Japs merely shrugged their shoulders.

"You see what happens to people who disobey. Better not permit any more of your people to try to escape this camp," was their only comment. But that didn't stop the escapes. It only made people more careful.

Men "went over the fence" nightly to join the forces at Bataan and the guerrilla bands in the hills. Most of those who escaped knew the hills and had hideouts arranged. But one night three Britishers escaped, only one of whom was a resident of the islands, and none of whom had any well-made plan for hiding. This was Laycock, an Australian. He had been a mining engineer, and had held a hundred and one odd jobs in various Philippine communities. The other two were Englishmen, seamen off the *Anwhei*, caught in Manila Bay at the first bombing. Fletcher was the navigating officer. Weeks was, I believe, third mate.

The three went over the fence at night after roll call. They weren't even missed. But they made the mistake of trying to travel by daylight. A truckload of Japanese soldiers came along the road they were following. The three men didn't get into the covering jungle in time, and were caught.

The Japanese soldiers took them to gendarmerie headquarters, from where they were returned to camp for a beating—so that all prisoners could get an object lesson. They were then taken out of camp to an outside local prison. On inquiring what was to be done with them the commandant told our committee that they would be given a trial . . . but they would not be shot.

The next thing we knew the word came in that they *were* to be shot. The commandant confirmed this. He claimed he had tried to prevent it; that he would even go out that night to humble himself before his commanding officer to plead for their lives. He said he would do this because he had promised our committee the men would not be shot. Colonel Tomoyashu did go out that night, dressed in wooden clogs and his old clothes to "humble" himself before his commanding officer. Where he went no one knew. But when he came back he assured us there would be no shooting.

The camp was seething with rumors and was greatly agitated. A real demonstration was in the making. The Japanese realized this and doubled the armed guards. They uncovered the machine guns on rooftops around the camp. Japanese guards with sub-machine guns posted themselves in windows of Filipino houses overlooking the 52-acre compound.

At noon Earl Carroll, along with the interpreter we weren't sure of, the two room monitors representing the rooms these men had lived in, and the Church-of-England minister were suddenly whisked out of camp in the commandant's limousine. Only a few of us knew this. It looked bad. By one-thirty the delegation was back, pale, shaky and uncommunicative. The Japanese military guard was again increased.

The three Britishers, Fletcher, Weeks, and Laycock, had been shot, sitting on the mound of dirt beside their common small grave. They had been shot from a distance by automatic revolvers and after toppling into the grave were buried alive—groans could still be heard as the dirt was shoveled on top of them.

After the mound had been piled up a marker bearing their names in Japanese characters was stuck on top of the grave. A Japanese soldier then went over to a fence covered with purple bougainvillea, snipped off a spray, laid it across the mound, and laughed.

That night it was only with the greatest of difficulty that Carroll and the committee were able to restrain the prisoners. But the Japanese were in a firing mood. They'd have killed the first objector. The committee, however, filed into the commandant's office and made an official protest over the shooting of civilians.

The next morning the daily Japanese newspaper carried an account of the attempted escape of the three prisoners and told of a "trial" and their being "executed" for attempting "to join the resisting fighting forces still holding out at Bataan and Corregidor." The entire city of Manila rumbled with indignation.

That same morning a special Mass was held for the three men in the Roman Catholic Chapel in the building in which the Spanish Fathers still lived in one corner of the compound. The Japanese had forbidden the Mass and warned internees not to attend.

Japanese guards were present at 6:45 A.M. when the crowd gathered. This was the critical moment. Would the guard interfere?

The guard stepped up close. The crowd of men surged toward the chapel. No one spoke. But you could hear the heavy breathing. The guards looked around. One fingered his rifle. He shouted some kind of a command and walked through the crowd to the outside of the ring of men. There they "presented arms," shouted again, and stood "at ease."

We all went to that Mass, Protestants, Catholics, and non-church-men alike. Just as many as could crowd into the chapel. Hundreds of others stood outside.

After the Mass was over the guards again took their posts.

But three days later Commandant Colonel Tomoyashu was "replaced" by Consul R. Tsurumi, of the well-known Tsurumi family. Colonel Tomoyashu told the committee he was being promoted to go into active service at Bataan. Within a month we heard he had "died of malignant malaria," in the jungles of Bataan. More likely lead poisoning. There was undisguised rejoicing in the camp. And from my own personal point of view, I felt considerable relief. At least one of my more persistent enemies was dead.

XXVI

IT WAS mid-March when General MacArthur was ordered to shift his headquarters from the depths of Corregidor to Australia. We in camp who had been following the campaign closely knew the end was near. By the 9th of April Bataan had fallen, and the horror march from Bataan to Tarlac and Camp O'Donnell became World War II history's leading military atrocity. Within a month Lieutenant General Jonathan W. ("Skinny") Wainwright decided there was no strategic value in trying to hold out at Corregidor until every man and every Army nurse in the fortress was dead. And he surrendered to Lieutenant General M. Homma in the city of Manila.

Undoubtedly the story of General Wainwright's surrender will be recorded by historians who dig deep into War Department files for the report on the fall of Corregidor as presented in typical War Department phraseology.

I was told the story of the surrender firsthand by a Japanese correspondent who was present, and who claimed to have done some of the interpreting. This correspondent, Kazumaro Uno, an American-born Japanese originally from Los Angeles, wrote the story in a Japanese propaganda booklet called *Corregidor—Isle of Delusion.* Uno told me his story after I had been transferred to Shanghai. He had called me to his office (he was then Japanese editor of the *Shanghai Evening Post and Mercury*) to ask me some questions about General MacArthur, questions for which I had no answer.

Uno spoke perfect American. In fact he had trouble with his

Japanese, which he spoke with an American accent. This made him
suspect among the Japanese. But there was little need for that. He
was, and still is, a loyal Japanese subject; also bitterly anti-American
because he says, "I was treated like a yellow skibby and not an
American citizen, although my education was as good as any other
American's. So I decided, the hell with the United States. I'd go to
Japan where my knowledge of the States would be appreciated."
And it was. Uno was obviously a privileged character in the Japanese Army Press Bureau. From those of his stories which I read I
think he was a more factually accurate reporter than most Japanese,
probably because of his American training. However, he could be
just as screwy as all the rest when it came to the hay-wire type of
propaganda they try to peddle as emotional come-on.

I want to give Uno's story of the surrender of Corregidor for two
reasons. First, it is the generally accepted Japanese version. Second,
it will probably be some time before we get our own official version
and I believe Uno's report is probably close enough to what really
happened to repeat. Here is the story that he told me:

Corregidor took its worst beating from the air and from the shore
guns at Mariveles and from the Batangas shores during the night of
May 5. The first Japanese landing barges hit the small beach opposite Mariveles on the north flank of the island in the dark of the
early morning. Most of the first Japanese landing flotilla was completely wiped out. The same went for the second and the third. But
the Japanese came on and on, finally getting a sizable force ashore
before dawn and forcing the Marines on the beachhead to withdraw
up the slope of the rock. There weren't many of the Fourth Marines
left to withdraw.

Uno was on the Bataan shore at Limay when word arrived that
General Wainwright had arrived from Corregidor to surrender.
The Japanese correspondents rushed to the small wood-frame house
where the historic meeting between Lieutenant General M. Homma
and Lieutenant General Wainwright would take place.

General Wainwright was already waiting at the shack when Uno
and the few Japanese correspondents arrived. Uno said Wainwright
leaned heavily on a cane. He was very thin and drawn, although his
eyes were exceedingly clear. He wore no necktie. His uniform was
worn and wrinkled. There were several American officers accom-
panying General Wainwright. One was an Army colonel, another
a Marine major. A staff sergeant stood near by with a large white
flag.

Japanese soldiers began to set a narrow table on the rickety porch of the shack. There were iced beer and orangeade, and some dry Japanese cakes. These were for the celebration *after* the signing of the surrender.

Several Japanese photographers tried to snap pictures of General Wainwright and his staff as they waited uncomfortably in the hot sun. The General always turned his back.

After nearly a half-hour wait a line of army limousines rolled up the narrow dusty road. General Homma and his staff alighted and proceeded immediately to the porch where they sat down. An aide approached General Wainwright indicating he was to come up onto the porch. He did. General Homma rose and gave a curt bow. General Homma spoke first, through an interpreter, although his English is letter perfect.

"I suppose you are tired, General?" he asked.

General Wainwright did not acknowledge the greeting.

"General Homma," he said, "I have come to surrender my men and myself."

General Homma sat down and motioned to Wainwright and his staff to be seated.

"In the name of His Imperial Japanese Majesty, I accept the surrender of all the United States forces in the Philippine Islands," General Homma declared.

There was obviously something wrong on the American side of the table, Uno said. General Wainwright hesitated a moment. "But, General," he protested, "I can surrender only the forces on Corregidor and Fort Drum. When General MacArthur left I was placed in command of these forces only."

Homma flared back, not waiting for the interpreter even to begin repeating.

"You are in command of all the forces in the Philippines. This has been true since MacArthur left. I will accept the surrender of *all* American forces—or you can go back to Corregidor and expect the full force of our attack to continue."

General Homma got up. So did everyone else. He shot a parting order to General Wainwright, whom Uno described as "wilted."

"When you see fit to surrender you may surrender to the Commanding Officer now on Corregidor. He will bring you to me in Manila. . . ." And he and his staff roared away from the little wood shack and the small palm clearing in a heavy cloud of choking Philippine dust.

General Wainwright and his staff were obviously worried, according to Uno. In a few minutes, the U.S. Army colonel came over to where a Japanese lieutenant, a colonel, and Uno were talking.

"General Wainwright wants General Homma to know he will accept full responsibility for surrender of the American troops in the Philippines. And he asks your courtesy in recalling General Homma before he gets away. Because the lives of so many men are at stake he requests that you be good enough to contact General Homma quickly."

The Japanese colonel asked Uno to translate. He said there was nothing he could do.

The American colonel replied, "General Wainwright will send me under your flag of truce to Mindanao to contact General Sharp in charge of our forces down there."

The Japanese colonel replied, "It is too late now."

Uno said he and the lieutenant talked with the Japanese colonel who finally agreed to accompany General Wainwright and his staff across to Corregidor and to take General Wainwright to the headquarters of the Japanese commander.

"I will go to Corregidor to see that you surrender to the right man," the colonel told Wainwright. "Then he will take you to Manila to see General Homma."

It was after dark when General Wainwright "and his dejected staff" landed on the beach at Corregidor. Since the Japanese Higgins landing boat was too deep draft to get in close to the shore, two of the American noncoms made a hand-chair and carried General Wainwright the remaining few hundred feet to the shore. The other officers waded in. One American staff officer was very sick "from lack of food" and had to be helped ashore.

Uno went with the party until they got to the headquarters of the Japanese officer to whom General Wainwright surrendered himself. Later General Wainwright was taken to Manila where he met Homma, officially surrendered, and was ordered to broadcast his surrender terms over station KZRH. This ended Uno's story.

Not so many days later I found myself in the unique position of being able to watch the Japanese drive the bedraggled group of gallant Corregidor defenders through the city of Manila in a disgusting "gloat" march. And during that march I saw many an American and many a Filipino soldier helping each other limp and drag themselves along the route from where they were dumped ashore outside the city to the station, to Fort McKinley, and even to the dungeons at Bilibid prison, not far from our camp at Santo Tomás.

On that steaming-hot Philippine day I found myself released from camp with a pass which permitted me to remain out until 3 P.M. Ostensibly I was given this pass—one of three during my entire eight and a half months in the Santo Tomás concentration camp—to go into the city of Manila to purchase camp supplies. We were still feeding ourselves, and providing all our own sanitation and other equipment at this time.

I had completed my purchasing at Aguinaldo's Department Store and was eating a meal in a small restaurant when a Filipino came in and said, "Seer, they are marching the men from Corregidor into the city."

"Where?" I asked.

"In from Pasay. I think along Dewey Boulevard . . ."

I rushed out, jumped into a *carretela* (two-wheeled horse-drawn cart) and told the driver to take me quickly to where the men were being marched into the city.

I found that the Americans and Filipinos whom General Wainwright had surrendered at Corregidor had been brought onto the beach near Manila in Japanese landing barges, dumped ashore, formed into ragged groups of two to three hundred each and marched off to the city.

Many of these men were so sick and weak they could scarcely drag themselves along. Hundreds were obviously suffering from the effects of the heavy aerial and shore battery bombardment they had received for days prior to the surrender. Scarcely any seemed to be in good condition. A few had hats. Most had dirty towels or torn shirts over their heads to protect them from the terrific heat of the tropical sun.

The first prisoners I saw after I sidled into the crowd of Filipinos gathered along the street were Naval officers. The Japs had them packed into army trucks. Most of them were without caps or insignia. A few of them had been able to get cleaned up. Most of them were just as they had been when captured—tired, drawn, and so much thinner than when I had seen them last. Those I recognized looked older, peaked, but defiant. Japanese guards with drawn pistols rode in the trucks with them. There was no opportunity to catch their attention, although some scanned the street crowds for familiar faces.

There were only a few Americans and British who witnessed this march. These were "sick" internee-prisoners who had been released temporarily from the camp, and a scattering of mothers who had small children, and who had been permitted to leave camp for a short time.

The Japanese guards who paced along at 20- or 30-foot intervals were utterly wanton in the way they jabbed their sharp bayonets into the arms, buttocks, and backs of the stragglers. The Jap had decided he was going to show the Filipino spectator who was "superior." Now the Jap was gloating. Hadn't he just cleaned the white man out of what proved to be the toughest stronghold in all the Far East? (It took some 150,000 Japs to take the 85,000 Filipino-American troops we had at Bataan and the 13,000 or so left on Corregidor.)

Some Japanese guards patrolled the ragged groups of prisoners, beating stragglers with the flat of their swords. I saw one American beaten to the street for half-heartedly raising his arms to stave off the brutal, frenzied beating. Two of his buddies lifted him to his feet and dragged him along.

But it was the so-called "rest periods" that were the worst. These were nothing but moments of extreme torture for our men. About every half hour—or twenty minutes—the Japanese command to halt would come down the line. "Stop . . . stop . . . stop . . ." the Japs would shout.

Our men would slump to the street in exhaustion. Only a few would prefer to remain standing. It was too painful for some of the bandaged to get down and get up again. No sooner would the poor beggars—and they looked like a great line of tattered beggars—get relaxed on the pavement than the Jap guards would rush among them, bayonet points jabbing, prodding, drawing blood.

"Up . . . up . . . up . . . !" they'd shout. Some of the men just couldn't get to their feet without assistance. Sometimes this assistance was slow in coming. I saw a Jap right in front of me put his bayonet clear through the arm muscle of a soldier who raised his arm to protect a friend from vicious bayonet jabs.

At such atrocities the crowd of Filipino spectators would murmur disapproval. And at times like these the Japanese guards would wade right into the crowds swinging their rifles like clubs, felling any hapless spectator who wasn't quick enough to dodge out of the way.

Filipino women cried and fainted as they caught sight of their husbands or sons in the long trailing lines of Filipinos who followed the Americans. When some Filipino hysterically stepped out into the mass of marching men to go to the arms of their men, Japanese guards slapped their faces, even going so far as to shove rifle butts into their faces and stomachs. This procedure was particularly amusing to the Japanese. In fact the whole "gloat" march caused great hilarity among the guards and the many Japanese civilians who watched the march in groups.

During the short torture rest periods when Filipinos tossed packages of cigarettes and handed out bottles of beer and water as well as vitamin tablet packages and other medicines to the soldiers, the Japs became furious. They waded among the prostrate men using rifle butts to break the beer and water bottles, and lunged into the crowds along the curbs to try to catch the "culprits who aided and befriended the enemy." Those they caught were badly slapped and beaten. Some were taken away—I don't know where. Probably for more beatings.

One woman standing next to me carried a four- or five-year-old child on her shoulder. I felt her stiffen; heard her gasp. I looked to see what had caused this. She had spotted her husband. The baby started to cry "Daddy . . ." but the mother clapped her hand over the child's mouth. "Just look at Daddy," she whispered. "Don't speak. The Japanese will hurt him if you do." The baby was puzzled, but obeyed. Baby hands opened and shut in silent greeting.

You couldn't miss the father. His eyes filled with tears, he started through the marching crowd. A wiser friend caught him, held him. He just couldn't look any more. After a brave nod and attempt to smile at his wife and baby, he turned away and looked out toward the bay shimmering golden in the afternoon sunlight.

Yes . . . all this and more confirmed everything I had heard up until that moment about the "horror march from Bataan." And later when I heard the story of that forced march of an even sicker and more tattered mass of prisoners, from the mouths of men who had made the march and survived to escape, I knew my estimate of the Jap had not been keen and alert enough. I knew then that to the Jap the atrocity was merely doing his duty. What appeared on the surface to be the fanatical, the sadistic, the hopped-up Jap, was the ordinary *sane* Japanese soldier.

When I was shown actual photographs of the march from Bataan by Japanese newsman Uno later in Shanghai—pictures of long lines of gaunt, starving, often shoeless men wading ankle deep through the choking dust of the rutted Philippine roads—I longed to be able to bring only one such picture home to prove to the people in the United States what kind of an enemy we were fighting.

Most of the men from Corregidor were packed into small boxcars and shipped north to Cabanatuan where many of them still survive. During those first weeks as many as seventeen Americans died daily in these camps from beatings, forced labor, starvation, dysentery, and lack of medical care for wounds and other ailments. I had word directly from a "contact" at one of the war prisoner camps telling me of the death of Harry Morton, the young U.S. Navy lieutenant who had tried to be so helpful and sane during the wartime censorship debacle. He had monitored most of my broadcasts. Now, I learned he had died of dysentery because of lack of any medical care. Harry Morton's mother and sister lived in the next room to mine at camp. His wife and their nine-month-old baby were still on the outside. Somehow I couldn't get up courage to tell them about Harry. But it wasn't long before they got direct word themselves.

In many instances Japanese Army doctors who visited the American and Filipino camps first at O'Donnell and later at Cabanatuan would not treat an American or Filipino unless the prisoner could pay for the medicine. And typically Japanese, many a Japanese doctor, after a slap-dash treatment, would take the money and report the prisoner for having forbidden money hidden on his person.

But the Filipinos had the last word—even at this time. Shortly after the "glorious victories of the forces of His Imperial Japanese Majesty at Bataan and Corregidor," Lieutenant General Homma and the top officers of the naval landing party ordered a "victory parade." The line of march took thousands of cocky, bandy-legged Japanese troops through the business section of Manila across the Passig River bridge and past the Government buildings to the green Luneta at the edge of Manila Bay.

There, framed against the background of angular masts and stacks of ships sunk in the inner harbor, stood the deep-chested Lieutenant General, an admiral in stiff whites, and thirty or more military, naval, and civilian aides. The victorious army afoot, and in trucks and tanks, passed in review. Thousands of Filipinos watched along the route of the march. Some turned their backs when the color guards passed.

The Japanese insisted that Jorge Vargas, chairman of the Executive Commission, and members of his Commission march in the parade in the sweltering heat, carrying small Japanese flags. This was designed to be the supreme insult. This was planned "enforced victory." The Filipino population of Manila was to note hereby that the Japanese Government had taken over for keeps, and that the Filipino Government was openly subservient.

At such occasions there must be martial music. A parade without music, even discordant Japanese band music, is pretty flat. The Japanese Army had a few bands in the Philippines, but not enough.

There was only one answer. Order out some Filipino bands to be spotted in the parade.

The parade went off as scheduled. The Japanese were exultant! The bands stumped past the reviewing stand. Ancestral swords and gold teeth flashed in the morning sun. This was victory; this was superiority at its height! A Filipino band passed in review toward the end of the parade. As these Filipinos approached the reviewing stand, the drum major chirped on his whistle, and gave the down beat with his baton.

Every Filipino within hearing turned, startled at what he heard. Then broad grins, followed by cheers from the crowd. The conquerors, somewhat surprised at this "spontaneous recognition of victory," graciously acknowledged the cheers. The band marched on and dispersed. And so did the crowd.

The band had passed the reviewing stand playing "The Stars and Stripes Forever."

XXVII

WHAT infuriated the Japanese conquerors of the Philippines, and the exploiters of Manila in particular, was the increasing lack of respect shown them by the average Filipino.

The Jap missed his chance at winning over any Filipinos who might have been "on the fence" after listening to all the Japanese promises of "co-prosperity for Greater East Asia." The invader came into the Philippines, as he did into Malaya and the Netherlands East Indies and China, with utter disregard for the well-being and the feelings of the native population, and immediately antagonized the very peoples he needed to assist him in this East Asia grab.

After brutal slappings and beatings in the open streets, and the very apparent disregard of native customs and of the native himself, the Jap in the Philippines soon became known among the Filipinos as "the termite." The Filipino, when ired, is not a man to be trifled with. This the Japanese soldier soon discovered. Within four weeks after the occupation of Manila, and while the battles for Bataan and Corregidor still raged across the bay, it was unsafe for less than three or four Japanese soldiers to walk any but the main streets of Manila after dark.

The number of dead Japanese soldiers found stabbed and dragged up back streets startled the military administrator of the city into action. Wherever a Japanese was found dead ten Filipinos were ordered killed. If a dead Jap was found in front of a house, the military police just went into that and other houses in the area, picked ten Filipinos at random, killed them and left them in the street in the broiling sun for several days—an object lesson.

Undaunted, the Filipinos continued to kill Japanese soldiers. In the hills and outlying districts guerrilla organizations improved and guerrilla activities increased.

And this is the most dangerous business in the world—espionage and guerrilla action. If your *coup* doesn't come off, you're finished. It takes guts, this business. It takes intelligence, and the Filipino has both plus a type of national spirit that makes him a most dangerous antagonist for the Jap.

The Philippines' guerrilla forces includes the pressure columnists, the counterpart of the Axis fifth columnists. The pressure columnists work underground. When the pressure is great enough it blows through the top and volcano-like takes everything else with it.

Since the fall of Corregidor the Japanese have been only too well aware of this movement. They have been constantly "mopping up," as they say, the remnants of the Filipino guerrilla forces. But somehow these forces have refused to stay "mopped up." Only the week before the repatriation ship, the *Teia Maru*, picked up 151 internees from the Philippines in September 1943, the Japanese announced the "final cleanup of all guerrillas on Luzon." But two days later guerrilla bands in southern Luzon machine-gunned two northbound trains, killing several hundred Japanese.

Earlier, some of these guerrilla bands organized raids on jails or Japanese compounds holding small numbers of Americans and British. This was before the Japanese had found time to ship their prisoners into the Manila or Baguio concentration camps. One guerrilla band of several hundred Filipinos raided a southern Luzon town where about sixty Americans were being held in a rat-infested jail. After the Filipinos had killed every Jap in the town they freed the Americans and took them off to the jungle hills—women, children, and aged alike.

Gradually this particular group of prisoners broke up. Some joined other groups. Some tried to get passage in native sailing craft down to the Island of Mindanao where there was still a considerable U.S.-led fighting force. But about ten of these people were surprised one day by a Japanese patrol and recaptured. Among them were some children about eight to twelve years old. They were taken back to the town from which they had been freed. Again they were shoved into the same vermin-filled jail. They received almost nothing to eat.

"This is so you will not run away again," one Jap told them.

The second day they were ordered out into the bright sunlight. "The captain wishes examine you," their English-speaking guard said.

When they reached the second-floor bare board office of the captain he examined each prisoner thoroughly, brutally—even to slapping some of the women. It seemed to those waiting their turn that he would never stop. Suddenly he did.

"Too hot!" he snorted. "These men these r-ady . . . they too dumb. I shoot you!" He gave a sharp order in Japanese. The men were lined up on one side of the office; women and children on the other. The men's hands were tied behind them. Then the women were shoved down the narrow staircase ahead of the men, out into a small open patio. They were arranged in a double line and left standing in the sweltering heat for nearly an hour. Finally, their worst fears seemed about to be realized. A squad of soldiers carrying rifles marched in and stood facing the Americans. The captain looked out an upstairs window and gave an order. This was the end. But no one spoke.

They could hear someone clattering down the stairs in heavy boots. It must be the captain. He appeared, half drunk. His collar was open, his suspenders were hanging down behind him. He was in an ugly mood. Still nothing was said. Obviously he was trying to get one of the Americans to speak out in protest.

"Now, I shoot you!" he bellowed. He gave an order in Japanese. The soldiers stood at attention and fingered their rifles.

Then the captain reached in his coat pocket and pulled out a black leather case which at first glance looked like a small revolver in a holder. Suddenly he held the black case out before him and burst into an uncontrollable fit of laughter.

It was a camera.

"I shoot you . . . yes . . . see . . . I shoot . . . you" (more laughter) "with camera" (increased laughter as he caught the unmistakable looks of relief in his prisoners' faces). He "shot" their pictures all right, highly pleased with the mental torture he had put his enemies through that muggy afternoon. One of them told me this story after he and his family had been transferred to Santo Tomás.

This is Japanese humor at its highest pitch.

I heard that this same captain was killed during another guerrilla raid on his town, when the Filipinos returned to release these same prisoners. But the prisoners had been shifted by that time.

Sometimes the Filipino bands got too cocky after a couple of such raids, and, overconfident, exposed themselves. The Japanese would ambush them then with a larger force, capture the leaders and massacre the others as an example to near-by guerrilla groups. It seemed for a time there that the Japanese were having extraordinarily good luck in breaking into the "G" organization, as the Filipinos called their setup. But this was due mainly to a fluke. The Japanese Military Intelligence caught the secretary of the "G" headquarters for being out after curfew. He showed signs of knowing more than he told. Naturally he was given a very rough time and no one ever saw or heard of him again. But it was evident that he did give the names of a few "G" group leaders. These were leaders of groups of up to two hundred guerrillas.

In a class by himself among the Filipinos who constantly harass the Japanese is Juan de la Cruz—or "John Smith" to the Filipino—the people's hero of the Philippines, the mythical radio personality who caused more trouble and actual embarrassment to Lieutenant General Homma, conqueror of the Philippines, than all the Fil-American troops at Bataan or Corregidor.

What's more, Juan Cruz remained free. He remained free, ready at a moment's notice to radio blitz any Japanese general, admiral, corporal, or geisha when the hour should come to arouse the Filipino flame of resistance into a mighty consuming fire of elimination of everything Nipponese. His regular broadcasts—short and long wave from portable sets "somewhere on the Island of Luzon"—were made, as he told his listeners, "just to keep my hand in for the big day." These broadcasts were made in Tagalog, Spanish, and English.

From the very beginning Juan Cruz had a price on his head. Ten thousand pesos were offered by the very much worried General Homma at the height of the first series of broadcasts. To match the offer for his scalp by the bald-headed, Oxford-accented Japanese general, Juan Cruz countered the next day with "exactly 5 centavos (2½ cents U.S.) for your ivory-plated dome, you—— No skull is worth more!"

Juan Cruz understood the Japanese psychology. He did everything possible over the air to rile the Japanese Command. He even poked fun at His Imperial Japanese Majesty Hirohito, whom he addressed familiarly as "Charlie"—the name coined by foreigners in Japan for the Emperor. He pricked the Japanese in their soft spot—

their inferiority complex—constantly. He was the unseen but not unheard sniper. To be sure the Japanese had put a strict military ban and death penalty for possession of short-wave radio sets. But not for long-wave sets. The Japanese wanted and tried to put out their own long-winded propaganda over stations KZRH and KZRM. Thus it was most perplexing to the Japanese propagandist to hear Juan Cruz break in on a program and then announce a time and wave length over which all might hear him.

"John Smith" had the best news sources in the Philippines. Some of his broadcasts, copies of which I saw, showed sources right at the elbow of the commanding Japanese administration, as well as of Japanese puppets. His intimate knowledge of what went on everywhere in the Islands was phenomenal. For instance, he could tell you all about events happening inside the concentration camps where more than six thousand American and British were sweating and starving out the war. When the three civilian British internees were shot without trial on February 16, 1942, Juan Cruz had the whole story—and accurately—the following day.

Whatever he reported on he had the facts. He used them effectively. His people soon found he was telling the truth. His greeting of *"Mabuhay-mabuhay-mabuhay."* (long life) became familiar household words.

At one period Juan Cruz had to tone down his sensational messages because he was arousing his people too soon. The Filipinos were rising in an unorganized way in various parts of Luzon, rising against the Japanese at the wrong time, too soon, causing their subjection to needless, ruthless punishment of the type only the brutal Japanese could think up. Thus, when it became evident that the broadcasts were inflaming the people too soon and without a proper pattern, they were temporarily discontinued.

Several times the Japanese claimed to have captured Juan Cruz. And he had some close calls. Obviously he moved his broadcasting unit constantly, even while broadcasting. His story fully told would make a Hollywood thriller-producer gasp. One day at the height of the Japanese dragnet campaign for him he escaped by the brazen device of halting his broadcast in the midst of a sentence, leaving his equipment to be disposed of by other Filipino patriots, and walking serenely through the Japanese cordon. He showed the Japanese which way he had gone. With his next broadcast he upbraided "the stupid ——" for their thick-headedness. His profanity was profuse, but to the point.

He had two purposes. First, to arouse his people against the tyranny of the Japanese invaders. Second, to infuriate the Japanese into making blunders through the ever useful means of ridicule. The Japanese can't stand ridicule. Their inferiority complex doesn't permit it.

The original plan for Juan Cruz envisioned the possibility of his being captured. Thus his successor was picked and ready to replace him if it ever became necessary, for this voice of freedom had to be kept on the air.

Careful planning was imperative for the guerrillas' operation from the hills against the Japanese-operated mines, roads, power lines, dams, munitions dumps, and railroads, and in the cities where there was more direct counter-espionage and passive resistance against the Japanese, and more assassination work.

"Elimination" jobs called for special assassins. One of the most sensational and the most hushed up was the elimination of Alejandro Roces, Jr., who with his wife was killed in a *carretela* in front of his own house. His father who witnessed the violent murder from his front porch died on the spot of shock. It appeared that Roces, Jr., was working with the guerrillas on the one hand and playing with the Japanese on the other. The story is that his wife didn't know of his connection with the guerrillas and unknown to Roces turned over to the Japanese two guerrillas who appeared at the house one day for some money. The guerrilla group leader ordered the elimination of Roces, Jr., because of this double cross.

The Japanese tried hard to cover up his death, merely announcing that his father had died from heart failure. But at the father's funeral there were three coffins.

The attempt to assassinate José Laurel, President of the Japanese-controlled "Free Philippines," was unsuccessful although the guerrillas stood over him after the first shot had knocked him down and fired point blank into his chest. This happened on the Wack-Wack Golf course. But José Laurel and Benigno Aquino, head of the Kalibapi (Japanese-inspired Filipino co-operation political society) are marked men by the guerrillas.

Such blatant action as this fires the other Filipinos and they want to do their part to remove the "termites." In July 1943 word was passed via bamboo telegraph and chain-letter system that "Now is not the time to strike. We will advise you when that time comes. Keep alert. Never fail to report what you see. Never fail to note traitors nor how the enemy moves in our midst. Watch where he keeps his arms and ammunition. Watch! The time will come. We are planning for it. We will let you know. *Mabuhay!*"

But this organized resistance is not the only sort of thing which is worrying the invader of the Philippines. Within two months after their occupation of the Islands, the Japanese realized that they were up against something far greater than the guerrilla bands in the hills and the remnants of the USAFFE forces on Bataan and Corregidor. During a period of questioning the Japanese asked me to comment on the following statement which supposedly came from the Japanese Army Press Bureau headquarters in the form of a report back to Japan on the Filipino attitude. The statement read:

"I believe it is conservative to estimate that about 50 per cent of the seventeen million Filipinos are still loyal or nearly loyal to our enemies. In other words, any action on America's part that is felt in the Philippines will draw these people along, led by a sizable aggressive anti-Japanese group. The pro-Japanese element is about average for occupied areas, including about 10 per cent for whom we have created special privileges and those who were antagonized by the Americans. There is an element of something over 30 per cent that does not know what is going on and does not care. These are most of the hill and outlying Island people. That leaves about 10 per cent who want to be convinced. They have not come into too close contact with us but have heard our propaganda."

This easy flow of English could have come from any Japanese graduate of Harvard, Princeton, Stanford, or any other American university. And there were many such graduates.

There are about seven million Filipinos on the Island of Luzon—the heaviest populated. Mindanao in the south has three million, and Cebu one and a half million. It is from this population group that the main opposition will be formed against the Japanese when the right time comes. Despite anything the Japanese can do the Philippines still remain the reddest, whitest, and bluest spot in East Asia. And when the time does come the Dunkirk and Sicily retreats will seem mere beach parties. The Japanese will never be able to crowd all of their troops into a much improved Corregidor and Bataan defense area.

And the Filipino hatred—you've heard of *juramentado* or fanatical berserkism—will wreak a terrible vengeance on thousands of Japanese.

It can be argued, and convincingly, that America's principles of liberty, equality, and justice failed in the Philippine Islands. But actually when contrasted with Japan's New Order for East Asia, the American way stands the test. The first thing the Japanese military administration did under General Homma to win over the average Filipino was to magnanimously cut workers' wages in half. The Filipino was told that he was thereby given the much-sought-after opportunity of co-operating with the great liberating movement. He would share in the co-prosperity sphere for East Asia. But first, he would have the privilege of sharing in co-poverty. And reducing the average pre-war wage of one peso, or 50 cents U.S., of the Filipino to one-half that amount, was poverty with a capital "P."

XXVIII

WHAT can we expect when we get back into the Philippines? Much depends on *how* we re-enter the Islands. If we go back via the conference-table route our reception is likely to be negative. If we go back fighting—as the Filipinos expect us to do—the Filipino reception should be effectively helpful. It's the Japanese reception we'll have to worry about. The Jap has rebuilt, and is still building, the defenses of the Islands. But by the time we get to the Philippines across the mid-Pacific and South Pacific routes there should be United Nations aircraft operational bases close enough along the China Coast, and enough bombers, bombs, spare parts and gasoline to slap the Jap from east and west.

Once in, the rehabilitation job will be immense. Cities and villages throughout the Islands today are like ghost towns. They've just been stacked together after the fighting and burning. There has been little new construction and no general repair. Thousands of shops and stores still remain boarded up. Business generally is at a standstill. The financial situation is only as strong as the thin Japanese paper peso.

The transportation job to resupply, rebuild the Philippines, in the face of all our planning for Europe, Russia, China, will be heavy. Since, however, the Philippines are our only territorial possession out there, our Washington planners must realize that the Philippines are *our first responsibility* for rehabilitation planning. Then China, the Netherlands East Indies, Malaya, Siberia, and Japan follow in their proper perspective.

Businessmen here want to know the future plan for the Philippines. Do they get full freedom and independence immediately? Or is the movement toward independence to be gradual? They want to know whether it is going to be worth putting money into the Philippines resources of sugar, mining, pineapple, coconut, by-products and even light industry construction. All this must be clarified before the cessation of hostilities. What we do in this matter of Filipino rehabilitation and independence will set a standard for the native populations under the British and Dutch. What happens to the Filipino will have repercussions as far distant as India. How we do *what* we do probably means the difference between peace and future native-population revolutions in India, Burma, Malaya, and the Netherlands East Indies.

Because of the original hold-back from Washington on what to do with the Philippines, there were two attitudes expressed in the policy-making quarters. Both of these were based on Japan's rather clever psychological lead in giving the Filipino independence in name only.

The Japanese long-range political warrior—with an eye to continuing the fight even after the physical warfare ceases, for the Japanese is determined that there will be no peace in East Asia—feels the early Japanese-offered "independence" means added future political trouble for America in the Philippines and Britain in Burma, after the two areas are retaken. This is indicative of the Japanese "peace" intentions. There's much more in this than meets the eye at first glance. Close attention was given to the two attitudes by government policy makers on the questions, "Full and complete economic and political independence for the Philippines—or not?" It's all part of a new foreign policy to be formulated for Far Eastern relationships.

The first group said: "Restricted independence—dominion status —yes. Full independence—never. When the war is over, despite everything President Quezon says, the average Filipino won't want full independence. He won't be in any position economically, politically, or defensively to accept it. What the Filipino will want and will accept with alacrity is full freedom and independence of life within the American scheme, including defensive protection."

This group visualized the new Philippines Administration this way:

Following reoccupation—"and there must be a battle-won Philippines, not conference-table won—"

1. American military naval administration. This may last for a year or more. During this time civil life including all municipal and Philippine-wide civil service will be re-established.
2. General Department of State supervision. Take the Philippines

out of the Division of Territories and Insular Possessions and install them—perhaps even Alaska too, due to its proximity to the Far East—under diplomatic supervision and full naval and military protection. This to come only after Far East rehabilitation and International Police Force control, International Economic Commission control, and general Five-Power (U.S., China, Russia, Netherlands, Britain) supervision of Far Eastern affairs has become evident.

3. Heavy U.S. operational force installations: The United States must keep military and naval operational force installations in the Philippines.

The second groups said: "Full independence for the Philippines by 1946—as promised. If we haven't gone back into the Philippines and haven't beat the Jap by that time, give independence just as soon as is practical after victory."

They state that since Japan gave the Filipino "a type of independence" the United States must give more. We couldn't defend the Philippines, they argue, but we told the Filipinos left on the spot to make the best of a bad situation. If they have now received "a kind of independence—even though it is in name only—our full responsibility is to live up to our 1946 promise. And secondly, we must give them more than the Japs have offered."

This group visualizes the new Philippines Administration this way:

Following reoccupation (and both groups agree on this point) "no conference-table deal on the Philippines will regain lost American prestige in the Far East, nor repay our debt to the average Filipino, who has turned out to be a loyal American."

1. Establishment of a military naval administration. This should hold only so long a time as it takes President Quezon and his cabinet to get back and reorganize a new Philippines government, together with proved loyal Filipino leaders who have remained through the trouble.

2. Defense. Japan will have been destroyed as an aggressive military and naval power in the Far East. Thus there is no one to defend the Philippines against. Let our Army staff train a Filipino army of 500,000 much in the manner of MacArthur's unfinished defense scheme. Let the United States Navy—and British, Russian, and Dutch Navies—use international bases in the Philippines. These bases to be under international control.

3. Philippines Foreign Policy. Keep close watch over it. It's to be expected the independent Filipino will feel his oats and thumb

his nose at Uncle Sam now and then. But he should be independent to do so. We can watch him from afar and if necessary can check him.

On June 30, 1944, President Franklin D. Roosevelt signed two Resolutions of Congress, the first of which "lays down a policy for the granting of independence and for the acquisition of bases adequate for the mutual protection of the United States and the Philippines." It is important that history record the President's statement. The Oriental will never let the Occidental forget a single implication. It rated only page six in *The New York Times*. But from it will come headlines in the future if we don't live up to its letter.

The President said:

"In that resolution it is declared to be the policy of 'the Congress that the United States shall drive the treacherous, invading Japanese from the Philippine Islands, restore as quickly as possible the orderly, free democratic processes of government to the Filipino people, and thereupon establish the complete independence of the Philippine Islands as a separate self-governing nation.' The measure makes it possible to proclaim independence as soon as practicable after constitutional processes and normal functions of government have been restored in the Philippines.

"It is contemplated that as soon as conditions warrant civil government will be set up under constitutional officers. It will be their duty forthwith to take emergency measures to alleviate the physical and economic hardships of the Philippine people and to prepare the Commonwealth to receive and exercise the independence which we have promised them.

"The latter includes two tasks of great importance: Those who have collaborated with the enemy must be removed from authority and influence and the political and economic life of the country; and the democratic form of government guaranteed in the Constitution of the Philippines must be restored for the benefit of the people of the islands.

"On the problem of bases, the present organic act permitted acquisition only of naval bases and fueling stations, a situation wholly inadequate to meet the conditions of modern warfare. The measure approved today will permit the acquisition of air and land bases in addition to naval bases and fueling stations.

"I have been informed that this action is most welcome to Commonwealth authorities, and that they will gladly co-operate in the establishment and maintenance of bases both as a restored Commonwealth and as an independent nation. By this we shall have an outstanding example of co-operation designed to prevent a recurrence of armed aggression and to assure the peaceful use of a great ocean by those in pursuit of peaceful ends.

"The second joint resolution signed today brings into effect the joint economic commission first ordained in the present organic act, and enlarges its scope to include consideration of proposals for the economic and financial rehabilitation of the Philippines.

"We are ever mindful of the heroic role of the Philippines and their people in the present conflict. Theirs is the only substantial area and theirs the only substantial population under the American flag to suffer lengthy invasion by the enemy. History will attest the heroic resistance of the combined armies of the United States and the Philippines in Luzon, Cebu, Iloilo and other islands of the archipelago.

"Our character as a nation will be judged for years to come by the human understanding and the physical efficiency with which we help in the immense task of rehabilitating the Philippines. . . ."

The final answer is in the hands of the big offensive in the Pacific; in the world-stability plans in the briefcases of the "peace makers."

But I can tell you from personal knowledge that, whether he gets it or not, it is full independence that is deep in the heart of the Filipino.

XXIX

CARL MYDANS and I were told by Commandant Tsurumi one day about mid-August (1942) that he would give us just three minutes to place our names on what was called the "Shanghai List." I looked at Carl in amazement. He looked at me in amazement. Then almost together we said, "What have we got to lose?" We scrawled ours and our wives' names down on the so-called list, made the customary enforced bow to the commandant and went in search of Marjorie and Shelley to tell them the news. After seven and a half long months of imprisonment it looked as though we were "on our way," although where, we weren't quite sure!

Another month passed before the seemingly mythical ship (a great majority of the internees were certain this ship would never become a reality) actually did sail for Shanghai. Why such a transfer was made and how we got on such a ship are questions hard to answer. Why the Japanese military administration took 113 assorted prisoners out of a concentration camp of nearly 3500, placed us aboard a troop convoy and sent us 1200 miles from Manila to Shanghai, is one of those Japanese unanswerables.

Commandant Tsurumi would give us no guarantee that we wouldn't be put in prison or camp again upon reaching our destination. He wouldn't say "exactly" why he'd given us "the chance," as he put it, to go to Shanghai. For months Carl and I, singly and jointly with Jack Percival, had written letters to the commanding general of the Philippine Islands and had paid innumerable visits to the office of the commandant requesting—even demanding at one stage—our exchange as accredited correspondents with the Far Eastern diplomats.

"You have no status," was the only answer we were given.

The local Manila newsmen had given up hope from the very first. But we three, together with Russell Brines, refused to take no for an answer. We were the only accredited "in transit" correspondents in Manila. When the first exchange had taken place in July 1942 we had done everything possible to be included in it, pointing out time and again that as "in transit" journalists we should be exchanged. But the boat left without us. The Japanese were not ready that early in the war to have correspondents leave the Philippines to tell their story—a story of Japanese brutality, of plunder, of rape, of maltreatment of prisoners of war and civilians alike.

When the commandant told us, "You will go to Shanghai," without any further explanation, seemingly without reason, we were astonished. But we were also delighted.

Jack Percival finally decided against going. His wife had had her baby only three months previously, and little John, Jr.—the first internment-camp boy—had weighed 8 pounds at birth and had continued to do very well. Jack felt he shouldn't take the chances which the trip obviously involved. Joy and the baby were still outside in a convent where they had gone directly from the hospital. Joy would be allowed to live in the convent until the baby was a year old, which assured them of clean living quarters, fairly good food and medical care. And it was well that Jack managed, because of the baby, to get their names stricken from the Shanghai List. Nearly every one of the "convoy gang," as we called ourselves, was ill after arrival in China; some had a lingering illness for months; one man died.

Those of us who left the camp that hot noon of September 12 comprised a cross section of British-American prisoners from Shanghai Taipans, missionaries, and Rockefeller Foundation nurses, to mothers and babies whose husbands and fathers were in Shanghai. Others included a few able-bodied seamen and Philippine bamboo-Americans, and a Polish refugee. Down on the pier we were joined by a Norwegian sea captain, seventeen third party nationals including Spanish neutrals, and in addition forty-four Indians who were being returned to Japan. The total was 174.

As we stood on the Manila pier looking up at the tin-can freighter, *Maya Maru* (about 5000 tons)—one of the ships that had brought Japanese troops to the Philippines on that December of 1941 when eighty Japanese transports were sighted off Lingayen—we wondered how we would ever manage to get through the ten or twelve days which we must spend aboard. However, I know that at that stage had we been offered an open raft we'd have taken it rather than return to the Santo Tomás concentration camp.

We sat on the dock without a slit of shade in the heat of a tropical sun from mid-day until after 5:00 P.M. The horses were being loaded. We could wait. We'd had many lessons in patience.

"Look over there," Marjorie nudged me and spoke in a low voice. "There's Sancho, and Ike is with him."

Sancho was standing with his back against a bale of hay seemingly paying no attention to what was going on around him.

"Don't wave," I cautioned Marjorie. "Don't pay any attention. He'll let us know when he thinks it's all right."

"There are too many guards around just now," Marjorie said looking about her in an offhand manner.

We sat for at least fifteen minutes before Sancho left the bale of hay and quickly came over to us. The guards were down at the other end of the pier in a huddle over something or other.

"Sancho!" Marjorie took both his hands in hers for a moment and gave them a gentle squeeze. "I could kiss you," she said with a little laugh that sounded more like tears than laughter. "And you too, Ike."

Two friends who had stood by us from the very first day of the war. How Sancho had bought the food, the necessities that he had sent into the camp for us during that period when we had had no money, we shall never know. We did know his small salary could never have covered it. And all the little thoughtful things that he had done for us without being asked to do them, things that had made us laugh and cry—the bright red nail polish for Marjorie; the package of Aunt Jemima pancake flour because he had remembered that I was fond of pancakes; straw hats for both of us to "keep the head not to mind the heat of the sun"; two bright red pillows "because I see the people sit on the ground and it is hard"; a small book of prayers: "It will help you in our trouble, Seer. I pray for you and for Mum every day."

Before leaving camp we had given Sancho all the money that we had left. Three hundred pesos—not much, but to Sancho it was nearly a year's salary, measured by former days. I wish we had had more. But Sancho had said to me, "This will last a long time, Seer. Now that they send you away I will go to the provinces. It will be cheap to live and I will not see the Japanese so much."

Until that moment it had never dawned on me that Sancho had stayed in Manila only to look after Marjorie and me. But he had.

Now as he and Ike stood before us we didn't know what to tell him. We were sad. None of us really spoke what was in our hearts. But Marjorie and I knew that Sancho and Ike understood. Because they did not have to tell us in words what was in their hearts. We knew.

"I bring you the cake, Mum," Sancho said, holding out a large cardboard box. We lifted the cover. I've never seen such a cake. It had white frosting with fancy green edging and pink swirls like a cartwheel toward the center.

"Thank you, Sancho. It is a lovely cake," Marjorie said.

"Don't forget, Sancho," I reminded him, "when it is time for Ike to go to college I will send for him. He will come to the United States and he will go to the big university. We will take good care of him."

"The war will be ended then, Seer. I will send Ike to you. He is always a good boy. And he is very smart."

There was silence for a few seconds. It was hard for us to say anything.

"We know the Japanese are sending you away," Sancho finally said. "It is good you go to Shanghai, Seer. Then perhaps you will get home to the United States. Before the war ends. Then you can help my people there. And you can tell the Americans that we wait for them here. We will see you when you return, Seer."

"Here come the guards," Marjorie warned. "You must go, Sancho. They mustn't catch you here."

"Do not worry about me, Mum. No one will bring harm to me. But you will be all right? I wish I could carry your bag, Mum. It is too heavy for you."

"Never mind, Sancho. It is all right."

"Good-by, Mum. Good-by, Seer. I will wait for you."

Before we could say anything further Sancho and Ike were gone. The guards were coming toward us kicking bags out of their way with their heavy boots. Marjorie couldn't keep back the tears, and I didn't try to make her.

PART FIVE

Out of Manila: into Shanghai

XXX

IT WAS late in the afternoon before the order came for us to carry our luggage aboard the *Maya Maru*. By that time many of our group were faint with hunger and thirst. To make it just a bit more difficult the gangway was placed so that it was like walking the rungs of a ladder between two roofs. Instead of earth, there was open water 20 feet beneath. There was no railing on either side— only a useless swinging rope to grasp. As we edged our way up, a constant jostling file of Japanese and British Indians squeezed past us, and this on a ladder not more than 2 feet wide.

Marjorie went ahead of me. I was afraid to look. But up she went to the top. She was loaded to the point of desperation for we were not at all certain that we would be allowed to go ashore again to pick up any remaining baggage. We'd been told we could take what we could carry. Thus we tried to carry everything possible aboard in one trip. Marjorie's handbag dangled from her left arm. She carried two heavy coats and two raincoats over the same arm. In her left hand was a straw basket filled with canned food, towels, tin cups and plates, toilet paper, and bananas. In her right hand she carried a suitcase weighing about 35 pounds. How she did it I'll never know. It's one of those things that had she stopped to think about she never could have done. Not in a million years.

I was loaded too. A zipper case under my left arm, a suitcase in my hand. A bedding roll containing some canned foods and fresh fruit on my shoulder held in place by a long rope which I grasped with my right hand which already held a pullman case. I accomplished the impossible and so did everyone—especially the women with babies—who went up the ladder that night, balancing precariously, peering down through the open rounds into the oily water.

Once on deck we were ordered down—way down! A steep iron gangway brought us to the deck well. Another stairway, this time without railing on either side, a ladder that was almost perpendicular, brought us deep into the hold. Our hold. The next hold below held 250 steaming, neighing horses.

On either side the full length of the ship, as well as straight down the middle, were double-decker shelves, with about 8 inches headroom when you were seated. These shelves were for sleeping. This was where we were to live—exist—for the next ten or twelve days. The aisles between were barely 2 feet wide. Amidship, people had to sleep in a T fashion. Marjorie and I managed to get spaces near the stern of the ship which narrowed considerably. Thus we had no one sleeping at our heads crosswise for there was just enough room to stretch full length with our feet touching the bulkhead. The shelves were spread with thin straw mats. No bedding was furnished. Fortunately we had brought two blankets and a pillow each.

Marjorie slept on my left. Next to her was Shelley Mydans, then Carl. On my right was Russell Brines, and then Bert Covit. We called this "the press galleyry." As we lay looking up at the shelf above, it appeared to be moving. There was a constant and unending line of cockroaches marching solemnly along in single file. Each morning I would brush off of Marjorie's back the dead cockroaches that she had flattened as she rolled over in the night. Then she would do the same for me.

Cockroaches running riot all over the place; rats skipping across our feet and faces during the night; Indians holding tea parties at all hours of the night; Indians jibbering with neighbors 100 feet down the line in voices that made you feel you really didn't care what happened to India so long as you could get the Indians out of your hair.

There were forty-four of these Indians quartered on the shelves opposite us. Some of them had two or three wives and half a dozen or more children. We were never quite sure when they were merely conversing or when they were fighting. They were being sent to Japan.

The children were always plunking themselves down in the 2-foot-wide aisle just by our heads and piddling on the floor. There was almost a riot over this before we could get the mothers to understand that we could not and would not stand for it. The privy just at the top of the stairs was bad enough. Three wooden booths built on the deck served as toilets, for all the troops and the prisoners as well. The privy was supposed to be hosed down every day but usually it was every second or even third day. Next to the booths was an open urinal which nearly always had a long waiting line of soldiers in front of it, all in readiness. When the wind blew in the wrong direction—wrong for us anyway in the hold below—the odor was overpowering.

The first night we stayed tied up at the dock. We were not to sail until the following morning. The heat was stifling. When we saw huge canvas ventilators being pushed down into the hold we cheered—mentally. You say nothing on a Japanese troopship. Through these long canvas arms or bags the air from above is blown into the hold. Our enthusiasm was premature. The canvas bags went right on past us down into the next hold below. Ventilation was provided for the horses. Not for us.

As the days passed the odor from the horses became more and more intense. Before we left Formosa some of the horses died from the heat. How many we didn't know, but one dead horse is as bad as half a dozen, so the number didn't matter. The dead horses were left in the hold until we arrived in Shanghai.

If you'd gone up the mast and looked down on the afterdeck of the troopship *Maya Maru*, the first thing you'd have noticed would have been the small amount of deck space available in the afterdeck well for the 250 troops, and over two hundred others, including enemy prisoners. Aft of the superstructure and forward of a high poop deck you would have seen a double-hatched deck—the deck well itself. (We prisoners weren't permitted fore or aft of the deck well although there was plenty of space on the poop deck.) You would have noticed on the starboard side of the forward hatch a pile of baled hay. This was for the horses. Across on the port side you would have seen the cook shack—just a wooden shack some 20 feet long to cover three cooking *kongs* and a tea *kong*.

Looking down from the mast you would have seen four winches with helplessly twined, greasy cable between the fore and aft hatches, the after hatch being closed tightly with a shiny Cadillac staff car riding on top. You would have seen on the starboard side of the after hatch another wood shack—the open-sided three-hole privy—and just behind that a 3-ton U.S. Army truck. On the port side aft of the cook shack you would have noticed a small metal water tank alongside of which was a stack of twelve loosely bound 4 x 4-inch planks—life rafts. Large bamboo water kegs for dish-washing stood along the steel rail.

The thing that probably would have struck you most forcibly was the fact that there was no shade and no sitting space except atop the water tank and the cook shack. (We were not permitted to touch, much less sit on the running board of the looted staff car.)

No comfort, no convenience, no shade—nothing; not even for the Spanish neutrals, one of whom I saw slugged by the Japanese Consul when the Spaniard protested as a neutral passenger against being placed in the hold with the horses and the prisoners. Broiling sun on metal. It was like standing on a griddle. This was our little section of the *Maya Maru* for the transfer from Manila to Shanghai.

Each night on the entire trip we slept the sleep of exhaustion. By the third day Marjorie told me she literally ached in every bone in her body. There was not a muscle that didn't shriek.

The first night aboard the transport was bedlam. The noise of loading was deafening. There were no lights in the low-roofed 'tween deck section. The hatch above us was closed; the other just a bit forward was left open. But the smell—we called that *Eau de Maru*. And there's no description strong enough, no duplication possible, except aboard another Japanese troopship.

We hadn't eaten since breakfast, and that had been camp fare. By eight o'clock we were pretty fagged. The heat and the odor got most of the women. The babies were crying and sick. We were permitted on deck by the brusque gendarme officer whom we came to call "Surly Joe." There, amid a maze of twitching, greasy winch cable which at any moment was likely to coil around your ankle, we tried to elbow our way through the hundreds of soldiers to the outside rail.

"It's not the heat, it's the humanity," Marjorie murmured in my ear as we finally made the rail. Russ Brines, who spoke some Japanese, wangled a bucket of rice and some cold, dried fish and sea-weed from a mess sergeant. We washed it down with boiling tea. It was something to eat, anyway. Then the soldiers noticed we were eating, and the jibbering and jabbering that went on was deafening and threatening. Why should the prisoners be given food, and they not? The gendarme, Surly Joe, shoved the few of us who had gathered around Russ and the bucket of rice down the steep ladder into the hold. We wriggled in under the shelf above. The winches roared on the deck overhead, yet we slept exhausted to the crescendo of neighing horses, the high-pitched giggles and shrieks of the Japanese whores doing business across the alley from us, and the constant soprano gibberish of the forty-four Indians who kept shoving up and down the alleyway, constantly spitting, spitting, spitting.

Morning brought nothing more than greater heat, making it impossible to touch the steel deck and rails with bare hands. But we sailed, after much wrangling between the ship's officers and the army officials on the pier.

I was standing on a pile of baled hay—one of the few places we could find to get off the narrow, crowded deck—when a gendarme pricked me in the back with the point of his bayonet. He yelled something unintelligible with the usual scowl and show of teeth. I rubbed my back and replied with the usual bow, and asked Brines what the hell the fellow wanted so early in the morning.

Russ interpreted: "Oh, he says you can't stand around on deck without a shirt. It isn't polite to the captain of the ship, especially when we are pulling out of port. He also says you've been most insulting and you'll have to go below." Which I did.

Soon the rest of the prisoners, and peculiarly enough all of the 250 soldiers quartered in our stern section, also came below. We were not permitted to watch the passage of the *Maya Maru* and convoy through the Manila Harbor mine fields past Corregidor and into the China Sea.

When you're placed aboard an enemy troopship and sent in a convoy through seas in which you know American submarines are operating successfully, your reactions are mixed, to say the least. There's nothing you'd rather have happen to the convoy than have it attacked. From watching the loading I had estimated it carried some three thousand officers and soldiers, a good complement of artillery pieces, horses, trucks, and automobiles that had belonged to the United States forces in the Philippines, and considerable crated loot from the Philippines.

Yes, it would be quite a haul for a submarine. That was my first reaction. But after boarding ship and being told that in case of submarine or air attack it will be "officers and soldiers first, enemy aliens, including women, last," I had a different reaction. It's quite natural under these circumstances to hope that the convoy, or at least the ship you're in, will slip through.

Just before I had left Santo Tomás a fellow-prisoner had told me that if he thought we had even a 51 per cent chance of getting through he would have applied to go with us. "Frankly," he had said, "I don't think you have a prayer." And that opinion had been voiced countless times by many internees during our last few days in Manila. Now aboard the troop transport those words kept echoing. I had thought of them as instructions were given to us to wear our lifebelts at all times. I thought of them then as I sat in the hold during those sweltering hours while we slowly wound through mine fields past Corregidor. I thought of them later as I watched from the deck well our zigzag progress through waters that I knew held our own submarines.

With no more than a fifteen-minute breather for the lunch of rice, seaweed, and dried fish, we stayed in the depths of the ship from shortly after nine in the morning until about five that afternoon, when the convoy assembled and began to zigzag out of the mouth of Manila Bay. Then we were ordered to come up on deck, but first put on our life jackets, and be ready for any emergency.

It was here, we knew from our bamboo telegraph sources, that only the week before three ships from a forming convoy had been sunk by a submarine. And now two black destroyers funneled blacker smoke and churned circles around and around the ships as we eased out of the mouth of the bay and northward through the purple sunset along the Bataan coast; the coast the Fil-American troops had held so long with nothing but bluff and a few cans of corned beef.

The lead destroyer finally blinked an okay from its bridge just at dark, and we breathed easier. It was cooler now that we were at sea and a few of us stood atop the small water tank to try to get out of the deck well into the breeze. Any ideas we may have had of sleeping on deck that night, or any other night, were quickly dispersed. Surly Joe came along with his bayonet and herded all of us below onto our shelves with our cockroaches and rats.

XXXI

THE days aboard the troop transport passed slowly. Although conditions became worse with each added day and sanitation was something in the faint and distant past, we became inured to the filth. No one complained. The important thing was we were on our way and Santo Tomás was behind us.

There seemed to be little sense in trying to keep clean. But we tried anyway. I shaved daily in the boiling tea that was always available in varying intensity from a great iron *kong* just forward of the mess shack. About 4 A.M. Carl, Russell, and I would go up on deck and try to get a bath of sorts at the small water tank. Marjorie and Shelley would come up about 5 A.M. just before it got light. There was no one around at that early hour. During the day we had to fight off the Indians from the spigot at the small water tank. They would let the precious water run on the deck while they rinsed their sari and pantaloons.

When the Jap soldiers came and let the water run there was nothing we could do about it. The tank was filled only once a day. The wizened old seaman who did the filling delighted in appearing suddenly from behind the cook shack with his hose and sweeping a stream of water across the top of the tank which was the only place we had to sit beside the baled hay. After the first drenching we didn't mind since the drying off process was quite cooling.

One evening just at dusk before we were routed down below deck a little missionary woman was wetting her small handkerchief at the dripping spigot of the water tank so she'd have something cool to place over her face to keep the bugs off when she tried to go to sleep. I was on top of the water tank thinking I'd do the same thing, when there suddenly appeared at her elbow a Jap soldier stark naked but for a towel tied around his head. He was going to bathe. Sensing someone beside her the missionary looked up. What she saw nearly made her swoon. She stuttered and got up off her knees. Such embarrassment I've never seen before or since.

The soldier was determined to be polite. He bowed and waved and hissed and insisted that the woman finish her ablutions before he started. The more the woman tried to back off the more insistent the soldier became. "But I'm finished," the missionary stammered almost in tears. "You wash. You wash." The soldier bowed toward the spigot and stood aside to wait. His words were Japanese but there was no mistaking their meaning. So the flustered, embarrassed little lady stooped down and rinsed out her handkerchief once again, made a show of dabbing her hands and face, rose and fairly flew across the deck to the hatch. The naked Japanese stood hissing and bowing until she disappeared. Polite to the last drip. You never knew what was going to happen next.

Our existence aboard the ship was one of two roll calls morning and night; standing in line for fish and rice; trying to find a place on deck to stand or sit; going up and down, in and out of the hold two or three times a day—"by order." Sometimes the lookout high above would jabber out a warning. Sometimes it meant down-below for us. At others we would see frantic rushings about of the Japanese while we stood by bewildered. Finally we discovered the few small plank life rafts and edged toward them when the Japanese obviously began to worry.

There was no gun on the aft deck and what we thought was a wicked-looking pom-pom atop the wireless shack turned out to be a wooden dummy gun. We learned, however, there was a heavier artillery piece on a shaky wooden platform forward. We weren't permitted to go off the deck well inside the superstructure nor through to the forward deck well.

However, Carl and I made one or two before-dawn excursions forward. On one of them we ran into tall, red-headed Ted Wallace. Ted was a former radiocaster in Manila who had enlisted at the outset of the war. He with three other Fil-American soldiers was being taken to Japan. I didn't talk to Wallace, but to one of the others who said they'd been brought down from the Cabanatuan war prisoners' camp and placed aboard just before we'd arrived. They had inside bunks and their kits had been carried aboard for them by Japanese soldiers. They didn't know what was in store for them.

During the four-day zigzag trip from Manila to Takao, southern-most Formosa naval base, we became acclimated for the two-day stay at Takao and the four-and-a-half day final dash to Shanghai. The pace of our convoy was estimated by the seamen in our group at about 6 to 8 knots. Our ship was the fastest in the convoy and therefore ran last. We'd creep up on the rest of the ships, then veer way off to starboard—fresh meat for a sub—and then zigzag back. The constant rattle of the rudder chain against the steel hull was the obbligato to the rest of the duck and dodge symphony.

Each night the leading destroyer would run up and down the convoy with signal men wigwagging the evening's orders. We were specifically told at the start not to throw overboard anything that would mark the route of the convoy. Not even cigarette stubs. One order read: "No smoking without smoke box—Captain, by order." The "smoke box" turned out to be a tin can.

But after each meal the soldiers threw overside cigarette boxes, all the excess rice, fish, and other food, including wooden crates, leaving a perfect trail. But let one of *us* toss a banana skin over and an awful row was raised by the gendarmes who were always on guard.

One night one of our group threw a banana skin over and the wind whipped it back full into the face of the officer in charge of the 250 troops in our hold. He was furious and ordered everyone below. He tried to find out who had thrown it. He put on such a show of livid temper that it became ridiculous to the point where we had all we could do to keep from bursting out laughing. There's nothing more ridiculous than a strutting, shouting, baggy-uniformed Japanese officer. But we dared not show the slightest amusement. One of our people, a Pole, had taken a heavy face slapping from this same officer because he had been late to roll call.

The evening we arrived in Formosa the convoy held off the low green coastline until just about dusk. Then the destroyer fired a small gun. It was the signal to run for the mouth of the bottleneck harbor. We got off to a bad start, but our superior speed put us in second. We all were ordered below as usual, but I managed to hide myself in the privy from which I watched us slip through a narrow mouth into the landlocked harbor of Takao. The mouth can't be more than a quarter of a mile wide. Its hillside fortifications give it a thoroughly protected appearance. On the sea side the shore slopes away and you find a long hooked sandspit protecting the large and apparently deep landlocked harbor.

That night occasional aircraft droned high over the harbor and powerful searchlights stabbed up at the stars from every possible angle. I counted seventeen lights at one time and there were many more. Morning revealed the reason for the protective activity of the night before. The harbor was packed with gray-blue camouflaged ships loaded to the plimpsol line with troops and military supplies. And more supplies were being lightered aboard. We estimated roughly 170,000 tons of shipping lay in the harbor or alongside the quays. A Japanese newsman aboard our ship, who used to come down to talk about his "daring experiences" at Corregidor's fall, looked very wise about this convoy in the making. "You'll read all about this in a few weeks," he said. "Too bad for your people this time." It was too bad all right—but not for us. These were some of the thousands of Japanese who were lost in the Japanese counter-attacks on Guadalcanal in the Solomons.

The seamen in our crowd picked out what was obviously an American President liner. They claimed she was the *President Harrison*. The Japanese got the *Harrison* when she was run aground off Shanghai at the start of the war. This ship had a gaping hole midships on the port side. She was ill kept with only a bamboo latticework masking the hole.

We were in port two days. During that time the convoy began to move out through the gate to pick up its naval escort of what appeared to be cruisers and destroyers pacing back and forth impatiently outside. What a free-for-all that would have been for submarines!

"Yeah," snorted a seaman, when I made that comment to him. "Yeah, but let 'em waste the fuel and energy they're going to use getting to wherever it is they're going, then we'll sink them there—that's smarter." It was.

At Takao the Japanese put ice aboard. Not for us. For the horses. But some of the ice bars broke against the side of the ship as they were hoisted on. If you've ever seen street urchins scramble for pennies that's nothing to what we did for this dirty oil-and-hay-covered ice we scrounged off the deck. Filthy and unhealthy? Yes. But it was cold. We were able to use some of the forbidden Philippine pesos we smuggled aboard to bribe crew members to buy bananas and pommolo (oversized grapefruit) for us. And the fruit was refreshing. The only clean food we had on the entire trip.

The second day about half the troops and their chippie friends disembarked. The chippies carried most of the officers' luggage up on deck and placed it in the slings for hoisting overside. Then they went below, painted and dressed themselves in their gaudy, cheap finery. On deck in the broiling sun awaiting their order to disembark they were haughty, quarrelsome, and noisy as a flock of jaybirds trying to light on a single tree branch.

One of them turned suddenly and sank her teeth deep into the shoulder of one of our crowd. She held on until she drew blood and the startled man, a former Manila movie owner, was so amazed at the action he seemed unable to pull away. Another of the chippies thoroughly slapped the mother of a baby boy who had spilled some of his lunch gruel on her dirty white shoes. The mother, a British woman, to avoid further row went down below, somehow found some white shoe cleaner, and there in front of all the grinning soldiers and chippies cleaned the shoe.

But if we thought we were going to be rid of half our afterdeck-well complement of soldiers and chippies we were disappointed. For no sooner were these ashore than new passengers arrived. These were Formosan recruits in charge of a hard-boiled sergeant who explosively warned them against us. These boys weren't as nasty as the regular troops. Before we got to Shanghai they were even trying to pick up a few words of English—when the sergeant wasn't on deck.

At mealtimes we lined up for our food in front of the cook shack after the officers and chippies had had their food. We were given chopsticks and small Japanese bowls: one to eat out of, the other for our tea. We were supposed to wash and return them after each meal. We had to wash these dishes in sea water that was sloshed into heavy bamboo tubs. The mess crews—one man for each fifteen soldiers—washed all their bowls and chopsticks as well as the rice and chow buckets in this water. They resented our trying to wash our dishes first or at the same time. So it behooved us to wait and try to get the bowls as clean as possible in the greasy water that was left. Actually the only way to do was to take two bowls and a pair of chopsticks for yourself and clean and wash them in the hot tea or boiling hot water we got from the tea *kong*. The tea *kong* in which some people finally washed their dirty dishes, thereby making drinking tea a bit precarious, was our savior.

Most of us had been wise enough to bring along some canned foods and fruits we had been able to get through the fence at camp and had saved for just such an emergency. Marjorie and I had just enough canned food for one can of beans or corned beef a day for the entire trip. We never went hungry. The Japanese ration rice was good, second-grade rice. Much better than any camp rice we ever had in the Philippines or later in China. The troops had the best available. Surprisingly enough they threw overboard all leftover food—about one-third of the rice cooked each meal. But they never reduced the ration. This amazed us, coming from a nation we had been taught never wasted or threw anything away.

The Japanese soldier, as I had noticed before in China and the Philippines, seemed to need very little food to keep going—and not too good quality food. The food served aboard the *Maya Maru*, one English-speaking soldier told me, was typical. "Good stuff, huh?" he asked me. "Your soldiers don't get so good, I think."

I told him I was only a civilian. I didn't know about soldiers. You never know when an answer to a leading question will put you in a spot.

Three times a day aboard the *Maya Maru* we and the troops got rice plus an assortment of small quantities of dried fish, dried salty seaweed, beancurd gruel, sliced cucumber, and a dab of squash or sweet potato. How would our troops go for this as a steady year-in, year-out diet? The difference in original standards of living benefits the Japanese soldier on campaigns in his East Asia warfare, since he demands little meat and lives almost entirely off the land in which he's fighting, a land in which the average person eats about the same thing as the Japanese is used to.

Fortunately we had no rough or nasty weather. The trip with the convoy to Formosa was smooth, if hot. The run by ourselves across the China Sea and up the coast to Woosung on the Yangtze brought us into cooler weather, if somewhat choppier water. The stench and filth aboard grew hour by hour, and as we neared Woosung, our Shanghai port destination, the Japs seemed to care less and less about the condition of the ship and the food served.

The afternoon we arrived in the muddy stream of the Yangtze and pulled up alongside the quay we had a scare. It looked for a while as though we weren't going to be permitted to leave the ship, and we knew from the crew that she was going on across to Japan. Orders came that we were to remain where we were—below deck as usual. The troops disembarked and stood in long sloppy lines on the quay with all their nondescript luggage in piles in front of them. Then came the loot from the Philippines—the shiny automobiles, the great crates of machinery, the small boxes of USAFFE uniforms, and the heavy ammunition boxes. This was the usual type of cargo, the crew members told us, that they carried on their constant trips to Java, Singapore, and Manila. These were loot convoys.

Some two hours after landing, we were told to carry what luggage we had up out of the hold to the small open deck on the superstructure. We formed a long line and promptly passed the stuff up. Now perhaps we'd go ashore. It was still a long way upriver to Shanghai. Were we to be put in the war prisoners' camp we understood was near by? Or what?

But we were premature again. Not the enemy prisoners next. No indeed. The horses. We were held in the hold while the horses, most of them scrawny, sick, and nearly dead, were hoisted steaming and screaming out onto the quay. I counted five dead horses left in the area just beneath us. No attempt was made to get them out.

Just at sunset we heard the whistle of a tug alongside. The gendarme, Surly Joe, came clomping down the ladder into the hold. Even he had to catch his breath at the odor. But he drew himself up with his best sneer stretched across his face. "You will go aboard the tug," he shouted. "The tug will take you to Shanghai. It is good riddance we have of you." We nearly shouted back with relief. But no one said a word audibly.

The general movement was toward the ladder down which Surly Joe had just come. "Not yet," he bellowed. He grabbed Russ Brines by the collar and shoved me ahead of him down the narrow alleyway aft. We stumbled ahead of him. He yelled something in Japanese, stopped and struck a pose, arms crossed over his chest.

"What's he want now?" I asked Russ.

"He has just told us we are dirty as pigs and asked whether we thought we were going to leave this hold in such a dirty condition. He furthermore added," Russ continued in an undertone, "that we certainly can't expect His Imperial Japanese Majesty's troops to come into such a filthy place as this after we leave it . . . and he told us to clean it up."

There was no other answer. Russ and I crawled in under the upper shelf and started brushing the dead bugs into small piles. We shook out the dirty mats that had been there since the Philippine invasion a year before, and generally gave the impression of working. Then Surly Joe grabbed some women and shoved them under the shelves on the other side. Seeing the situation, almost all our group went to work. The East Indians—the dirtiest of the lot—just stood by watching. The Japs wouldn't let them work alongside us. The idea was race humiliation.

After about half an hour of this Surly Joe tired of the dust and smell and went up on deck. We followed to find a large lighter alongside. Two white men in white ducks were aboard. You can't imagine how clean they looked, how refreshing. The tug was trim and well kept. We were to be moved up to Shanghai aboard her. Slowly we lined up and stumbled down the gangway to the deck of the tug. Mothers and babies first, aged next, and the rest of us followed.

The two men in white stood at the gangway of the tug. They looked horrified, and they told us afterwards they'd never seen such a scrawny, dirty, disheveled lot of people as we Anglo-Americans. One of the men was a Swiss consular officer, the other an American from the Shanghai American Relief Center. He indicated that we probably wouldn't be interned. No one had been interned in Shanghai, he told us. It was almost unbelievable that here, nearly a year after war had been declared, enemy nationals were still free to come and go. But it was true.

After the two-hour ride up the river to the familiar Shanghai Bund we were lined up on the pontoon of the customs jetty in British, American, and neutral groups. The Japanese consular and gendarme officials had their usual difficulty in counting us accurately and at least half an hour was spent in checking and rechecking. Finally the consular officer spoke:

"You will not be permitted to get your baggage tonight (it was about 10:00 P.M.). You will return to the jetty at 10:00 A.M. tomorrow for inspection. [Pause.] You may go now."

No one moved.

"What was that last?" came a voice from the rear.

"You may go now," he said.

Still no one moved. The shock was too great. Here after nearly a year of the roughest kind of treatment, a Jap officer was saying, "You may go [free] now."

"Come on!" I nudged Marjorie. "He may change his mind. Let's get out of here."

And with that the Mydans, Bert Covit, and Russ Brines and we hustled off the jetty onto the Shanghai Bund. As we glanced behind to see if any Japanese were following we caught a glimpse of the silhouette of the 1942 exchange ship, *Conte Verde*, then being fueled and reloaded for what we believed would be an almost immediate sailing for Lourenço Marques and, we hoped, freedom for us.

XXXII

UPON our arrival in Shanghai that night of September 21, 1942, we went directly to the old Palace Hotel, scarcely daring to hope they might take us in. But they did. They said, "Yes, sir, a room with a bath," politely failing to see our filthy clothes, dirty stringy hair, our lack of luggage, the look of "refugee" which was imprinted all over us. The Swiss hotel clerk also said, "The Grill Room closes at 10 P.M., but we'll keep it open for you if you'll come down immediately. That is, if you want anything to eat?" He smiled.

Did we want anything to eat? After ten days of rice, and fish, and seaweed, and beancurd? We were upstairs and down again in less than fifteen minutes. We paused long enough to stand in the middle of our room and just look. We were alone. Only two beds in a room large enough to hold at least eight by camp standards. Our room! Real beds—no camp cots these. We sat gingerly on the side and gave an experimental bounce. Yes, just as we had remembered. Deep springs and soft mattresses. The thing actually gave when you moved. A rug on the floor, Chinese blue; drapes at the windows, deep rose; two large upholstered chairs that looked as though you could most comfortably spend the rest of your life in them just sitting. "And I bet there are no bugs in them," Marjorie ventured. A polished mahogany desk and table; indirect lighting. Our room!

And our bath! No standing in line. No flushing toilets with buckets! No sharing of washbowls. Privacy!

We washed hands and face, a little powder and lipstick for Marjorie, a comb through her hair, and we went racing down the hall. Never mind that we were so dirty. We could wait another hour for a good bath. We'd already waited nine months. It was now past 10 P.M. and that steak "coming up" was something we had dreamed about for the past nine months.

It was better than the dream—just the right shade of pink, crisp French fried potatoes, green peas, a tossed green salad, and apple pie à la mode, with black coffee. We looked at each other and grinned. We looked over at Carl and Shelley Mydans and Russell Brines and Bert Covit at the next table and grinned some more. There simply weren't words to express our feelings. We had known hunger; we had known nausea from trying to eat greasy, unpalatable messes that were supposed to be food; we had gone without for nine months. And here we were. We couldn't talk except to keep repeating, "Isn't it wonderful? Isn't it wonderful?"—but how we could eat!

That night Marjorie and I each took three baths, one after the other, and finished up with showers. And again all we could say was, "Isn't it wonderful?"

To be well fed, to be clean, to have privacy—those are the three things that stand out in my mind above others, the three things that I shall never take for granted again. For internment, both in Manila and later on again in Shanghai, meant hunger, filth, and lack of privacy. And to me, if you take those three things and add them up it means lack of freedom.

Freedom! I'll never be able to hear that word again, to read it, to say it, without *feeling* it. For to me it's no longer just a word. It's a way of life—the American way of life. And that way of life means simple things—running water, crowded subways, church bells ringing, the smell of baking cookies, double feature movies, the right to walk down the street, the right to shut your door and be alone, the right to love and laugh, to work and play. The right to know all these things, to do all these things—without fear.

The Japs know all about fear. They know how to wage a war of fear with the enemy aliens in their occupied territories. "A war of nerves." In Shanghai they refused to tell the representatives of the American, British, and Dutch communities what was to be done with enemy aliens. And they refused to tell the Swiss who were looking out for American, British, and Dutch interests. "Keep 'em guessing" was the Japanese policy.

The Anglo-American communities had been lulled into a sense of false security during the first year of the war. For here in Shanghai and some other North China communities enemy aliens were allowed to remain in their homes. A few of them had been picked up and questioned. A few others had been picked up and imprisoned. But the majority, after registration, had been left more or less alone.

The first blow fell on November 5, 1942, six weeks after we arrived.

Even the weather seemed to work in favor of the Japanese, for November 5 was the first real winter day we had had. The fall had been clear and crisp with lots of sunshine. November 5 was rainy, and dreadfully cold. At seven o'clock that morning the telephone rang . . .

"They what? Say that again? Where are they taking him? Is he allowed to take anything with him? How many others did they get? . . ." "They" always meant the Japs.

"They got Russ," I told Marjorie as I hung up the phone.

"Where'd they take him?" she asked. I knew the one thing uppermost in her thoughts, as in mine, was Bridge House—the torture prison.

"I don't know. That was Art," I told her. Arthur Ladow had also been one of our gang who had come up from Manila with us on the troop transport. He and Russ had been rooming together at the Foreign YMCA.

"But why did they take Russ and not Art?" she asked, knowing full well there was no answer to that.

And when we finally got dressed and went down to breakfast we saw the room next to ours was sealed. "They" had got the old man, from Cook's Tours office, who had been occupying the room. I knew there was no answer to that either. Why the old man and not me right next door?

We called the room boy. "What happened to Master?" I asked him, nodding at the sealed door. There were Japanese characters all over the seal.

"Gendarmes come, Master, and take other Master away," the boy told us.

"What time they come?"

"I think mebbie five o'clock, Master. They take upstairs Master, too," he added.

"Which Master?" I asked holding my breath. Marjorie and I both

thought of Jack. Jack and Dorothy Janszen had introduced themselves to us the first week of our arrival as we were having breakfast in the grill one morning. A young couple from Chicago—Jack
was the Westinghouse representative—they had closed their home
two weeks before the second repatriation ship was supposed to have
sailed—the exchange ship that never did sail—and had gone to the
Palace Hotel for what they thought was to be a matter of fourteen
days. Before they left the Palace Hotel the fourteen days had passed
into six months, and they left, not for repatriation, but for internment. Dorothy and Jack are still interned.

"Not young Master on next floor," the room boy grinned. "But
Master on number five floor."

We breathed a sigh of relief.

"Did Master take anything with him? Any clothes, any bags?"
we asked.

"No, nothing. He dress. Gendarmes look see all time. They say
hurry, hurry. You no take this. You no take that. You no take nothing. Later you can catch—mebbie."

But it was more than two months before the room next to ours
was again unsealed. What happened to the old man's possessions we
never learned. Certainly he never saw them again.

We ordered breakfast. Marjorie said it was difficult to swallow. I
knew what she meant.

I telephoned many friends that morning asking each one the same
question, "Is everything all right?" When I called Dorothy Dunn's
home her sixteen-year-old daughter, Patricia, answered.

"They've taken Daddy," she told me. She sounded calmer than I
felt.

"We'll be right out, Patty," I said.

Tom Dunn was one of Shanghai's best known doctors. He was
taken, with Russ and the other men that early misty morning of
November 5, to the former Fourth U.S. Marine barracks on Haiphong Road, which soon became known as the Haiphong Road
Camp. This was a political prison. Obviously Tom was picked up
because a doctor was needed in the camp.

When Marjorie and I, together with Jack and Dorothy Janszen,
arrived at the Dunn home half a dozen Japanese were sitting in the
living room drinking tea. The gendarmes had turned the place up-
side down, looking for "documents." These droopy-trousered little
soldiers made such a ridiculous picture that the chubby two-year-old
twins, Beverley and Daphne, paraded around after the soldiers mim-
icking them and shouting, "Baby soldat . . . baby soldat," pointing

and laughing at the stocky Japanese playing detective. The Japanese, who didn't see the joke or understand the baby talk, laughed with the babies anyway. At that time Beverley and Daphne spoke as much Russian as they did English. Dorothy's father had been a U.S. consular officer in Vladivostok where she had learned Russian. The babies' conversation was an amusing mixture of Russian, English, and Chinese.

The gendarmes didn't find the "documents" they were looking for. What these documents might be Dorothy had no idea. The rooms in the house with the exception of the living room had been sealed early in the morning when the Japanese had taken Tom away. They unsealed the rooms and searched. The house was in a jumbled mess.

After they had gone Dorothy told us what had happened. "We were awakened about 5:00 A.M.," she said, "by the noise of heavy boots on the stairs. The door burst open and several gendarmes entered with drawn pistols. I simply couldn't believe my eyes. They ordered Tom to get up and come with them. They took him off."

Dorothy is naturally quick and high-strung. But there were no hysterics in her voice. She gave us a flat statement, without embellishment. This was a harrowing, torturing experience for both Dorothy and Tom from the moment the gendarmes had broken into their bedroom until they were reunited ten months later aboard the repatriation ship. Dorothy didn't try to put her feelings into words. She knew there weren't words strong enough.

Tom had been handed a mimeographed summons on which his name had been incorrectly filled in. The summons read in effect, "Due to military necessity, you are hereby ordered to Haiphong Road Center, where you will be confined. . . ."

Tom was taken off without knowing when he would see his wife and family again. Dorothy was told she could send food, bedding, and other necessities to him later. From our own experience we knew what Tom would need, so we helped Dorothy get these things together and pack them.

During all this, Dorothy's seventy-four-year-old mother, Roxanna Pray, had plenty to say. Grandma Pray is from northern Maine, and had encountered the Japanese before, when, as wife of a U.S. consul, she was in Vladivostok during the Russo-Japanese War. She went mumbling and muttering about the house, calling the Japs "baboons," "bastards," and "apes," and even the presence of the gendarmes didn't stop her, though it did make her keep her voice low. Later she sewed her money and a few pieces of the family silver into her petticoats and said, "I defy any one of 'em to take this away from me." And throughout all the searching, Granny's white hair and New England austerity kept the Japanese at a distance.

That November 5, 1942, was the beginning of the "war of nerves." Three hundred men were picked up on that cold, rainy morning just as was Tom Dunn—most of them in the very early hours before dawn. They were routed out of bed by a knock on the door. They were prodded in the back with bayonets. Some of them awoke to find gendarmes standing Nazi-Gestapo-like around their beds. They had to dress while the gendarmes watched. The wife merely put on robe and slippers. One wife started downstairs to come face to face with a gendarme who was proceeding cautiously up with drawn pistol.

Many of these men were allowed to take nothing at all with them. Others were permitted to take what they "could carry"; a suitcase with clothes hastily thrown into it, whatever might be at hand, and usually as happens in such a case, things that were needed least of all. Fortunate were those men who thought to throw in a can of something to eat—sardines, bullybeef, beans, anything that was food. A few were allowed to take bedding: a blanket, a pillow.

The next morning, in exactly the same way, sixty-five more men were picked up and also thrown into Haiphong Road Camp.

How long was this to go on? Was everyone to be picked up in this way? When would the knock come on our door? We waited for that knock on the door. Heavy footsteps down the hall. Would they pass? Early morning . . . noon . . . evening time . . . would we still be there in the morning?

We put our house in order. First we went out and bought a sleeping bag for Russ, flannel pajamas, soap, shaving cream, and the other absolute necessities which we knew he must have immediately. Most of all we bought food. We took these things out to the American School which had been established at once as a relief-sending center. Packages could be taken to the American School by friends and relatives. These packages were delivered to the men in the camp. The American School was also allowed to send in meals to the men for a while.

Then we went shopping for ourselves. We knew what to get. We had been through it all before; only then we had had no chance to buy. First necessity was a duffle bag nearly as tall as I am. We stuffed that bag clear to the brim—a sleeping bag and pillow, flannel pajamas, winter underwear, two flannel shirts, towels, a tin plate and cup, soap and toilet articles, a few books; and canned food—all the beans and corned beef we could get into that one bag. We tugged and hauled and finally got it laced together at the top. Then I tried to lift it. "Anything you can carry," seemed to be the general order.

I know it was sheer determination that made it possible for me to get the bag on my back. Sheer determination born of memories of our first days in Santo Tomás when we had been thrown into camp without food and without beds. If we had to go in again, this time at least we were going to have a few blankets on the first night, and would know where our first breakfast was to come from; for I would carry it in on my back. I got the bag on my shoulders. "It makes you bowlegged," Marjorie laughed. "Anyway, I can carry it . . . if I have to," I told her. "That's the important thing." We had found you can do almost anything, if you have to.

We put the bag in the corner of the room. When we went to sleep each night I knew exactly what clothes I would get into—if that knock came on the door. Marjorie had her bag packed too, for we knew if the knock came the room would be sealed and all her clothes would be left inside. We were ready—at least as ready as anyone could be who had been through it all once before. But we prayed daily that it wouldn't happen again.

XXXIII

THE Swiss welcome at the Palace Hotel had seemed like a home-coming on that night of our arrival in Shanghai. I learned later that the Japanese had correctly guessed we might go to the Palace Hotel. They had ordered the manager to give us rooms. Once "in," we were not permitted to move.

The Swiss consular officer who had been aboard the tug that had brought us up the river to the Bund directed us to go to the office of the so-called American Residents' Association, to register as Americans and to indicate our desire to be or not to be repatriated. We correspondents, Carl and Shelley Mydans, Russ Brines, Bert Covit, Marjorie and I went down together. But it was the Swiss Consulate, rather than the inefficient and obstructionist American Association, which gave us such friendliness and helpfulness as we were able to find in Shanghai.

The first week of our arrival in Shanghai Dick Iwatate, University of Missouri School of Journalism graduate, called at the hotel. He'd known Russ in Japan. Dick wanted to meet "the other journalists." We met in our room. Iwatate's flawless English was disconcerting.

The usual pleasantries. Didn't we want to let our families know we'd arrived? Yes, certainly.

"Well," Iwatate said, "since I am head of the English division of Domei and Radio Tokyo, I'll be glad to have your arrival announced over Radio Tokyo. It will be picked up in the United States."

We appreciated that. Iwatate then said he hoped we'd care to make a statement about the good treatment we'd received in Santo Tomás. We told him we'd make a statement, but he wouldn't print it.

"We could hardly call the herding together of hundreds of mothers and small children in a building like the children's annex behind the Santo Tomás main building as 'good treatment,'" I explained. "And that is what we saw."

There was a moment of embarrassed silence. Iwatate knew what we meant. "Well," he said lamely, "Jennifer White (wife of North China Associated Press correspondent) said the treatment was good when she arrived from Manila."

"That's where Mrs. White and I disagree," I told him, "if that's what she said."

Iwatate, tall, slender, and somewhat ill at ease, rose and we bowed him out. But I believe to this day that Russ's "friend" Iwatate, and Buddy Uno (Los Angeles-born Jap-American) and a few others "arranged" for Russ's imprisonment at Haiphong Road. Carl, Bert, and I expected to follow momentarily.

"You were our delegate," we used to chafe Russ later when we were being repatriated.

From almost our first day in Shanghai Marjorie and I discovered promptly that the Japanese had marked us as suspicious characters. We were watched closely. Whether they shadowed us the first day or not, I don't know. We were too busy to notice for we were trying to register at the American Association, check in at the International Red Cross to send Red Cross messages to our families and offices, and to orient ourselves.

But on the second day we spotted our man. We called him "the purple shadow." He wore a purple shirt, and slacks that were as close to Philippine purple as you'll ever see. His shoes were bright yellow and his suit coat gray. He wore this outfit day after day. We were grateful to him for this. It was easy to spot him. He went everywhere with us, or slightly behind us. Once we were sure he was following us, we clung pretty closely to the hotel. We kept regular hours. We went out only for meals, and for walks up and down the Bund. We contacted no one. Our phone was tapped, and our room searched every day or so. Marjorie said she hoped they'd get all the remaining cockroaches out of our bags before we had to be interned again. But they weren't after our livestock.

XXXIV

SHANGHAI, China's greatest commercial city, was slowly bled to death, like a stuck pig.

The Shanghailander didn't believe the toothy little man from Tokyo would do exactly what he said he would. Thus, when he found himself in a concentration camp with no servants, no money, very little food, and having to do every bit of his own work, from cooking to cleaning toilets, he shook his head in amazement.

The Japs did a neat job on Shanghai—a lot neater than on Nanking, or even Peking. They want Shanghai as a second Tokyo. The Japanese systematically planned it as such from December 7-8, 1941, despite their claim that Shanghai has been cleared of foreigners in order to make it wholly Chinese.

The Chinese saw and knew what was happening. They took the philosophical attitude, and offered traditional passive resistance. The Jap, understanding this slow, Oriental warfare, in turn gave the Chinese the slow squeeze play. Each knew and understood what the other was doing.

But the foreigner—the Anglo-American, the Franco-Russian, and the Italo-German—at first was only vaguely aware of what was taking place. The Italo-German thought he knew what was happening; he thought he had an ally in the Japanese. The Franco-Russian tried to be neutral, on the surface. And the Anglo-American who built Shanghai kept repeating to himself, "I'm an American. I'm a Briton. The Japs can't do anything to me."

I've had Shanghailanders say to me, "It's unthinkable that some of our best Japanese customers—even our close Japanese friends—could or would aid in stripping us of our homes, our businesses. It's incredible that after being entertained in our homes, they would assist in throwing us into prison and use our confidences as the basis for third-degree interrogation and torture!"

Many Shanghailanders taken for grilling by the Japanese found themselves confronted with dossiers bearing their names, containing complete records of conversations they had held with Japanese "friends" whom they had entertained in their own homes long before the war. Yes, the Japanese had been thorough.

Little Yamaguchi-san smiled pleasantly, drank your wine, and smoked your cigarettes. Little Yamaguchi-san told you, "My people want no war with your people. We do not understand the militarists who say, 'So sorry. There must be war. Japan must be leader in East Asia.' What do you think?"

Little Yamaguchi-san put down what you thought, carefully, thoroughly, and turned it in to the military. This was his duty.

While Hong Kong, Manila, Singapore, Batavia, Surabaya and Rangoon were taken over by the Japanese military and naval authorities, and all enemy aliens were slapped into concentration camps, in Shanghai life continued along almost normal channels. Here the Japanese took their time about cleaning out the foreigner.

After the first surprise at not being interned had passed, the enemy aliens at Shanghai got the idea that nothing much would happen to their city. Many of them were certain that they would be permitted to live in their homes, if not do business, for the duration. "Shanghai always has been an international city," they argued. "Why should the Japanese change it now?" When the Shanghailander asked his Japanese acquaintance whether or not this was the official Japanese plan, the acquaintance would give the usual toothy grin, politely suck in his breath, and reply, "Maybe so." The human mind usually accepts as true what it wants to believe as true. Certainly this fitted the Shanghailander. But Occidental logic couldn't find a place for vitriolic Japanese hate. That's why 90 per cent guessed wrong.

This city—the only city in the war where enemy nationals were permitted to move about freely for over a year, rubbing elbows with their conqueror—saw many strange things.

Marjorie and I landed in Shanghai just as the Japanese had started to move in on the enemy aliens and to begin to check on all foreigners—including the Vichy French, the Russians, and the Allies of Japan, the Italians and the Germans.

This was the beginning of the end of the foreigners' Shanghai. As at the fall of Manila, we were to be in on the fall of Shanghai. In many ways the pattern was the same. Those of us who had been interned in Santo Tomás in Manila, and others who had been at Stanley Camp at Hong Kong, could see it coming. We told our Shanghai friends what we saw. They didn't see it that way. And in view of their arguments and long Shanghai experience, at first we began to wonder if they might not be right. But we'd been through all this once before. It was like a recurrent dream. The pattern looked the same to us. We felt it was impossible for the Japanese to leave us alone.

As 1942 came to an end the Shanghailander saw the financial and commercial city he and his people had built up from a mud flat into the greatest trading center in all of China—Shanghai, International City of four million—knocked down in front of him like a rack of tenpins. It was the slow roll of the bowling ball that fooled him.

That initial internment of 365 men on November 5 and 6, 1942, was the actual beginning of general internment for all enemy aliens in China—about 22,000, of which 15,000 were in Shanghai.

But it was not until January 1943 that the Shanghailander actually awakened to the real situation. And by then it was almost too late to do much about trying to help himself or others in preparing for internment. When he did awaken, reactions were mixed. The hundreds of missionaries intoned from their pulpits, "The tower of Babel has fallen—the city of sin hath reaped its reward . . ."; the business Taipan cursed "the dirty little bastards . . ."; the Chinese businessman nodded his head knowingly, tucked his hands up the wide sleeves of his padded gown, and observed, "time is against the enemy . . . we will absorb him."

XXXV

WITHIN two weeks of our arrival at Shanghai all enemy nationals were ordered to wear numbered red arm bands to identify them either as American, British, Dutch, or "others." The "others" who wore "X"s we discovered were called "enemy neutrals." These were Belgians, Norwegians, Greeks, Poles, and some other nationals of nations occupied by the Nazis. The Danes, for example, were exempt.

The end was getting close. The signs were unmistakable. This was the first of a series of events designed to discredit the foreigner, to make him lose face in the eyes of the Chinese. But actually, it showed the Chinese who we were. We took the arm band as a badge of honorable identification. And most of the Chinese accepted it as just that.

At first the Chinese couldn't figure it out. Then they saw the "A," the "B," and the "N" (Netherlands). "Oh, yes, Master, now we savvy," they'd say. "This 'A' man, he belong number one man. 'B' man, he belong number two man." Then with a long, sly wink such as only the Billiken-faced Chinese can give, they'd show you a quick "thumbs up" and shuffle off down the street.

The arm bands also gave the Japanese the tip as to who we were. Before, we might have been Russian, French, Italian, or German. Now the Japs began to crowd us off sidewalks, jostle us in the streetcars and order us to get up and give them seats. They were generally disagreeable.

But all this, while hard on us, on the other hand was excellent anti-Japanese propaganda. The Chinese—most of them—didn't like the way we were being kicked around. For instance, one day on a streetcar so crowded that it made the New York subway during rush hour seem roomy, Marjorie was ordered to give up her seat to a Japanese soldier. I was standing just in front of her and as she got to her feet, we moved down through the crowd. The Japanese soldier and his friend laughed boisterously. An elderly Chinese doffed his tiny, black skull cap, and offered Marjorie his seat. Then he glared at the Japanese soldiers as if to dare them to say anything. They didn't. This incident gained plenty face for the Chinese, and didn't lose any for us.

Within two weeks of pinning arm bands on us the Japanese forbade any enemy aliens to enter places of entertainment. That meant cinemas, night clubs, or restaurants where there was music. Remember, this was ten months after war had started. And as January (the month internment began) approached, more and more restaurants were pressured into placing placards in their windows: "Nationals of countries at war with Japan unwanted." During this pressure period the Japanese began their first series of blackout drills.

What had happened was this. When Japan struck on December 7-8, 1941, the Japs grabbed everything they could lay hands on—at a distance from Japan. But places like Shanghai, Tientsin, Peking, Nanking, all close to Japan, were actually already in the bag. There had been no immediate need to do anything about them except to pick up what few American and British marines and military people were left and intern them. The rest could wait while more important matters were taken care of. When things were under control in the farther-flung sectors, then there would be plenty of time to come back and strip Shanghai and the other cities of foreign-owned properties.

The same was true for air-raid precautionary drill and other defense preparations. During the first year of the war there were very few planes, warships, or troops in the Shanghai or other North China metropolitan regions. There was no need for them then. When these first blackouts were ordered for Shanghai, it gave the Chungking Chinese, some of whom I knew by that time, an opportunity to move unmolested at night. They did. I was let in on one job they planned and watched it unfold. There was a large godown (warehouse) in Hongkew (Shanghai Jap town) full of American and British chemical and electrical equipment. The Japanese had sealed it, and, waiting for a later date when they would have more time to clear it out, had merely placed a few watchmen around it.

The first night of the blackout the group of Chungking "city" guerrillas, as they call themselves, to be distinguished from the "country" guerrillas, moved in on the warehouse. They bound the guards and with several hundred men working in the blackout cleaned out about three-quarters of all the goods inside before dawn. I took a streetcar down to Hongkew two days afterwards just to see where the "job" had taken place. There were garrison troops with fixed bayonets standing guard in front of the main entrance to protect what was left, since chemicals and electrical equipment obviously are among those materials most needed in wartime Japan.

During the daylight air-raid precautionary drills, which the average Chinese call "daylight blackout," the Japanese pulled the same stunts that they do in Japan. But they don't get the same co-operation from the public. Planes fly low over the city dropping smoke bombs. Where these bombs drop, ambulances and special air-raid wardens dash to the spot to pick up anyone they choose in the vicinity, wrap him in bandages and rush him to the nearest first-aid station. It makes no difference who you are or where you're going. They just grab you, throw you to the ground, dump you onto a stretcher and off you go.

One of these first episodes lost considerable face for the Japanese precautionary drillers. I happened to be on hand for the show. I was standing on the roof of the Palace Hotel overlooking the Bund and the entire waterfront, when three fighter planes zoomed not 200 feet over the Bund and the river traffic—sampans, barges, slipper boats,

and regular river steamers. Thousands of Chinese stopped their toil-
ing and looked up. The lead plane dropped a smoke bomb meant to
hit the wide Bund. The bomb was misplaced, however, and fell on
the top deck of a riverboat moored to a jetty pontoon. In a second's
time the smoke bomb had ignited some canvas and straw on the deck
and flames shot out.

For half an hour fireboats screeched their sirens and navy tugs
slipped alongside the ferryboat; while Chinese coolies scrambled up
to the deck to beat out the flames, navy officers rushed over from
27 The Bund, the Navy Office (formerly Jardine and Company)
jibbering and Jappering, but doing nothing helpful. Not until after
the coolies had beaten out the fire did the Japanese-operated fire
department arrive on the scene, to be confronted with hundreds of
grinning, mocking Chinese.

A Chinese who'd been standing at my side silently watching all
of this shook his head. "This Jap man, he just make play-play," he
muttered. "All time he make play-play. When comes boom-boom,
he plenty run. Never mind—bimeby plenty planes, bimeby plenty
boom-boom. No more Jap man." He patted me on the red arm band
and trudged off.

During this period, beginning in November 1942, the Japanese
fully closed in on the enemy alien community. They mopped up
last-minute details on the year-long takeover of foreign concerns.
They moved into enemy alien homes, stamped all the rugs and furniture and home utensils. They demanded property deeds, and in-
ventories of everything in the homes from babies' dolls to pickle
forks and beds. They stomped into homes at any hour of the day
or night. They'd demand coffee, "Ah-mer-ikan coff-ee!"—not tea.
They'd ask for American cigarettes. They'd admire a piece of bric-
a-brac. If it wasn't offered to them, they'd pocket it. The Japanese
were now "taking" Shanghai.

During this same period all radio short-wave reception sets and
long-wave sets of more than five tubes were ordered turned in at
gendarmerie headquarters. There were a few radio repair shops
around town to which neutrals, Chinese, and Axis aliens were ordered to take sets for sealing. The Japanese would take the sets, remove the extra tubes and sockets, and seal up the mechanism that
permitted you to hear KGEI or KWID in San Francisco, or Chungking, or Radio Delhi. Also they took out all the good copper wire
and the American-made tubes and replaced them with local-made
stuff that was next to useless.

The foreigners—including the Swiss, Italian, Russian, and German consulates—were strictly ordered to have their radios in by a certain date. The Swiss and Italians took their sets down to their consulates and left them, rather than give them to the Japs. The Germans refused to give theirs up. And the Russians said, "If you want ours, come and get them!" There are over twenty thousand Russians. A year later the Japanese had made no move to go after their radios.

But the enemy American-British-Netherlander group dutifully brought their radios down to the gendarmerie. It was different with them. Most of their radios had been registered previously. Thus it was wise to comply with the order. However, some people had two radios and many of them secreted one and turned in the other, or gave one away. Why give the Japanese radio equipment they'd eventually use to fight you with? And why not listen to what was going on in the world as long as possible?

One day when I was ordered to report to the gendarmerie headquarters for questioning, I had time to watch the turn-in of radios. There was an extremely long line. Of course you had to fill out forms in at least triplicate for everything. Most of these had to have your picture on them. When you'd filled them out it was a three to five chance that the Japanese at the desk would discover you'd filled out the wrong one and would hand you another. These forms were the bane of our existence. You had to be very careful, in filling them out, not to give conflicting evidence, or you would be brought up for cross questioning.

This day people were sweating over forms, sitting on their radios, or holding the radios under one arm while they filled out the forms. Somehow most of the instruments "unfortunately" had been dropped "accidentally" en route to the gendarmerie and weren't in working condition.

I saw an American seaman I knew walk in. He took a quick look around. Then he blandly walked up to the pile of turned-in radios stacked up against the wall, looked them over casually, selected a small but powerful set, bowed low to the guard and said, "My radio. Must stand in line to turn in. Left here last night closing time."

The guard who didn't understand any of it returned the bow. The seaman nodded, tucked the radio under his arm and walked out of the gendarmerie office with a good short-wave set.

Despite the final "listen and die" order regarding short-wave reception, all who could listened. There are hundreds of short-wave sets in the large Chinese community. These are used daily. They will be of inestimable value when the time comes to issue warnings and instructions to the Chinese population at the end of the Jap rule in

Shanghai. And the Japanese know it, but they can't stop up all of these listeners' ears. In the first place they'd never find half the radios, and secondly, search by Japanese soldiers of Chinese homes in a city the Japanese had turned over to his "friendly Chinese brothers" would hardly be the "thing to do."

The Japanese do not have it all their way in the occupied cities of China. The long arm of Chungking reaches down into Nanking, Peking, and Shanghai. It tosses homemade hand bombs at Japanese and puppet officials; hides time bombs to explode in railway stations or out in the country under railway or highway culverts, causes train tie-ups and truck wrecks.

Not only the Japs are threatened by guerrillas and terrorists inside Occupied China, but the "foreigners" are as well. Until the Japanese edict that all enemy aliens had to wear red arm bands, there was no way for Chinese to tell whether the foreigner was Nazi, Russian, or Anglo-American.

Shanghai in constant dimout has some pretty dark streets, and many bicycling foreigners have been slugged and relieved of their bikes and money. But before internment when the red arm bands first appeared, marking the United Nations foreigners, the order went out among the guerrillas and bike thugs not to lift bikes or cash from "Red Arm Bands."

I had a friend who was pedaling his bike home one night on the outskirts of Shanghai when he was stopped by three Chinese, shoved around, and relieved of his bicycle. The Chinese started off with the bicycle when on second thought the leader switched his flashlight on the foreign victim. The first thing that stood out was the bright red "A" arm band.

"Velly solly, Master—velly solly," the Chinese apologized. He helped rearrange my friend's disheveled clothing, returned his bicycle to him, and faded into the black of the suburban road without another word.

The next night this same man went to dine with a friend. During the meal he noticed the Chinese serving boy eying him curiously as if trying to place him. The vague sense of recognition was mutual. Before the evening was over, my friend had placed the houseboy as the bicycle thug of the night before. He told his host of his adventure.

XXXVI

ON DECEMBER 31, 1942, in Shanghai, I started to keep a diary. It was a dangerous business and I knew it was probably not wisdom on my part. However, from that date, until February 25, 1943, when we were finally re-imprisoned, I kept daily notes. After that I was able to add a few entries. But for most of the time in camp I kept the journal buried in a small Chinese powdered-milk tin. When it looked as though repatriation was actually coming I dug up the journal, making entries from the middle of August through September 15, when I had to secrete it in preparation for my inspection and for our repatriation from Shanghai on September 19, 1943.

How I got it out would make interesting reading. But undoubtedly there are others who will wish to do the same thing later. It wasn't an easy thing to do. I had several very close calls. The Japanese were thorough in their search of my baggage and my person, but not thorough enough. They missed the tiny journal and a small blue address book despite such careful probing as opening sealed packages of cigarettes that I was carrying for a friend, and feeling of each cigarette individually.

Naturally the journal is sketchy because it is so tiny. The notations were made for "reminders" of what really happened. I have expanded this material so that you can read exactly what comes to my mind as I read the notations.

"Repatriation!" What a magic word that was. To every American and Britisher that meant the difference of having to starve out the remainder of what we all felt would be a long Far East war, or getting home where we could really do something toward winning the war.

We all knew that the next repatriation ship would carry only 1500 people. Yet each of the 3000 Americans could think of some circumstance which he was sure justified him in expecting a place on the ship. The British, numbering perhaps 12,000, were just as hopeful as we that a British repatriation would come shortly. There was scarcely a week passed in which at least 50 per cent of the British and American community hadn't checked in at the Swiss Consulate General "to see what's new on repatriation."

The families with small children or aged parents were nearly frantic as it became more and more apparent that the Japanese were going to imprison all enemy aliens. The hope of repatriation was the last straw. Everyone was grasping at it.

The last week of the year—just before New Year's—the Swiss Consulate was increasingly active checking and rechecking repatriation priority categories. But no one knew for sure what the priorities were. Everyone had "the dope straight from the Swiss," but careful checkups proved that no one—not even the Swiss—was sure about anything.

Jack Janszen, his wife Dorothy, and Marjorie and I used to go up on the roof of the Palace Hotel at night and look down the Bund toward the Swiss Consulate offices on the ninth floor of the Messageries Maritimes Building. For four nights during Christmas week, lights burned down there until midnight. Marjorie contended this was "significant." Anything out of the ordinary those days was "significant."

Other afternoons Jack and I would climb up to the graveled rooftop just to watch the activity in the Whangpoo River. The Japanese river police boats were vigilant. They never missed a sampan. And they never missed an opportunity to confiscate something from the small cargo boats that passed up and down the muddy, meandering river in front of what once had been the busy port of Shanghai.

Once in a while in the downstream haze we would spot the huge former passenger liners such as the *Kamakura Maru*, or the French motorship *Aramis*. They were being used as troop transports and cargo vessels. We watched the Japs' ant-like swarming over these vessels, loading tons of white wheat sacks from sampans and from trucks ashore.

Of course we always kept one eye cocked on the Italian luxury liner *Conte Verde*—then our white hope for repatriation, since she had taken the first diplomatic exchange group out. New Year's week the Italian crew chipped paint and daubed red lead all over her in a measles pattern. They also restrung cables from her forward loading booms. All of us enemy aliens passing up and down the Bund would stop to watch the progress, and to pass along rumors on the significance of the painting. But even the Swiss who were closest to the repatriation program knew nothing more than the fact that the U.S. Department of State was constantly pressuring for speedy repatriation.

It was on January 5 during this upset period of false hopes and threatening imprisonment that I received the first word from home.

It was exactly one year to the day that Marjorie and I were first imprisoned at Santo Tomás. Hans Jost, Assistant Delegate at the office of the International Red Cross, called to say there was a message from my mother who was in the United States.

I was so nervous I could scarcely direct the rickshaw coolie. It was a delayed radiogram stating that she had received word that we had been transferred from Manila. She said Charlie Colebaugh (managing editor of *Collier's*), Dolph Opfinger at Mutual Broadcasting System, and others were exerting pressure on our case as well as urging a general "humanitarian repatriation." She said everything possible was being done. We debated whether that meant there was little hope, or that repatriation was imminent. But it was a great relief to know she was well, and an answer to our prayers.

Ever since the Haiphong Road political camp had been set up in November I had taken a weekly food parcel out to the American School Relief Center for Russ Brines. One cold January morning out at the relief center I saw Lieutenant Honda, the gendarmerie liaison officer at Haiphong Road. He is a surly, young, self-important Jap. He said Brines was well and was getting plenty to eat. I had been questioned at Bridge House just before Christmas by Lieutenant Honda and that experience made me distrust anything he said or did. I guess I wasn't "inscrutable" enough. For the next day I was ordered to report to the office of the Naval Landing Party at 5 P.M. I ought to have known enough by this time to have kept my mouth shut. Lieutenant Matsuda, a Princeton graduate, very pointedly put me through a forty-five-minute grilling on the question of Russ Brines and why I had been asking questions of Lieutenant Honda about Brines' condition. He wanted to know why I had written a short note to Henningsen, the prisoner chairman of Brines' camp. I told him that I was naturally interested, because Brines was a good friend and that I had been nominated by the Swiss Consulate as spokesman for our small group of American correspondents shifted from Manila last September. Matsuda was very nasty and caustic. However, I didn't get slugged. But I was worried that they'd keep me in a cell overnight. I was afraid that would set a precedent. But just before 7 P.M. they ordered me to return to the Palace Hotel.

On January 9 the Chinese puppet government declared war on the United States and Great Britain. This put the North and Central Coast Chinese in a spot. Until then they had been able to grin, shrug their shoulders, and say, "I am just Chinese. I do not take sides."

The day after the Japanese-inspired puppet declaration of war, Marjorie, Jack, Dorothy Janszen and I took the long tramcar ride out through Frenchtown to Dorothy Dunn's. We had a cheerful time at Dorothy's as usual, she being very practical about the problem of the expected future internment. She had Grandma Pray, the two-year-old twins, and sixteen-year-old Patty to consider. Pat proved a great help, especially since her father had been thrown into the Haiphong Road camp. At this stage, Dorothy was really in a spot. If there was a repatriation ship she would have to go with the twins, but probably without her husband. If not, she would have to take enough special food into camp to assure the babies of a specialized nutritious diet. Seventy-four-year-old Granny undoubtedly had an iron constitution and hated the Japs, but it was obvious she could not take an extended period of camp chow such as we had in Manila. We worked all afternoon on lists of food stuffs and other necessary articles for Dorothy to buy. This was typical of everyone's routine those days, in preparation for internment in Shanghai.

When we got back from Dorothy's that night the hotel manager telephoned the room to tell me the gendarmerie had been in looking for me about six o'clock. I knew if I went over to their headquarters there was every chance they'd keep me. I figured if they wanted me they'd come and get me. It wasn't long before the desk clerk rang the room and said, "There's a questionnaire been left down here for you to fill out immediately." Marjorie went down with me to get it. She was really worried and I wasn't too hopeful.

The manager handed me a mimeographed questionnaire. "You fill this out. You return this to Japanese supervisor of this hotel, Mr. Kanaya, immediately. We must have the answer." The questionnaire asked for my opinion on: (1) The meaning of the declaration of war by Nanking against the United States and Britain. (2) My opinion regarding the relinquishment by Japan of extraterritoriality in China. (3) My opinion regarding Japan's "gracious act" in turning over to the Nanking Government control and administration of the international settlement in Shanghai. I tried several answers, none of which seemed satisfactory, for I knew they would quote me over Radio Tokyo. Finally, I wrote: "Under the circumstances as an enemy alien, and since I do not know the full facts regarding this matter, I feel His Imperial Japanese Majesty's Government will understand when I say that I am not qualified to express an opinion."

Mr. Kanaya was politely upset at the brief answer. He said he was not certain this would be acceptable to "the gendarmerie gentlemen." Then Marjorie and I dropped into Carl and Shelley Mydans' room, realizing that they would also have received a questionnaire. They were still pondering. They thought a longer answer might be more effective and keep the Japanese from coming back for further questioning. However, we didn't hear from the gendarmerie again on this matter.

As a further indication that internment was closing in on us, all enemy alien businessmen were told to report to an open-air pavilion in Hongkew. Of course Jack had to go to represent Westinghouse. Mitsubishi had taken him over. Here they were ordered to remove their overcoats, as a mark of politeness to high Japanese dignitaries who were about to relieve them officially of everything they or their companies owned. These enemy aliens stood for two hours in the cold, bareheaded and without coats, while "receipts" for robbery were handed out like diplomas. Now the Japanese had officially taken over all enemy property.

At this point our imprisonment seemed so close that Jack and I went to the offices of the American Residents' Association to offer our services in any capacity in assisting in preparation for internment. They weren't interested. They were even resentful at what they indicated as "intrusion" on our part. James O. Nichols (acting head of the Association since Henningsen's internment at Haiphong Road) said, "No extra preparation is necessary. After all, nothing much can be done." I was so upset at this lack of a common-sense approach that I had to leave before I blew up.

Jack suggested we go over to the British Residents' Association, which we did. Braidwood, the B.R.A. chairman, was interested in ideas and suggestions based on my experience in the Manila camp. At the moment we arrived it just happened he had two or three people there, including Lawrence Kadoorie from Hong Kong, who had gone through the rough days of internment at Stanley Camp. We pooled ideas and came out with what seemed to be a workable setup for camp organization, and lists of "must" supplies and medical necessities. One of the biggest problems we had was to secure financial credit of sufficient size to enable the British and American Residents' Associations to purchase bulk quantities of necessities—from brooms, buckets, mops, and disinfectant to vitamins and medicines and even wooden army cots and hospital beds.

A few days later I ran into Nichols on the street all bundled up like a little pekingese in a jacket. "Banjo [the Japanese Consulate liaison with American and British Residents' Associations] has just told me that internment will come even if there is repatriation," Nichols said. "Then if this is true," I told him, "you fellows had better begin lining up beds, mattresses, medicines, and other equipment right away with the aid of the International Red Cross." Nichols' only reply was followed by a confident wave of his hand. "Oh, the Japanese will furnish us with everything!"

XXXVII

IN LATE afternoon of January 18 I received word that I was to be permitted to visit Haiphong Road Camp to see Russ Brines, along with about twenty others who were wives of British, American, and Dutch prisoners. Here was a chance to get a glimpse of the kind of treatment we might expect in a few weeks, when they picked us up again.

At the last minute Bob Biesel, who managed the American Relief Center, arranged through Lieutenant Honda for Art Ladow to come with me to see Russ. Russ had asked for Art. He wanted to find out what had happened to the clothing he had been forced to leave behind when he was picked up on November 5.

We were supposed to enter Haiphong Road Camp at 10 A.M. sharp. Our time inside was limited to one hour. When we were finally lined up in two rows beneath the red brick archway and were inspected by the Army guards, it was 10:15. Haiphong Road Camp isn't the way I thought it would be. It's the old U.S. Fourth Marines Barracks, but they're not barracks buildings. The 362 British, American, and Dutch are housed in one of two old three-story brick houses. The rooms are small. Floors are wood. Men are crowded in tightly.

The Japanese guard led us across the small open compound, where I noted a short volley ball court on one side and a small garden on the other, and into the building on the right. Henningsen, American chairman, was standing there with a list to check off our names. He looked pretty well but being a tall man seemed more gaunt. He was very pale. Cornell Franklin (former Shanghai Municipal Council chairman) was acting as a camp policeman. He was definitely thinner. He led us up two flights into a bare, cold waiting room. I had a chance to whisper a few words to him as I followed up the narrow winding stairs. "We're getting enough to eat now," he drawled. "This is a torture-chamber reception center. The Japs are constantly taking our boys out to Bridge House."

My turn came quickly. Lieutenant Honda said, "Ten minutes. No longer. And no whispering. If you do . . ." and he raised his hand in a threatening gesture. I found myself in a long room. There were eight stools, two in each corner. A tall civilian Japanese snooped around.

Tom Dunn came in first. He looked terribly tired and stooped. He shook hands briefly and turned quickly to Dorothy, Pat, and the twins in the far corner. The twins' squeals and laughter covered Russ's entry and we had several minutes of fast conversation before the twins quieted down.

Russ looked stuffed. But it was due to all the extra sweaters he was wearing, for it was a cold, clammy day. He's chubby anyway —I didn't think he'd lost much weight. He said he and his room-mates were eating pretty well, since most of them got parcels each week from the outside. I told him Honda was planning to cut down on the parcels but that Marjorie and I would keep sending them as long as we remained out.

The ten minutes passed quickly, but not before we had covered the ground. In the middle of our overcrowded conversation the tall, civilian Japanese stuck his nose in. Russ introduced us. The old bird laughed, "Brin-ess, he look good, eh? I think now we cut down his chow. Too fat."

"Yeah—ha-ha," I laughed weakly, "very funny—ha-ha!"

"The old astard-bay . . . ," mumbled Russ as the Japanese turned to the Dunn twins. "Is-thay ace-play ink-stays," he continued in a natural tone. And we talked for a minute or two in pig Latin. The Japanese never turned around. We often found pig Latin helped in a tight pinch.

Russ said what got him was the monotony, the threat of retalia-tion and torture questioning at Bridge House, plus the lack of space and exercise. "It's really a hell hole. . . ." He told of several roll calls daily, whenever the Japs happened to feel roll-callish. The prisoners usually had to run out onto the small compound and count off in Japanese. "Whenever the colonel-commandant enters camp if you are anywhere near him you have to bow deeply," Russ said. "Some-times in the morning at roll call the army lieutenant has us practice bowing toward Tokyo. The bastard!" That's like making every Japanese prisoner at home, say at Tule Lake Camp, stand at atten-tion each morning and salute the American flag accompanied by the Pledge to the Flag.

We got a lot done in ten minutes, thanks to Dorothy Dunn's twins making so much rumpus. The visiting time was cut for the others who came in after we did—they only let a few of us in the room at a time. Some wives merely got to say "hello and good-by." Honda thought this "very funny."

The other prisoners hung from windows in the second building or leaned on their rakes and shovels in the front compound watching us being marched out. No one made a sign. It gave me the strangest depressed feeling to see these men I knew—to see their wives just ahead of me—and to realize they were aching to wave, but knew punishment might accompany a signal. . . .

The axe fell on January 23. Internment! The Japs called the British and American Residents' Associations and told them that all single men between the ages of eighteen and forty-five were to report for internment on January 31. The Associations were ordered to cull these people out of their lists and to tell them to report the following morning at 9:45 at Church House for final instructions. Symbolic of their disregard for international law—or agreement—the Japanese completely ignored the Swiss who represented us Americans and British, refusing to deal with the Swiss at all on the subject of internment. About four hundred men showed up at Church House. The meeting was short and tense. This was the first group. What happened to them would happen to the rest of us. We were all anxious to find out. They were permitted to take four bundles, one to be a bed and bedding. The other three were to be at the prisoner's option but "must not be larger than a small trunk." This certainly differed from Manila where we had practically nothing. This so-called "heavy baggage" was to be delivered by the prisoner himself on January 29 and 30 at the customs jetty on the Bund. We learned the camp would be set up in an old British-American Tobacco Company warehouse, just across the river in Pootung. We were also told there would be a second group to follow this one in about two weeks. The total planned for the Pootung camp was approximately one thousand. We wondered then how it compared with the way our people rounded up the Hawaiian and West Coast Japanese when they were put into camps.

Jack and I went shopping in the rain that first afternoon following the announcement. We found four slightly bent iron cots in a little Chinese shop and bargained the owner down to $180 CRB—Japanese-issued paper money—about $6 U.S. The next day Carl and Shelley tried the same shop. The owner wanted $500 CRB per bed. And that's what happened all over Shanghai. The friendly Chinese is also a number one businessman who is alert to the rising demand market.

Here is my diary comment on the first Shanghai general internment:

January 31—Thousands of Chinese and other Shanghailanders assembled outside Church House at the Cathedral to watch the march
of the first foreigners to be interned. The 320 men assembled at
about 10 A.M. They were divided into squads—British and American
and Dutch. A truck was backed up to Church House to take baggage for the sick and aged. We piled the bags in. Just before the
march began Banjo ordered every man to carry his own baggage
regardless of age or sickness. We had to unload the truck. All the
men were trying to carry too much. It's lucky it was only two
blocks to the jetty. When the march began Japanese propaganda
corps photographers, perched in trees, took pictures of the marching men and the crowds. Instead of getting pictures of terrified men
and impressed spectators, they were making pictures of what appeared to be an hilarious send-off. This first gang acted as though
they were going to be repatriated instead of interned. The Americans and British have learned something about face, too. The Japanese were frankly puzzled and the photographers were ordered to
stop making pictures.

Banjo and a colonel of the consular police who supervised the
march were furious.

XXXVIII

THE day the Japanese called up all remaining unattached men
I worked on the telephone all afternoon calling people from the
American Association office. I tried to break it as gently as possible.
I just said, "I'm sorry to have to tell you that your number has come
up. You're to report at Church House Sunday to get your instruc-
tions. You'll probably have about a week before you go in."

Most of them said, "Okay, thanks." But their too calm brevity of
speech was but an attempt to cover up the extreme nervousness we
all felt.

Banjo came in after we finished telephoning. I overheard him talking about the ratio of men and women in the Chapei camp just outside Shanghai where Marjorie and I were scheduled to go. The point
was that we should be permitted to keep a number of able-bodied
single men out of Pootung to help with much of the necessary man-

ual labor in this American family camp. In checking over the cards, it looked as though the ratio was likely to be about one man to every nine women. This was mentioned to Banjo. His only remark was, "Let the women work. What do they think this is—a goddamn boarding house?" I could have slugged him. Other Americans have —pre-war. He was fired from Shell Oil at one time, I understand. If there are ever any post-war trials he should not be passed over.

During this pre-internment period Marjorie and I called several times on Karl von Wiegand and Lady Drummond-Hay (Hearst publications) who were held almost incommunicado at the Hotel Metropole. Karl's eyesight was slightly improved by a recent operation. But he was certainly in no condition to go into camp. He applied for both his and Lady Hay's suspension. I asked him why he didn't petition the Japanese to permit him to continue living at the Metropole. He was under virtual house-arrest there anyway.

The first note was smuggled out of Pootung by Lanny Davis of San Francisco, who had come up from Manila with us. He reported the food was worse than Manila . . . dirty rice, a little cabbage, and some tea. They got fish occasionally. Lanny had been over there nine days then. He said if the Japanese would fix it up a little bit, it wouldn't be much worse than Santo Tomás. The men lived in large rooms but jammed close together. About eighty in some rooms. It was cold and damp but there were stoves. The coal, such as it was, was plentiful. There were only a couple of toilets for the whole bunch. Lanny said lack of water and plumbing was really the biggest problem at the moment.

I was ordered to the gendarmerie office late that same afternoon for another quizzing and saw the gendarmerie lady sleuth, Mrs. Nogami, who was just as "pleasant" as she could be. But I didn't like the cutting tone of her voice when she talked to the stubby little lieutenant who quizzed me.

I was nervous, for I was afraid they'd found out about Lanny's note. But the lieutenant never mentioned it. This quizzing lasted two hours. After half an hour seated I was forced to kneel on a baseball bat and talk from that position, with the pain under my kneecaps growing more excruciating every moment. That's really hell. This time he wanted to know where I was getting my money. I gave him the story I had told before and hoped I didn't miss anything. I didn't remember much of the last half hour of it. My legs were asleep. But he did most of the talking. It was about the inferior white people and superior Orientals and about the Greater East Asia Sphere.

When I got out I went down to Jimmy's Kitchen and sat for about half an hour drinking coffee and eating a fried egg which cost me more money than I could afford. I had to get my bearings. From there I went to the Swiss Consulate where I reported to Ruf what had happened. He's a stolid little Swiss but efficient.

While at the Consulate I learned that Dr. Ralph Dunn, the dentist, had offered all his equipment to be packed and taken into one of the camps. I was flabbergasted to hear that Nichols had refused to accept the equipment since the Japanese refused to pay drayage into camp. On hearing about this, Janszen told Nichols that he would go out and get the money somewhere, but for Nichols to get permission to cart the equipment into camp. Nichols said he and the British had earmarked about $400,000 CRB (about $13,000 U.S.) for drugs and medicines for the camps.

As it turned out the British camps got some of these drugs and medicines, but we received only a few cans of disinfectant, some empty medicine bottles, and a smattering of medicines brought in by our own doctors.

It wasn't until February 13 that Marjorie and I learned we were to go "in" on February 25. Dorothy and Jack Janszen got their orders the same day. The Japs gave us prison camp numbers. Ours were C-219 and C-220. The "C" stood for Chapei.

When we got the order we started out to make a few last-minute needed purchases, such as soap and toilet paper. In one former foreign drugstore I found a few American products. It cost Marjorie the equivalent of $1 U.S. for a 10-cent bottle of Jergens Lotion. She got this for the "fishwater hands" she knew she'd soon get in camp. I bought a nickel package of wintergreen Life Savers for 50 cents U.S., just to have as a "morale builder" some dark day in camp. This sort of purchasing certainly had it all over the hectic occupation days in Manila.

It was arranged with the Japanese to permit twenty men to go into camp as an "advance guard" on the 23rd, to clean up as much as possible and prepare for the rest of this first batch of about 350.

As internment proceeded, the best exchange rate around town grew to between $41 and $52 CRB to $1 U.S. Of course, there was severe punishment for anyone caught with a U.S. dollar or trading in notes. When we were transferred to Shanghai in September, the exchange was about 27 to $1 U.S. When we left a year later it was 100 to $1 U.S.

Ten days before we went into camp Jack and I helped check and load onto barges in the Whangpoo the baggage and bedding the

Japs permitted the second bunch of 388 called to Pootung to take with them. It was a cold and wet day. While we were working we learned that E. Fontanel (Swiss Consul General) on February 10 had protested the harsh treatment of Pootung prisoners, stressing punishment, no hospital, and lack of food as the basis for the protest. The Japanese claimed they didn't know what he was talking about. It was a good thing to let this protest news get around town. It was good for the Chinese to know about it.

Again, as on January 31, there was a tremendous crowd watching when the second group was herded off to Pootung. A Japanese squad marched ahead of the column carrying tall poles flying white banners with Chinese characters which were translated to me as "Enemy aliens being imprisoned for their own good." I walked alongside the men to the Bund, where we ran into a Japanese "anti-foreign" parade. There was a lot of shouting and waving of fists. For a few minutes it looked as though something serious might happen but the parade turned up Nanking Road. This was the end of the Pootung list. There were about seventy single men left of whom some thirty had been temporarily suspended because of severe illness. The others just weren't called, for some unknown reason.

With ten days to go I worked at Church House, handing out forms and new internment numbers prepared by the Japanese Consulate for those of us who were to be interned at Chapei on February 25. These were the people we were to be with—perhaps for the duration. I was astounded at the number of sick and aged who showed up. The age average of this group was high—over forty. It was evident there would not be very many able-bodied men or women.

To facilitate routine at the American Association· offices, Ralph Schilling (Standard Oil) and Dr. Weiss (missionary doctor) were appointed by Nichols as the scrutinizing committee for all letters submitted by persons requesting medical or other exemption from camp. This was a vital job requiring infinite tact, patience, and an understanding of human nature when under extreme emotional stress. The recommendations of these two men, passed along to the Japs, could have life and death importance.

For several days at the Association office I listened to remarks and recommendations made regarding internment of women and children and the aged . . . recommendations to applicants for exemption telling them it was better for them to go into camp immediately, since they would have to go in eventually. I heard people told this when it resulted in splitting families. I tried to discuss it with these two men. But never having been in camp, and being unable to conceive of the utter brutality and hatred of the Japanese for foreigners, they merely shrugged their shoulders.

I talked seriously with Nichols and his assistant, Bill Gray, on the subject. I contended it was the job of every American, and particularly their association, to keep every person out of camp as long as possible. Neither of these men had much to offer, except to comment weakly, "Banjo says everyone has to be interned. Maybe they can be released after they get into camp."

In order that our nationals might have some funds once they arrived in camp our Government permitted the Swiss Consulate to make comfort loans to Americans, payable after the war, in the amount of $60 U.S. for a single American and $112 for husband and wife. The Swiss began immediately to try to establish a basis for continuing a smaller comfort allowance payable each month to interned civilians. But at first the Japanese refused to consider permitting it.

It was while we were trying to work out all of these last-minute arrangements—for what we felt certainly would be the "duration" sentence—that I was astonished to have Banjo take me aside one day to tell me that Riozo Tsurumi, former commandant at Manila's Santo Tomás camp, would be in Shanghai soon.

"Mr. Tsurumi is to be the chief commandant for all civil assembly centers in North and Central China," Banjo said, "and he has sent word that you are to report to him the moment he arrives." That really had me guessing. One thing was quite clear, however. The Tokyo people felt Tsurumi had done such a good job of keeping the hated enemy nationals "in line" at Santo Tomás that they were giving him a much bigger job.

Meantime there was nothing to do but to sit tight and wait for Tsurumi to arrive from up North where he was "inspecting camp sites."

One noon during the last days spent at the Palace Hotel waiting for Tsurumi to arrive and for our internment, we had a difficult moment. Four Japs at a near-by table—we ate one meal a day at the hotel—shoved back their chairs and marched around our table shouting, "Downfall with enemy nationals!" The whole dining room—there must have been three hundred people—quieted till all you could hear was heavy breathing. We kept on eating. After some more shouting in Japanese, the four Japs reeled out between the other tables.

This seemed to be our day for unpleasantness, for we were walk-

ing up the crowded Bund that same afternoon when Jack accidentally bumped into a scrawny Jap who was carrying a cardboard
calendar under his arm. Jack just murmured, "Sorry," and we went
on. Suddenly he was grabbed from behind and spun around by this
little Jap who was waving his broken calendar in the air. A crowd
gathered immediately. Jack bowed and said, "I am sorry." The Jap
just kept shaking Jack by the arm. Anything might have happened.
But Jack used his head. He bowed deeply three times and each time
repeated, "I am very sorry." A Chinese said something loudly and
there was quite a bit of murmuring in the crowd. The Jap looked
around uncomfortably, shouted something, waved his fist and the
broken calendar, and walked off.

These are the moments you see bright red. The Japs hope you'll
do something they can term "disrespectful" so they can call a gendarme and rush you away to be beaten! We wondered how those
Japanese who were free in America or Britain were being treated by
average Americans and Britons.

The Japanese civilians were getting very cocky in the International
Settlement and French Concession at this period. An order came out
forcing all "stateless people" (Jewish refugees and other Jews who
arrived in Shanghai after 1937) to sell out to the Japanese in the
French Concession and International Settlement. Of the sixteen thousand Jews in Shanghai, well over ten thousand lived outside of Hongkew, but the new order forced them to move to Hongkew's worst
slum to live within an area of one square mile.

A member of the French Legation told me that the Japanese Embassy at Nanking had advised his government that Shanghai was to
be developed as a second Tokyo. Everything pointed that way—that
is, everything except the attitude of the Chinese. Indicative of their
feeling is this story which I heard from another Frenchman. He and
two friends went into the steam room of the Foreign YMCA. There's
a line of electric steam boxes there which, as usual, were filled with
red-faced, sweating little Japs. "They looked just like hunks of raw
meat sticking out of the boxes," he said. One of my friends laughed
out loud and called to the Chinese boy in attendance, "Hey, boy
. . . what you cook here . . . sukiaki?" The Japs, who were locked
in, were furious and clamored to be released. But the Chinese boy
said, "Never mind . . . this man belong Frenchman . . . he no belong
red arm band . . . never mind." And he left them locked in the cabinets, to cook a little more.

On Washington's birthday—with three more days before camp—I
called on Egle at the International Red Cross to check on the lists I

had given him of fundamental necessities from disinfectant to brooms and mops, mosquito netting, butcher knives, "plumbers' friends" and clothesline rope, not to forget medicines of all kinds. He promised to send them in as soon as the Japs permitted. Seven months later when I was repatriated, he still had not been able to secure the needed okay.

I left $1000 CRB at Scharpf and Guenther Transfer Co., which was a designated International Red Cross center for receipt of comfort parcels later to be sent into the camps. This money was to assure that parcels would be sent as before to Russ Brines at Haiphong Road after we were interned.

Two nights before our reinternment, we joined Jack and Dorothy Janszen for our last real Chinese chow at Sun Ya's on Nanking Road. We ate until we were stuffed, feeling just like the condemned!

Jack and I were at the Columbia Club before eight the next morning. Three Scharpf and Guenther trucks were there ready for the first trip to Chapei. About twelve consular police were on guard. About nine o'clock Tsurumi showed up in a big shiny car with two civilians and Banjo. The Japs were bowing all over the place to Tsurumi because of his rank. After we got Watson's gang (the twenty men who went into camp two days early to get it cleaned up a bit) loaded onto the trucks, Tsurumi told me he wanted to talk to me in his car. He wanted to know what kind of a trip we had from Manila to Shanghai on the *Maya Maru*. I told him, "Not so good." He laughed, showing all his bad teeth. Then he wanted to know how I liked Shanghai. I told him, "Better than Manila," which he also thought was a very big joke. "I know," he said. "You did not like Manila camp. I will tell you something. Neither did I." With that he signalled his driver and drove off. His big car led the three-truck caravan led by Watson and the clean-up crew of twenty on its first trip to Chapei.

Tsurumi returned in about an hour. Another car followed his with a military and naval officer inside. Tsurumi sent for me. He was very polite. He asked very formally about Marjorie's health. So I asked about Mrs. Tsurumi's health. He said he was pleased to see me. I said nothing. It was obvious that this was an official opening to something. The Army and Navy officers—one a general, one an admiral —just sat there and grinned.

Finally Tsurumi said, "I have had very great honor—high position given me. I have been appointed by my government chief commandant for North and Central China for internment and control of all enemy aliens," he explained. "This is very great honor."

He waited expectantly but I didn't tell him I was glad he had the job. Then came the surprise.

"Gun-san, I appoint you as chairman all internee's committees. I make my headquarters at Chapei Camp. I have ordered you to be placed at Chapei. I do all negotiating for people your camp—people other camps—at Chapei. I know you from Manila. I want this camp run like Manila camp. I want other camps run like Manila camp. You know how. Gun-san, I do all negotiating for enemy aliens through you."

I looked at the admiral and the general. They nodded emphatically. After the usual formula of stating that this undoubtedly was a very great honor, I told him I was sure he realized the only one who could negotiate with or for us prisoners was the Swiss Consul General, M. Fontanel, who represented British and American interests. He jumped to his feet and banged his fist on the table.

"Never mind Swiss. Never mind international law. I do not negotiate with any Swiss. I make my own law. I negotiate with you. This is my order."

I explained carefully the setup of the American and British Residents' Association, and how they had been working to organize the internment. "I am not Shanghailander," I told him. "You understand people here will want someone they know to be chairman. I am outsider. It will be better for you if you have committee. You will have better camp because people will co-operate."

He and the admiral and general had quite a talk in Japanese. Then he turned to me. "We negotiate with you. But we will have committee. What man you think for chairman? No British, no Dutch. Just American. I have plenty trouble with British in Manila. We do not like British. They treat my people bad in India. What Shanghai man make best chairman?"

Here he had me. Henningsen was by far the best man but he was in Haiphong Road Camp. Nichols was out of the question. I said, "Mr. Watson. He is the man who went into camp this morning with you. He is leader of the twenty men."

"Okay. Wat-son chairman. Gun-san vice-chairman."

"I think perhaps we have a woman on the committee, Mr. Tsurumi. And two or three more men. It may be better. Look at list of names, then talk with Mr. Watson."

"Why one woman?" he challenged.

I told him of the preponderance of women and children on the Chapei list. I reminded him that we had much trouble in Manila because we had so many women and children and it would be better if he appointed one woman to look after all women's and children's affairs.

He decided to wait until Thursday when we were to go into camp. I reported this to Buergin and Ruf at the Swiss Consulate late that afternoon. They agreed that I had done the right thing.

Before we knew it Marjorie and I were back in a Japanese concentration camp again. Twice in one war; and this time the barbed wire looked twice as high, twice as sharp. And the dilapidated buildings and compound looked even more discouraging than Santo Tomás.

PART SIX

Internment in Chapei

XXXIX

THE first night in camp was cold, damp, and filthy. The two large school buildings were still being patched up from having been wrecked and left to the elements since the 1937 Chapei District fighting. I knew the Japs were going to spring a surprise roll call on us. That would mean terror for the few hundred aged men and women and the tiny children, many of them two and under. One was six weeks old.

We also had two pregnant women, one of whom we had to send out to the hospital in a hurry the next day because of a miscarriage caused by excitement and the rough, bumpy ride into camp. The baby died and the mother almost died. Even she was ordered to stand roll call that night. There were two other such infant deaths from miscarriage during the first months of the camp due to the fact that the Japs would not extend the internment dates of the mothers until after the birth of the babies. Later a six-months-old baby died from improper care due to lack of equipment in our camp hospital. This baby dehydrated before the mother's eyes. At the last minute the child was sent to an outside hospital, but it was too late.

In order to beat the Jap at his own game—that of surprises—we moved fast that first day. Early in the afternoon I was able to get a skeleton camp organization set up, knowing that in all probability if we could present our plan first to the commandant he would not bother to work one out himself. Naturally we would much prefer our own plan to anything cooked up by the Japs. Despite the confusion of the baggage inspection—during which the Japanese guards helped themselves to anything they found in the limited luggage, from diamond rings to food, and carpenter's tools to coats—the internees were primed and ready for the first roll call.

It was after nine o'clock when it finally came. The deputy commandant—a pudgy, bespectacled, toughy named K. Inaba—had had several too many drinks and was in a nasty humor. He insisted on everyone "numbering"—counting off. Many of the old people were bewildered and frightened. The youngsters were asleep in their parents' arms. Everyone had to stand in the cold, wet hallways, until the entire roll call was over.

Immediately afterwards, Inaba (a former gendarmerie, or Japanese Gestapo officer) ordered everyone in camp to line up along the stairs in front of the commandant's office to come before him "to sign the oath." The oath proved to be innocuous enough. It stated —and I can quote directly because I smuggled out a copy:

OATH

On the occasion of my entry into the Civil Assembly Center, I ....
do hereby solemnly pledge

(1) that I will not attempt or conspire to commit any act which is likely to benefit the enemies of Japan or to prejudice the interests of Japan,

(2) that I will not attempt or conspire to escape from the Civil Assembly Center,

(3) that I will abide by any of the regulations enforced by the Civil Assembly Authorities.

But Inaba-san, full of "wheesky" and hatred for "you superior white people," took issue with the manner in which many of the internees placed the signed oath before him on the desk where he sat glowering.

One girl placed her hand on the desk; two men—one a former member of the Shanghai Municipal Council—neglected to hand the oath to him right side up; another girl who was asked why she was in camp replied, "Because I was forced to come." Inaba threatened them with prison—meaning Bridge House. Purple-faced, the veins in his neck throbbing, he talked like a tyrant. Shouting, waving his arms, he looked more like a mad ape. He made these prisoners stand in a corner, like naughty children, for more than an hour. Fortunately, he struck no one. At the height of his display of temper we, the committee, asked if we might not "take full responsibility for the behavior of these internees." This was a compromise to give Inaba a way out. After much bluster he accepted. It was then clear that this had been just an act to frighten the new prisoners. He had succeeded. But he'd also made us mad.

This was the same Inaba-san who insisted on a three-month "disciplinary period" before we were permitted to purchase a single egg, or extra vegetables for our 135 children aged five and under, or the more than one hundred internees over sixty, or the constantly mounting infirmary list of dysentery cases. This is the charming fellow who was mainly responsible for the preamble to the camp rules and regulations, beginning, "This is your home. It must be loved and cherished. . . ."

The men at the Pootung camp, just across the river from Shanghai, felt just as strongly as we did about Inaba-san. The British at other camps throughout the area also felt the sting of his keen hatred. If it hadn't been so serious it would have been ridiculous. Here was this pompous little man, about thirty-four years old, who wore green and red-checked race-track suits, trying to impress committee members with his self-styled "smart business manner." His most frequent expletive, accompanied by pounding with his fist on his own fat chest, was: "I Inaba. I make the international law history. I am God."

Inaba and Tsurumi worked out, with their superiors at the consulate, the regulations which they presented to all of us on our induction into camp. They called it "matriculation."

The morning after our arrival in camp the commandant crowded us all into the lobby of the main building at Chapei to read these rules to us. Guards with drawn revolvers stood on all sides of the room. Two guards placed themselves behind the commandant and the captain of the guard, Sugahara, who stood on the stairs above the internees. The three of us who made up the camp internee committee stood behind the two guards while still another guard with fixed bayonet stood behind us. With the stage thus set the commandant read these rules for all camps, which I later smuggled out:

The provisions prescribed hereunder shall be observed by the Americans and British subjects living in the Chapei Civil Assembly Center.

The Civil Assembly Center being the best home for those who live in it, *must be loved and cherished* by all of them. Each person shall take care of his health and live in harmony with each other. There shall be no disputing, quarreling, disturbing or any other improper demeanors.

In the daily routine enforced by the Civil Assembly Authorities, the turn-out, the roll calls and lights-out shall especially be observed with precision.

Food and other allowances being fixed by the Government, no alternation in them shall be allowed. Complaints or manifestations of discontent against the food provided or against its quantity, or any complaint against living conditions or equipments of the Civil Assembly Center shall not be made.

(There was anticipation of such complaints on the part of the Japanese. Lack of food, medicines, and inadequate living conditions were a definite feature of the "plan" for hated enemy aliens.)

The orders given by the Japanese officials and police guards shall be strictly obeyed and there shall be no act of defiance.

For the time being one letter a month, subject to censor by the Japanese officials, will be permitted for each person. Such letters must be typed or written in clear and legible handwriting; letters hard to read shall not be accepted.

As all members of living sections shall be held responsible and punished for run-away of its member, caution should be taken by each of them to prevent such an occurrence.

(And at the close of the reading the commandant threatened death by shooting if anyone attempted to escape . . . death for civilian noncombatant internees, who were not prisoners of war.)

No argument shall be made nor any rumor shall be circulated concerning the world situation, nor any criticism against Japan shall be allowed.

(They had spies planted among us who reported overheard conversations to the commandant. Usually these spies were Eurasians—half-breed Chinese or Japanese.)

In case when the dining room cannot accommodate all the members meal may be served in three or four turns. In such a case each person shall take his meal in less than twenty minutes.

(This rule was superfluous because our dining rooms were very shortly taken away from us to be used as living quarters. We ate in our rooms. However, by mentioning such dining rooms, the Japs felt they were "covered" because they recognized such rooms should be in camps.)

Members shall take care of the sick; when medical treatment is necessary, request shall be made for it to the Japanese Officials in charge through the Executive Committee.

(The Japs never furnished a single medical item, with the exception of some poor quality vaccine, nor a bed to my knowledge during the entire internment period. Everything we used we bought ourselves at graft prices.)

Violation of the above shall be dealt with disciplinary measures of short allowance, detention, etc., and in certain cases with severe punishment.

As the committee member who did most of the negotiating with the Japanese these were the rules I had to angle around in trying to secure improved living, eating, and health conditions for the interned Americans, British, Dutch, and Belgians. My neck was way out most of the time.

Compare these regulations with the type of loosely constituted but undoubtedly fairer rules imposed by our United States Government on the Japanese internees in the United States. If these Japanese regulations give an insight into the hate mentality of the Jap, then what derision must have been felt by the Japanese-born internee in the United States when he saw the type of what we call "fair treatment" our government gave him?

XL

THE women in camp were Spartan. Few of them were young. They had difficulty in acclimating themselves to the rugged existence forced upon them. Because there were more women than men, the able-bodied women had to take on many more of the camp duties than was necessary at Manila. That meant even carrying buckets of water upstairs to the elderly women in their rooms. Of course men helped when they could, but able-bodied men were at a premium. Sickness took its toll; weakness from malnutrition struck the camp like an epidemic. We even had children's epidemics of whooping cough and measles. Parents were frantic. Mothers tried to get their babies and smaller children sent out to the hospital. Some mothers wanted to go along. The Japanese refused in many instances. In others, they returned children from the hospital before they were well. I've asked Marjorie to write a chapter here from the women's point of view at Chapei. Since Marjorie served on the Women's Committee, her point of view gives an intimate picture.

BY MARJORIE HATHAWAY GUNNISON

Life for the women in the Chapei camp in China differed primarily from that of Santo Tomás in Manila in the fact that we had our own organization and a much-needed representative on the executive committee. Dorothy Janszen, who was our representative, was tireless in her efforts; and she was honest—therefore she got results in spite of her inexperience in handling women and in dealing with the Japs.

Dorothy is slight, blue-eyed, brown-haired, and in her early thirties. Barely over 5 feet tall and weighing only 100 pounds, she is a good soldier for all that. She has done more for the welfare of the women and children in Chapei than any other single individual. When it's all added up, what she has done and what women in the other camps have done, and still are doing, is this: They are trying to live normal, healthy lives; they are trying to keep cheerful, keep happy . . . to do their part in the war.

It sounds simple. Just what everyone at home is trying to do. But naturally there's a big difference. These women are trying to live normal lives under circumstances far from normal. Their living space is on an average of less than 30 square feet per person. Try living on your 9 x 12 rug—you, as part of a family of three. Just try doing all your eating, washing, sleeping on that rug—and even at that you'd have more than 30 square feet per person.

These women are trying to live as healthy lives as possible in filthy, sordid surroundings and under circumstances that give them too little food and food that's poor in quality and low in vitamin content. Despite the poor food and lack of medical care these women must do hard work, back-breaking, exhausting, endless work.

It was their duty to prepare and clean whatever vegetables came into camp—a job that had to be done in a cold scullery with no benches to sit on, and a wet stone floor underfoot. It was their duty to clean fish, which meant long hours with hands in cold water, and it was their duty to clean rice, a job that was particularly hard on the eyes. It meant hours of bending over trays, attempting an impossible task—to clean out the bugs, the worms, and the rocks and dirt. Over 40 per cent of the rice the Japs supplied us was dirt, bugs, and rice husk. The rice was rationed to last us for a certain number of days. So we had to spread it thin to make up for the weight lost in dirt and bugs. There were other regular camp duties which had to be done by the women—cleaning their own lavatories, teaching school, caring for the children on the playground, washing laundry for the sick and sheets for the infirmary, preparing food in the baby kitchen in an effort to give the small children a special diet, nurses' aides in the infirmary and office work for the internee committee. All these things had to be done in addition to the work of caring for our own families, and doing our own laundry, and cleaning our own quarters.

These women in Chapei and other China camps are trying to give their children a feeling of security, of well-being in a situation that's definitely one of hand to mouth. The youngsters have had a difficult period of readjustment, especially the smaller ones. At first no one had any time for them, and there was no place for them, no real home. Wherever they went the words were: "Go away . . . don't bother me . . . leave that alone . . . don't do this and don't do that." Many of the children developed an "unwanted" complex. They felt keenly they didn't belong anywhere. From this developed behavior problems which were difficult to unravel.

Dorothy saw immediately that something had to be done for these children, and for the mothers. A nursery school and kindergarten was established with trained teachers and workers. The school met six mornings a week. In the afternoons a supervised play period was organized. It took many weeks of wheedling and maneuvering to get the playground fence.

Johnny was found one morning up to his waist in a mud puddle, his blue eyes filled with tears. Mother was rabid on the subject. Johnny might have drowned! Teacher was so upset she almost resigned on the spot. How could she pull Johnny out of mud puddles, stop Beverley and Michael from killing each other with the sticks they had found, and keep Mary from throwing sand in the nearest eyes when the youngsters were covering twice and three times the area they should? She wasn't a centipede and had only two legs. The playground had to be fenced in—or else!

Dorothy promised the fencing, not knowing how she was going to get it. But she knew she had to get it. First it was merely a rope fence donated by parents and woven by parents. But that was too easy to crawl under. Finally old pieces of canvas were stretched from post to post for half the fencing, a gate was made by our own carpenter's shop and bamboo used for the remainder of the fence. But it was Dorothy's constant tireless effort that made the fence a reality. This was typical of other women's problems, found and worked out in similar manner.

Dorothy had an efficient welfare committee headed by Mrs. Edwin Kilbourne, an outstanding missionary. These women worked constantly, visiting the various rooms daily, making arrangements to care for children when the mothers became ill, to do the laundry for them, carry water, stand in line for their food. Dorothy also established a sewing department where residents, especially men, could get mending and patching done, where aprons were made for heavy kitchen and butcher shop duty, for garbage gangs, and where the constant and unending taking-in of waist bands was done.

The greatest problem was food—always food. Not enough, and not good enough. The children five and under had a special baby kitchen where the food was prepared separately. Dorothy battled a hard-boiled pilfering ship's-crew kitchen gang constantly to get the best food for the children; for even the best was far from what babies should be eating.

Dorothy worked from eight in the morning until twelve at night for the first few months of her camp life, and she is still giving her services to the camp. She and Jack were left behind when we sailed from Shanghai aboard the *Teia Maru* to meet the *Gripsholm*. She was broken-hearted when she finally realized that, although Jack was a Westinghouse man, his business category wasn't high enough. They would not be repatriated. But she was a good soldier right up to the last minute when she said good-by to her many friends who were more fortunate.

I can still see her that final day helping to serve the noonday meal to repatriates, running back and forth to the main building to fetch forgotten belongings, helping mothers through the baggage-inspection line by taking care of the children. She kept what we call a stiff upper lip. And she needed it—she and all the other women who were left behind.

"Tell my mother," she said to me—and it was then she made a desperate effort not to break down—"tell my mother Jack and I are quite all right; that I want to see her more than anything I can think of, but not to forget we'll be coming on that next boat—oh, I hope it will be soon." She kept back the tears, but some of us couldn't.

Those camp days—endless, drudgery days—are still going on back there.

Take Joan and Eddie and their babies, little Joanna and Gail. They have been repatriated but their life in the Chapei internment camp was typical and is typical of those who are still carrying on.

Joan's a Shanghai girl. Her father was formerly financial advisor to the Chungking Government and returned to Washington. Eddie is from St. Petersburg, Florida. Before the war he was a cotton controller. But after internment he became a one-man laundry with a galvanized iron pail. Not only that but he became floor scrubber, dish washer, family waiter, water carrier, and nurse as well. He and Joan played at keeping house—enforced play at the point of a Japanese bayonet.

Besides all this Eddie carried coal twice a day 100 feet from the coal pile to the kitchen, and it took a ton a day to keep the fires burning. Tall and lean, slightly bald, and with a definite twinkle in his blue eyes, Eddie never lost his sense of humor. He needed it during those seven months in the internment camp.

Joan of the very dark brown eyes and brown hair did nearly all those things that Eddie did, in her turn, plus a few little odd jobs such as darning and mending, trying to whip up an appetizing extra little dish out of dried prunes and glucose to tempt the children, bathing the youngsters, telling them stories, and doing all the little things that all mothers do. Oh, yes. Joan worked in the camp scullery cleaning vegetables for the camp chow.

For Joan and Eddie there was no privacy. They lived in a room 16 x 45 feet with four other families—ten adults and five babies under four years of age. They had three flights of stairs to climb to their "deluxe" apartment—16 x 12 feet wide, large enough for two iron cots and two cribs, a couple of highchairs, a folding cardtable and two wooden stools which Eddie made out of an old packing case he had brought into camp packed with food stuffs that were all too soon gone.

In this space, trying to ignore the family life—the give and take, the parental discipline, the little quarrels, the laughs—on the other side of the painted floor line, Eddie and Joan, Joanna and Gail ate and slept, and played, and entertained.

Friends came to call and Joan served tea. Dry canteen cookies, or if it had been camp baking day Joan would serve cake she had made, for she still had a little flour left and had received the camp monthly sugar ration of one pound on the previous day. The cake called for water in place of milk, no shortening, and no eggs, although some of the more extravagant housekeepers used eggpowder. You forgot it was eggless and milkless for there were lots of raisins and dried prunes saved from the monthly International Red Cross package. The cake was always a definite success.

There was a birthday party for Joanna when she was three, and then later on one for Gail, her first. At night there were sometimes bridge games, for the babies had learned to sleep as soundly under the glaring light, and in spite of the constant bustle around them, as they had formerly in their own quiet rooms in the big house on Amherst Avenue where they had their own amah (nurse).

On Sunday—well, Sunday was just another day after all, a camp day that held all the daily tasks that must be done Sunday or no. But on Sunday little Joanna could go to Sunday School instead of Nursery School, and in the afternoon Eddie, who is a good athlete, played baseball, and Joan and Joanna and Gail got all dressed up in their camp Sunday best which wasn't quite like the dainty muslins and fine linens of Shanghai Sundays or Country Club days. But Eddie thought they looked very pretty in freshly washed gingham, or perhaps clean white shorts for Mama and blue overalls for the little tadpoles. And he had a right to be proud of those clean clothes —he had washed them.

He could see them sitting on the grass on the sidelines, or if they were lucky, on one of the newly made benches which the grounds work crew had just completed, watching the game, cheering for Daddy, and in between getting the latest camp gossip from Mrs. Brown and Mrs. Smith. Then back to the third floor for supper and baths and bed for small-fry. Dish washing for Eddie and Joan, a walk around the compound circular drive—once around took five minutes if they didn't walk too fast—and another day ended. Nothing accomplished—except one day nearer the end of internment.

But that was important . . . more important than anything else in their lives!

(End of Marjorie Gunnison's story of Chapei.)

XLI

IT WAS seldom Tsurumi's practice to give a flat "no" to anything. Rather, he used the "I-will-consider-this" method and usually pocket-vetoed everything we really wanted or needed. He gave us a typical Japanese run-around—which we may expect at the Peace Conference table if there is one—and after.

One of the earliest examples of these tactics came less than two weeks after we had arrived at Chapei. Under the Geneva Convention for treatment of prisoners of war one of the first requisites is that the prisoners shall be permitted to send cards or letters outside, stating the condition of their health and whether or not they are safe. I approached Tsurumi on this matter of letters, either to Shanghai or to relatives abroad. He had mentioned letters in his rules.

The first time, he said, "This is too soon, we cannot consider now." About three days later I mentioned it again, reminding him that he had permitted us to send communications once from Manila.

He said, "Okay, you write letters."

I asked, "What are your regulations?"

He replied, "Only regulations: write on one side of paper, must be clear writing, cannot criticize Japanese Government, cannot describe treatment in camp."

When I told the building monitors who passed the news around camp, there was great excitement. Nearly everyone carefully penned or pencilled a letter to somebody on the outside. I checked each letter to be sure the Japs would not punish anyone for a slip of the pen—also to check on any statements that might be utilized by the Japanese propaganda corps to their advantage. Then I took the letters to Tsurumi. There were probably five hundred.

He looked up in amazement. "What are these?"

"These are the letters which you gave us permission to write."

"Never! Too many letters . . . too much trouble . . . too much writing . . . must make shorter. Take them away."

I suggested a word limit, such as one hundred words.

"Okay, one hundred words—put on small piece paper."

He returned the large sheets and I had them distributed back to the writers with the new regulations. Three days later, I returned with the rewritten communications.

Tsurumi showed surprise again. "Why you bother me with these letters? This not important. People outside already know everything all right inside camp. This is best camp in all Far East. I am best commandant." I made no comment. He stood up and pointed his finger at me. "You think I am best commandant in all Far East, yes?"

I thought fast. If I told him what I was thinking, I was finished.

"Mr. Tsurumi," I said, "it is possible that people in this camp, some day when they are repatriated, *may* say Mr. Tsurumi was a just and fair commandant, *if* you permit these letters to be sent. These people are your prisoners. To write one letter means much to them; all same as to write one letter means much to Japanese interned in America. I am sure these Japanese in America have written letters back to Japan saying they are safe and well. It is only fair that the Americans, British, Dutch, and Belgians in here should do same."

"Okay," he said, "okay. Maybe I can get somebody to censor this."

I suggested one of his several assistants in the next office.

About a week later I saw the pile of letters on his desk again. "These are all ready to go?" I asked.

"No," he replied. "Too much trouble . . . still too many words . . . only twenty-five words. Must have smaller piece of paper."

I went out of the office with the letters and passed the news throughout the camp again. Not discouraged, the internees all re-wrote and condensed their messages. I returned the letters to Tsurumi and saw them day after day lying on his desk. Finally, Inaba began to check through the communications. One morning he pressed the buzzer that called me in from the executive committee's crowded office.

"Hey, Gun-san. What you mean letting people say they want vitamins this camp? This look like we do not feed you properly. You cannot say this, by order."

"But, Mr. Inaba," I explained, "these people are not openly complaining in their letters about food you furnish us, although you know and I know it is not sufficient for foreigners. If you permit people to ask for vitamins, this cost you nothing. People stay well longer. Maybe you get credit as deputy commandant for having healthy camp."

"Never mind," he replied, "whether healthy or not healthy. I do not care. You cannot send these letters. Take them all back."

I suggested that maybe the best way would be for him to tear up the letter he did not like and let the others go through.

"Okay, okay," he said. "Where is letter *you* write?"

I looked through the pile of communications and found my letter which was to the International Red Cross office and was harmless enough.

"Okay," he replied again, "if you write letter like this and you do not ask for vitamins, I let other letters go."

It was several days before he finished censoring the letters. They lay on Tsurumi's desk for about a week longer. One night when Tsurumi was leaving camp, I picked up these letters from his desk, carried them down to his car and handed them to him. "I believe you forgot these letters, Mr. Tsurumi. Weren't you going to take them to the Consulate?"

"Ah—so," he said.

A few days later, I noticed the letters back on his desk. "But, I thought these letters had been approved?" I asked.

"Approved all right, but now must have envelopes."

"But you know we have no envelopes. We must send out and purchase five hundred envelopes."

He agreed but it was several days before a member of his staff left camp. I asked this man to purchase some stamps as well for I saw an added delay if we didn't move quickly.

After the envelopes were typed in the internees office, Tsurumi insisted that two members of the consular police had to supervise the stuffing of letters into the envelopes, noting that the addresses on the letters and the addresses on the envelopes were identical. This finished, the commandant's chop (stamped signature on end of a piece of bone or ivory) had to be stamped on each envelope. Since Tsurumi was constantly going in and out of camp, he had to take the chop with him. Further delay. Finally, after two months had passed, the letters were addressed, stamped, chopped, and ready to go.

Just before the letters finally went out, a story appeared in the local Shanghai propaganda papers—the *Shanghai Times* and the *Evening Post and Mercury*—stating that the Japanese were fulfilling humane treatment agreements under international law by permitting internees to send letters "to loved ones." Because the Japanese do or start to do something *once*, they then claim they are fulfilling such a law, even though they may never do it a second time.

This long period of discussion over such a small matter as these letters was typical of what we went through in the constant daily hammering in trying to get even bare necessities to maintain the health of the camp. In the Japanese mind the expression of good intentions is more often than not the same as fulfilling those intentions. This is something we must never forget in dealing with the Japanese after the war is over.

The Japanese in several instances gave an indication of fulfilling their obligations to civilian internees. "We intend to supply milk for babies. We intend to give fresh vegetables for the sick. We intend to supply beds, medicines for hospital. . . ." But they never did. However, to read the local papers regarding what they were doing for the "formerly arrogant Americans and British," you'd think they were "magnanimously" (the word they used most often in describing their own actions) living up to their agreement with the United States by acting in accordance with the Geneva Convention. We found hourly application of three qualities absolutely imperative in dealing with these Japs. These were: patience, persistence, politeness—mostly persistence.

XLII

NOT only did the Japanese strip the enemy aliens of their possessions before imprisoning them, but they confiscated every dollar they could lay their hands on belonging to the prisoners themselves. The practice was different in each camp, but the idea was the same—robbery. We could see it coming from the very first, and the word was passed to the outside to let the Swiss Consulate know what was happening. The Swiss protested to the Japanese that they couldn't steal the money of the civilian prisoners. The Swiss maintained that each prisoner was entitled to a certain comfort allowance each month from his government, distributed through the Swiss Consulate. The Swiss continued to maintain that if the Japanese confiscated the money taken into camp by the prisoners, full international repercussions could be expected when the war was over. The only answer made by the Japanese was, "Never mind." However, from what actually happened it proved that the Swiss protest was effective.

Late in March, Tsurumi called me to his office and said, "My government orders every internee must turn over all personal money to me for 'safe keeping.' How much money you think people have in this camp?" The greed practically dripped out of his eyes.

I replied quickly that I thought there was very little money in camp—although I knew of one man alone who had $90,000 CRB in his room. I thought if the Japs felt there were not more than a few hundred thousand dollars in all, they wouldn't be interested in taking it. At this time, I did not know whether the Swiss had protested or not.

Tsurumi insisted that I make a quick survey to find out how much money was held by all of the internees. I went back to our internee office to talk with Scotty (Charles Scott—Standard Oil accountant) who had set up our internee books. We estimated roughly that there was close to $2,000,000 CRB in camp, and at an exchange rate of $40 CRB to 1 U.S. dollar, that gave us $50,000 U.S. That was too much just to hand over to R. Tsurumi and K. Inaba, Inc.

Scott and I decided the best thing to do was to wait until Tsurumi brought the question up again—use their own tactics: stall, delay. But the next morning Tsurumi said, "How much money you think in camp?"

I was noncommittal. "Oh, a few hundred tnousand."

"I order you collect this money . . . give each man a receipt and turn all this money over to me immediately. This is my order!"

Inaba chimed in, "This is Mr. Tsurumi's order!"

I spent over two hours attacking the matter, first from one side and then from another, politely and bluntly, but their minds were made up. They were going to have the money, or else. But I still stalled.

Our internee committee discussed the matter thoroughly. We were determined not to give up a single CRB unless actually forced to do so. We learned (through a means that I obviously can't disclose) that "the squeeze" was being applied at Pootung, Yu Yuen Road camp, and Lung Hua, the large British camp. At Pootung, the men flatly refused to turn over their money. In effect, they said: "If you want it, come and get it." And for several days there was a very tense situation. We did not feel we had the right to jeopardize the aged and women and children by taking such a flat stand.

Scott, Watson, and I spent several hours for several days discussing ways and means with Tsurumi and Inaba. Inaba was money-mad. Many times he had told me, "When war is over I will be rich man. I will be member of Japanese Diet. I will buy way into Japanese Diet. I am very smart businessman. That is why I join internment commission staff. That is why I become appointed chief commandant's special deputy. I am very clever. I can make plenty money through my friends, who supply all camps in China. You wait, one day I will be very great man in Japan."

Although Tsurumi was chief commandant, Inaba was the spark plug, and insisted that the money be turned in. Scott worked out a banking idea, based upon our discussions, whereby each internee would be issued a bank book which would carry the original entry as a deposit of the amount confiscated by the Japanese. Scott and his staff would keep the books. The Japs would keep the money. The internee would be permitted each month to draw in credit at a canteen to be established later, and through a supplementary food allowance, also to be established later, a certain specified amount.

At first, Tsurumi designated this amount as $200 CRB per adult, $300 per family. (The Swiss on the outside negotiated for $700 CRB per month per person.) The head of the family signed the notes. Scott framed a very carefully worded letter—our final protest—urging that the authorities permit us to collect the money and keep it ourselves, thinking we could work out some kind of compromise. But apparently this was a downtown Consulate order. Tsurumi and

Inaba would get a cut, and the Consulate officials as well. We finally turned over two trunks containing $1,952,092.80 CRB (about $50,-000 U.S.) which was deposited at the Mitsubishi Bank. I have smuggled out a carbon copy of the receipt issued by Tsurumi.

CHAPEI CIVIL ASSEMBLY CENTER

10th April 1943.

The Chairman:

Receipt is hereby acknowledged of two (2) trunks containing CRB dollars, One million, nine hundred fifty-two thousand, ninety two, and cents eighty, (CRB $1,952,092.80) being personal funds belonging to Residents of Chapei Civilian Assembly Center.

THE COMMANDANT.

Scott, as finance man, and Watson, as chairman, were permitted to go out to the Mitsubishi Bank with the trunks to see the money deposited in Tsurumi's name.

The Japanese got their cut out of this money by charging us full price but getting sizable reductions in actual purchase price of canteen and supplementary food supplies. They paid the bills themselves, submitting to us the voucher stubs. It was only for the actual purchasing done by Janszen or Scott that cash funds were brought into camp. This way the robbery was made to appear honorable and legal.

XLIII

IT WAS right after the Emperor's birthday late in April that Captain Sugahara called me into his office. E. L. ("Bud") Kilbourne, our ace-interpreter, was along with me. Bud's interpreting did more to prevent serious consequences from events the Japs considered "incidents" and to take advantage of situations of face for us than all the action any individual member of our internee committee ever took.

Bud translated that Captain Sugahara was most chagrined at the attitude I had taken over the celebration he had planned for the camp on the Emperor's birthday. The Japs had planned a sports day for the children, a series of races for adults, and an all-star

Japanese-American baseball game. Sugahara had planned a holiday. I had pointed out to him as delicately as possible—it's like treading on time bombs and bayonets to mention His Imperial Japanese Majesty—that we would be unable to participate in any such celebration.

He had seemed surprised. But when I told him that Tsurumi-san had not permitted celebration of America's Fourth of July at Manila the year before, and that "I personally would not consider it honorable for us to celebrate the birthday of an enemy . . . ," when I told him this as politely as possible, he had no alternative but to accept.

But now he had me. He wanted his Japanese baseball team to play our all-stars. He'd had his boys out practicing and in his opinion they were ready. I'd seen them, too. They were terrible. I knew what would happen. We'd win. They'd lose face . . . and then anything could happen, from cutting down on food to extra roll calls . . . anything. But he "ordered" the game for Sunday afternoon.

Although baseball is strictly an American "hated foreigner" game, the Japanese like to play it, just as they like foreign movies, foreign clothes, foreign manufacturing plants, foreign type aircraft, and foreign territories.

Everybody came out to see the game, even some Japs from the Consulate and Embassy. I had a talk with our boys. All agreed to take it easy. It was softball and when the Jap pitcher insisted on pitching overhand I felt better. At least his pitch would be harder to hit, I thought. But I was wrong.

We were home team. The Japs were in the field. At the end of our half-inning at bat—before the Japs even got to bat—the score was 27 to 0. Then the seriousness of it hit our all-stars. They tried to give the Japs runs. They fumbled the ball. They dropped sure flys. They fell across bases and made fools of themselves. There were more than one thousand watching the game, and it was all we could do to keep from laughing out loud at the sincere antics our boys went through trying to lose the game.

At the close of the 1st inning the score was Internees 27, Japs 1. Obviously, something had to be done. It was. Everyone struck out or grounded lightly. At the end of the 5th inning the score was 28 to 2, and stayed that way until the 7th, when the fat Sugahara-san came stomping over across the diamond to speak with me. I got Kilbourne and went out to meet him. Here it comes, I thought. Here it comes.

"Gun-san," he began, with the customary polite intake hissing of breath between his teeth. Maybe that was a good omen. I knew if he were sore he wouldn't be politely hissing. When he finished Kilbourne interpreted.

"Captain Sugahara says he and his men have greatly enjoyed playing this game, and they are going to enjoy finishing it. But now he says maybe we better not play for score any more; maybe we better just play for sport." Which we did. But there never was another Jap all-star game. Anything could have happened. But nothing did.

That is, nothing happened that you could exactly put your finger on. But after that Sugahara used to come out to the ball field in the afternoon grinning as though he'd just received the Order of the Rising Sun. Then he'd disappear and right in the middle of an exciting inning one of the English-speaking guards would show up and pick out eight or ten players. "You go build fence," he'd order. Or, "Now time fill up sacks with tin cans. Captain Sugahara orders so can sell to man at gate."

According to the letter of international law we civilian internee-prisoners were not supposed to do any labor for the Japs. But to mention international law in the Far East today is like sentencing yourself to the dungeon. How many times have I had some Jap spit in my face: "International law! Bah! There is no such thing. Japan makes its own law. I make the international law history!" And they did.

Rather than cause any incidents in family camps like ours by flatly refusing to do work for the Japs—such as putting up barbed-wire fences, or hauling "night soil" (fertilizer) for their garden—we'd just pull the old W.P.A. gag. We'd go along as ordered. But we'd lean on our shovels, take it as easy as possible, play them at their own game—seldom refusing anything, just stalling and never acting. We had too many small children and too many aged in camp to chance their full wrath—which we'd get now and then when I'd go into the office to make what I called "a reasonable complaint" because of the fact that the bread had gypsum in it to make it weigh more.

Then is when the venom would come out. Then is when you'd have to count to ten; bite your lip and hold your breath for fear of saying something that not only would get you into trouble but would jeopardize the existence of others in camp. Once you lost your temper with these boys you were through. The British tended to bang the table more than we Americans, and as a result they got less in their camps.

For instance, we received International Red Cross parcels in Chapei and at Pootung—both predominantly American camps—

before the British did in their camps. When these 20-pound limit parcels came it was like Christmas. They were sent in by friends, former servants (at considerable risks to themselves because the Japs checked up on the donors) or by the Swiss storage firm, Sharpf and Guenther, where some duration-minded prisoners left money before internment for just such parcels.

No parcels were permitted in for the first three months—the disciplinary period. In May we received two. But I believe we showed too much enthusiasm, too much satisfaction at their receipt. The guards, of course, inspected everything that came and took what they pleased in the way of fresh fruit, sausage, cigarettes or candy. They reported there were "too many luxuries" and we were immediately cut to one delivery each month. The Jap wants his white "foreign" captive to realize at all times that he, the Jap, is much more Spartan and can live on much less.

In our internment camps in the United States we give the Japanese what we as foreigners consider a proper nutritious diet—typical U.S. Army chow. The Japanese permitted us an 1800 to 2200 calorie diet, over three-quarters of which was protein content. The average Occidental needs some 3000 to 4000 calories daily if doing manual labor, as all of us were.

Yet, although we never had enough to eat, we always seemed to have plenty of garbage. Our internee garbage-hauling gang dumped large tubs of refuse at the gate daily. These containers were later hauled away by Chinese who paid the Japanese guards for the garbage which was fed to their pigs.

Typical of the toothy, hilarious pleasure the Japs showed at the slightest opportunity to use their authority to humiliate an internee was an incident that occurred one afternoon when a guard stepped up to the man pushing the garbage cart and cracked him a hard wallop across the face—apparently for no reason at all.

The man dropped the cart, startled, puzzled as to what had brought the blow. The Jap guard, red-faced, bellowed and belched orders at the increasingly bewildered American. Finally, sensing a beating in the offing by several guards who gathered menacingly, the garbage gang executed a series of to-the-ground bows and "strategically withdrew" to their living quarters.

The incident was reported immediately. After a long hour of palaver with Sugahara, captain of the guard, we learned that the gate guard had felt his importance as a soldier in His Imperial Japanese Majesty's service that afternoon and had decided that the man wheeling the garbage cart was to drop the cart and bow to him.

But since it had not been the custom and since none of the gang were mind readers they could hardly be expected to anticipate the slugging. This was carefully pointed out to Sugahara, but he insisted the gang should have known what the guard was thinking. (He had to save face for his men before the enemy, even though he knew they were in the wrong.)

However, in this case we held the top hand. Sugahara was told that in the future no garbage would be delivered to the gate. If he and his men wanted the garbage to sell to the Chinese for pig food and thought we were going to haul it down there for them to make money and slap us around in the bargain, he was greatly mistaken. Of course this answer was couched in slightly different phrasing by Mr. Kilbourne but the captain got the idea. No garbage was hauled for two days. We buried it out by the back fence.

Finally, to save his own face with his men—who knew we had defied the captain—Sugahara concluded that the garbage gang did not have to bow to the guards at the gate while hauling garbage since (and he saved his face with us in this way) in the Japanese army men on garbage detail don't have to salute.

Thus in this small, but serious to us, concentration camp incident, prestige or face was saved three times; once for the guards and twice for the captain. Yet it happened in this rare case that we gained face. To you this may seem like a lot of childish "play-play," as the Chinese sometimes call Japanese antics. But it is typical of what you are up against in any dealing with the Japanese—and what our military-naval-diplomatic forces are going to have to contend with when fighting ceases in East Asia.

Just as in Manila, Commandant Tsurumi insisted on much "pomp and circumstance"—and pretty drab it was—upon his arrival at camp in the morning and when he left each night. He lived about 4 miles distant in one of the "confiscated residences" of a British internee.

As an official he was allotted a car. But it wasn't what you'd expect. No shining black limousine for the Chief Commandant for all China's Civil Assembly Centers (Internment Camps). Tsurumi-san rated only a baby Austin. When he and Sugahara got into the official Austin, the tires were almost flat under their weight and neither could budge in the seat. Sugahara's sword invariably caused trouble too, getting tangled between his legs as he got out.

But the evening and the morning ceremony always brought smiles to the internee-prisoners who might be lounging around the entrance to the west building, or passing the entrance on some camp chore. We needed a few laughs. Actually I'm sure it was an ingrained sense of humor that kept us on an even keel. Things some-times would get so petty that finally you'd just have to laugh at them.

And then for a regular daily "brightener" there was always the captain's morning "guard mount." The entire platoon that guarded us lined up on our baseball diamond in an open formation. They had no rifles. But they carried swords that were extremely sharp. Captain Sugahara stood out before the platoon, his tight high-water pants revealing his dirty white socks and emphasizing his fat-boy figure. Each day it was the same. He'd screech his orders in a high raspy whine.

It went like this: First whine—swords out of scabbard and high over head like a cavalry charge. Second whine—great confusion try-ing to get sword back in scabbard without cutting fingers. No set return as used by American and British officers. Third whine—right hand over left breast pocket; next whine—button unbuttoned; next whine—small black book pulled out and held in both hands at eye level like a church festival soloist. At the next sound each soldier fingered through the pages of the notebook in practice. Final whine of this series—notebook back in pocket; pocket buttoned; hands to side.

Next series of high whines and toy-soldier movements went into right breast pocket from which came a pencil and larger notebook. These had to go back "by-the-number." This ended, the platoon went into the side pockets—search by order—and out came hand-cuffs from one, and a thin stout cord (for tying up prisoners) from the other. Pants pockets—"by-the-number"—revealed a pocket knife and a cloth gag for prisoners' mouths.

As a committeeman on duty, I seldom missed the morning drill, which took about half an hour. It fascinated me. One of my friends used to come out to watch each morning. I asked him why.

"Maybe some day one of these bastards will forget something, or pull out the wrong thing . . . and I want to see him catch hell!" That was worth waiting for.

XLIV

ONE day we had orders from the commandant's office to see that every room was cleaned up, since a high officer from the consular police was to make an inspection. By this time we were on to the "inspection" gag, or thought we were. Building and floor monitors merely got out a bucket of water with a little disinfectant in it. They went down the halls and into the rooms, sprinkling just enough water on the floors to leave a disinfectant odor. Anything that smells clean is "clean" to the Japs. But the consular police officer was very tough. He went into each room. He looked under each bed, he opened suitcases, he pulled things off shelves and particularly pointed to the few cans of extra food that the people had brought in with them. I could sense something was up.

The next morning the buzzer rang. I went into Tsurumi's office to find Inaba and Sugahara waiting for me. There was no greeting. Tsurumi let Inaba do the talking.

"Hey, Gun-san," he said, "your people have got too much food." I made no comment. "Who give you permission to bring tin food into camp?" Before I could answer, he went on, "Mr. Tsurumi orders you to gather all extra food you bring into camp and take down to red brick house across from guardhouse. This food we keep for you."

"This is my order," Tsurumi chimed in finally.

This was serious. If the Japanese confiscated our extra food, we would be in a bad way, particularly the babies, because at this time we were not permitted to purchase supplementary food. There was no canteen, and International Red Cross comfort parcels were not permitted in the camp at this time.

"Mr. Tsurumi," I began, "this is most serious. I must discuss this with other members of the committee."

"Never mind committee," Inaba cut in. "You do! Mr. Tsurumi makes this order. This is very serious order."

I arose, bowed, and left before they had a chance to give any more orders.

I checked with Watson and Dorothy Janszen, the other two members of the committee. We dug out of our files the internment orders and the "subpoena" for our imprisonment. The one that be-

gan, "Due to military necessity, you are hereby ordered to report.
. . ." Way down in a typically Japanesque clause we discovered the
phrase, "You are permitted to bring with you tennis rackets, sports
equipment, *any supplementary food that is considered desirable* and
such clothing that may be needed." There was our permission!

I waited a day before approaching the office. I went in with the
subpoena order in my pocket. Inaba was there. I began something
like this: "Mr. Tsurumi, I have read many places since my imprisonment, and I have been told for many years in the Far East that
Japanese people are honorable people. Is this so?"

Both Inaba and Tsurumi couldn't answer fast enough. "Yes, this
is so."

"And," I continued, "is it true that every Japanese man is a man
of his word?"

"Yes," replied Inaba, "Japanese people always tell truth."

"I am very glad to hear this because this answers a question for
me that has been bothering me for several days," I said. Then I
pulled out the subpoena order and showed them that permission had
been granted to bring in supplementary tin food. They were greatly
excited and talked back and forth for several minutes in rapid-fire
Japanese.

Then there was silence. After what must have been three or four
minutes, Inaba looked up. "Never mind this order."

"But, Mr. Inaba, this order is signed by His Imperial Japanese
Majesty's Consul General, Mr. Yano."

"This makes no difference. Yano can give permission to bring
food to camp, but after food passes entrance of camp, then food
becomes property commandant of this camp."

"Quite true, Mr. Inaba, but you and Mr. Tsurumi just told me
that Japanese people are men of their word. When your guards inspected our baggage, they permitted us to keep this food. By doing
this, Mr. Tsurumi, who was commandant, gave his permission for
us to keep this food. Is this not true?"

No answer. I continued, "It would be very bad thing from many
points of view if you confiscate this food."

"Ah, but you do not understand," Inaba interrupted.

Tsurumi put down his paper. "We do not *confiscate* this food.
We *keep* this food for you in safe keeping."

First victory—I could see they were weakening. I pressed my
point.

"Prisoners in this camp do not expect good treatment from you.
After what they have been through," I continued, "they do not ex-

pect any Japanese man to be fair or to be honest—and they will not give up their food without trouble. You have told me you do not wish trouble. You have requested this committee to co-operate with you so that there will be no difficulty in operating this camp or any other camp. I can say this—we will co-operate with you only so long as we feel that we are able to improve our conditions of living through negotiation with you. If you take this food now, neither Mr. Watson, Mrs. Janszen, nor I take any responsibility for what happens. You will have to go to each room yourself, and take the food by force. I think there will be plenty trouble. This is too bad." I started to leave.

Inaba said, "Hey, Gun-san, you don't understand. I am socialist. I believe every man should have equal amount of food."

"But, Mr. Inaba, I did not know there was a socialist party in Japan. This is very interesting."

"Never mind," he said, "not many socialists, not German National Socialists—just plain, honest socialists. Equality for everybody."

"In that case," I thrust back, "you will not take away food from these people."

Mr. Tsurumi stood up. "I am ordering you to deliver food to storehouse because some people have more food than other people. This is not equal. Therefore, nobody should have any extra food. We supply equal ration each day." [1]

Here was a chance for compromise and a way out for the Japanese who were obviously now in doubt about the advisability of confiscating the supplementary food but had to save face, once having passed an order. It was up to me to find a way to save their face and save our food. Otherwise, the order would stick and there would be "plenty trouble" and probably physical injuries to our own people to whom the committee would not suggest giving up their food.

"Perhaps," I suggested, "Mr. Tsurumi will consider *this* idea. If you think some people have more food than other people, we can easily remedy. Our committee will request donations for those who do not have any extra food. This food that is contributed we will keep in *our* supply office under lock and key—all same your keeping it down at the brick building, but easier to get at. Then Mrs. Janszen will have special welfare survey made by women's com-

[1] The Japanese food ration at Chapei for 1054 people was: bread, soggy brown, 550 pounds a day, 8 ounces per person; rice, .16 kilo per person daily; vegetables, 420 kilos daily; fish, later meat unboned, 240 kilos daily—total calorie content about 1900, of which over one-half was starch. A kilo equals 2.2 pounds.

mittee and we will allot extra food to those who do not have enough."

Their faces lighted up. Inaba laughed loudly. "Gun-san, you do this. This my order. This my idea. I am very smart businessman. Have some tea," and they rang for the coolie.

This is only one example of what happened daily. Patience in dealing with these people was a necessity. Table pounding was fatal.

My own interpretation of the food incident was that Inaba and Tsurumi had cooked up a plan whereby they would confiscate our food—thinking we would not protest—and sell it in the black market. At that time, such a sale would have brought them several hundred thousand Chinese dollars. But when they realized they would have to take the food from us forcibly and that undoubtedly there would be an incident which would reach the ears of their own Consulate and the Swiss Consulate, they were not willing to take the personal risk. If there were trouble, they might lose their jobs, especially where squeeze was concerned and where higher-ups at the gendarmerie or consular police officers did not get a cut. Actually, the amount that they would have received for the confiscated tin goods would have been nothing compared to what they later squeezed out of us—200 and 300 per cent profit on a very inadequate canteen—operated ironically by a man they called "the honest Mr. Sugyama."

XLV

MR. INABA did very well for himself with the cut he made from our camp-food allotment. He'd been given a budget to work on by the Consulate and was cutting quality in order to pocket money. He arranged for a lower grade of low-grade rice to be sent in. He saw to it that the 8 ounces of brown bread we were getting were cut in quality. One day he came into the internee office. He was in a good mood. I had an idea.

"Mr. Inaba," I opened, "next week is big religious week for foreigners . . . like many big Japanese religious festivals."

"Ah—so?" he queried. "What you call this?"

"We call this Easter. You have heard of this?"

"Yes. But never mind. You can have church. You can sing songs.

Okay. You have my permission." Then he laughed heartily. Big joke. He gives the white man permission to have church services.

Then I tried another tack. "Mr. Inaba, I am sure in Japanese camps in America our people permit Japanese to have special things on religious festival days."

"In America, never mind. You are here. Never mind America." Then a slow take . . . curiosity . . . "Hey, Gun-san, what you mean Japanese people permitted 'special things' on festival day?"

"Why, Mr. Inaba, just like in Japan, they permit Japanese to have special food this day. Think what this would mean to people in this camp—to babies, children, old people."

"Never mind all this talk . . . you talk too much . . ." Then another slow take. I could see the dollar signs begin to spin across his horizon. Here was a chance to make some additional easy money off the prisoners and no one would know the difference. "What kind of food you talking about?"

After that it was easy. We made a deal. He would get some eggs, some Chinese candy, and some vegetable—perhaps carrots (remember we had had nothing but fish, rice, and cabbage of very low grade for nearly three months) and he "thought" he could get some meat. But this might cost us $12,000 CRB. This was about $330 U.S. for over one thousand people. We had some money on hand—we'd set up a "general fund" for just such an emergency use.

Easter Sunday came and we had the meat, and potatoes, and vegetables, and the children had some eggs and candy. The day was a success. Our first change in diet, and our first meal when we actually had all we could eat.

But the pay-off, in several ways, came the next day. Inaba and Chief Commandant Tsurumi ordered me before them the first thing in the morning. Tsurumi had just heard of the "feast," as he called it.

"Who gave you permission to eat this meat?" he asked. "Where is this meat. You must return it."

I took a long chance and kidded back. I nodded out back toward the sewage system. "You'll have to go out back for it if you want it now!" That's just the sort of backhouse gag that catches this type of dirty-minded Jap. It worked. They guffawed. Then they wanted the money. "Right away!"

I got hold of Charles Scott, who always did a miraculous job with our camp finances. He had the "general fund" tucked away under his mattress. Scotty got the $12,000 and came up to our office. He and I waited around a few minutes for Inaba to come in and get it. Scotty said, "I guess I'll take it in to him."

In a few minutes Scott came back, a blank expression on his face. "What's up?" I asked.

"I think there was something wrong about all that," he puzzled. "There was another Jap in there when I put the money on the table. And from the tone of things, and the way Inaba ordered me out, I think someone got caught off second."

What had happened was that the supply officer and his staff for all the camps in North and Central China had happened in on a typical "surprise" visit and caught the "boys" in a special off-the-cuff deal. But it ended well enough. Inaba told me later he'd had to split a bit with the supply officer. "But," he continued, "I think maybe you have another religious festival day we do this again, huh?" I suggested that as far as we were concerned, every Sunday could become a festival day, and we could pay—and did. But that was the beginning of the breakdown of the disciplinary period. The final breakdown came after Inaba and Tsurumi found the food contractor—"the honest Mister Sugyama." Mr. S. was a bigger crook than either of them. He handled our so-called canteen and "supplementary food" allotment. These two items were eventually handled the same way in all the camps, to give the local commandants their cut.

After several months each internee-prisoner was given a chance to "borrow" on his own personal note—repayable after the war—from his Government about $7 U.S. per month. This was arranged through the Swiss Consulate in Shanghai after months of negotiations. It only came about because it meant money in the pockets of the commandants, not because the Japs thought we needed supplementary food or were living up to any international agreement.

We weren't able to buy much for the $7 but what we did get was worth it. We tried to buy in bulk to get some blue-green bloated water-buffalo meat, and some pretty fair carrots, tomatoes, onions, and white potatoes. We also got eggs later on. When we left on September 19, 1943, the camp canteen was supplying cookies, rancid peanut butter and jam, some crackers, some shrinkable Japanese socks and women's kimonos and wood clogs and a few other items. But of course we were rationed as to what we could buy since the $7 we were loaned each month from our Government didn't go very far.

When things had begun to "loosen up" a bit after the Easter affair, one day Inaba called me into the office of the captain of the guard. It was evident, in their smugness, that he and Sugahara had cooked up something.

"You like sukiaki, Gun-san?" asked Inaba.

I had visions of steaming hot thin sliced beef, vegetables, eggs, and all that goes with a sukiaki meal. "Indeed I do, Mr. Inaba."

"Captain Sugahara and I—we give one banquet for you and committee tonight at guard house."

I didn't like this idea at all. I tried to hedge out of it. But finally, Sugahara snorted something and I could see I was getting in deeper.

"Sugahara says he orders you and committee to come." At that both of them guffawed. So we went—four of us—when an "escort" came after us. There were twenty-two guards and our two "hosts" all in their kimonos. The sukiaki was cooking away on the electric hot plates they had taken from us the day we arrived. Boy, it smelled good!—after fish and cabbage and rice sweepings.

I kept my chopsticks in the cooking dish all evening, snaffling out piece after piece of meat as it became nicely browned. The drinking of saki started slowly and increased until all the Japs were a deep mahogany. Then Captain Sugahara wanted "quiet." He was going to sing. And sing he did. It was like short-wave radio on a bad night of static.

Everybody beat time with their hands and swayed back and forth. Next Inaba-san insisted I do something to entertain. But I passed the buck to Jack Janszen, as "Shanghai's Westinghouse expert with the beautiful baritone." He sang "Rose Marie," "Auld Lang Syne," and "Workin' on the Railroad" in which we all joined—including Inaba, Sugahara, and the other boys. That gave me an idea. I shouted across the low table to Jack and Ben Watson, "Let's sing 'God Bless America!' They'll never know the difference." There was so much noise no one heard me. I clapped my hands together for silence and climbed to my feet.

"Mr. Inaba, Captain Sugahara—we will sing you a song famous in America, with great meaning to all of us here at this table this evening."

Applause.

We sang—and lustily, I can tell you. When we'd finished the song we switched to "There'll Always Be an England" and the Japs were clapping their hands keeping time throughout.

"Come on—everybody sing!" I shouted. The Japanese is a good mimic and since we'd tried to follow one of their songs, they followed ours. Only a few of them understood any English words, but they made a stab at it. That topped the evening, and soon after we put on our shoes and left with the guard to get back to the buildings before "lights out" at 10 P.M. That was a real "victory dinner" —a little pre-victory day.

XLVI

"YOU'RE wanted up in the commandant's office." The young messenger boy from our own internee committee office was breathless. "They're practically killin' a Chinese they caught down by the gate. . . ."

I was out of hearing before he finished. Up in the commandant's office, on the third floor of the school building, I found the messenger was right.

As I entered the office of the captain of the guard, I bowed according to prescribed rule, advanced to a spot some 2 feet in front of the captain's desk and bowed again. The guards across the long room were just finishing giving the poor Chinese the "water treatment." They were filling him with water until he looked as though he were going to burst.

My entry stopped the proceedings. The guards were laughing and hopping around the hapless red-faced, pop-eyed Chinese boy like screwball college sophomores around a fraternity pledge. But despite the hilarity, they weren't kidding.

Captain Sugahara snapped some kind of a command, and automatically the "pranksters" stood at attention. Lieutenant Kuahara, with the three silver front teeth, came over to interpret. He had learned "American" somewhere besides "the Tokyo Commercial College" as he steadily maintained. More likely San Francisco Commerce High School.

"Captain Sugahara . . . he think . . . you know . . . this man . . . yes?" came the expressionless question.

I looked at the poor vomiting Chinese again. I'm sure that if I had known him I'd never have recognized him. I merely shook my head.

Sugahara pulled his eyes down to mere slits. When he did this you knew he was mad—mad clear through. He barked a question at Kuahara.

"This China boy . . . he say . . . he boy-san . . . for one J. Smith . . . inmate this camp. You know this Smith?"

"Yes, I know Mr. Smith [which obviously isn't his name]. He is very number one man. Never cause any trouble. I think maybe boy makes mistake."

Kuahara repeated something to the captain.

"Better you go catch this man," Kuahara ordered. "You bring him here."

I went down to find him. He was outside working on a sewerage ditch-digging gang. That was his daily job, just as mine on the internee executive committee was that of daily, hourly negotiation with the Japs over all kinds of internee problems.

Smith and I were able to establish that the Chinese was Smith's former houseboy, and to convince Sugahara that Smith was not trying to communicate with the boy through the fence. To communicate with the outside was the worst crime you could commit. Just the appearance of trying to communicate was fatal. That fact became increasingly clear to this curious houseboy who thought since his former "master" was inside the barbed wire he'd try to get a glimpse of him.

Fortunately, the boy had no note on his person, and Smith had been working at a distance from the fence. This much proved, Sugahara permitted Smith to leave the office. I tried to intercede for the Chinese, saying that certainly no Chinese would try to communicate with anyone in the camp as openly as they claimed this boy had tried. If he'd wanted to slip a note in or talk to Mr. Smith, why, I asked, had he walked up to the front gate? That made sense, they thought.

But even though they shoved the cowering boy downstairs and out across the compound to the gate guard house, they didn't let him go until late that night. I heard his cries all afternoon and in the early evening from inside the guard house. The "playful" guards were just teaching him a lesson. Of course the news of his treatment would spread around the whole district as soon as he was released. The Japs figured this information would frighten the Chinese into behaving; would show them how mighty the Japanese were. But such things only make the already sullen Chinese coolie and shopkeeper nod knowingly. If you could understand what the Chinese spectators of these things mumble to themselves as they turn away, you'd hear the equivalent of "There'll come a day . . . and when it comes . . ."

The fact that we had blue-uniformed consular police guards in China, while at our Manila camp we were prodded around by regular Japanese army guards, made little difference in the treatment handed out. Certainly in Japanese military circles it isn't the uniform that makes the man.

One day I asked Tsurumi how he compared the camps in the Philippines and China—from the Japanese administrative point of view. I was sure it was because he had done such a good job of starvation and repression as commandant in the Philippines, where I first met him, that he was put in charge of the China camps.

"In the Philippines, we operated freely," he said. "There was no Swiss Government to report to your Government anything we did to you. That made it easy. We could shoot people if we wished [such as the three Britishers who were shot for attempting to escape]. We could use any method of punishment without a chance of its being officially reported to your country. That was ideal. But, here in Shanghai, we must not shoot you. We can slowly starve you," he paused and smiled significantly, for I had just been protesting about some very low-grade rice and some very stale fish, "if we wish. We will, too, if things get bad for us. If we shoot you, the Swiss will report this, and that causes a few 'complications.'" He smiled toothily. "If we starve you—well, that might happen in any camp. And we can make excuses to the Swiss. But we are required to be more careful here for the Swiss watch us very closely."

XLVII

IMMEDIATELY upon entry into camp, as I mentioned previously, I had buried my diary, for safe keeping. As an internee committee member, Japanese guards and commandant's staff officers were constantly calling in my room to check on nearly everything from blackout regulations to the babies' whooping cough ward—we had over thirty youngsters at one time in this ward, all with whooping cough. It was too risky to keep anything like a journal in my quarters.

As the newness of environment wore off, as we got somewhat used to the never-ending feeling of gnawing hunger, as run-down physical conditions brought on melancholia and irritated tempers, this camp, like most others, went through its throes of "internal politics." Selfishness, greed, and petty personal disputes took on undue importance. These factors highlighted more critical personal problems.

The most serious point of contention among the internees was the kitchen, or "galley" as it came to be called, since it soon developed into a closed corporation run by three seamen, two from the Jap-captured *President Harrison,* and one a river pilot. In June a camp election was held over the manner in which the kitchen was run. I fought the galley gang on the basis of inefficiency, mishandling of food, and just plain misappropriation of food that should have been going into daily rations.

My first whirl into reform politics found me ousted by fifty votes by the kitchen machine, which was headed by camp chairman Watson. The replacement committee continued at good pace until the internees suddenly found some 700 out of 1051 ill from stomach disorders. They also found that they were paying over one-half of the $700 CRB monthly "comfort allowance" permitted through the Swiss Consulate loan for supplementary food (food to supplement the basic poor quality ration the Japs supplied). Also the internees suddenly realized that there had been no change after the election, except for the worse, in the operation of the galley.

Petitions came to the defeated reform committee to ask Tsurumi to oust Watson and his committee on the charge of negligence. But the reform committee pointed out that it would never do to show dissension among the internees, for this would be playing into the hands of the enemy. Furthermore, the new committee had been elected for six months. We were still trying to act in a democratic manner inside a concentration camp.

However, there seemed to be nothing to prevent a petition signed by more than one-half of the internees receiving the comfort allowances, to demand that Watson change kitchen crews, and replace the chiseling galley gang with an honest, experienced, and intelligent food man such as Jimmy James who, before imprisonment, had run several Shanghai restaurants. A petition was prepared, signed by irate internees and presented to Watson, who had no choice but to act. The galley gang had to go. Volunteers—mostly British, in view of impending repatriation—filled the kitchen jobs.

Watson's committee continued in office, but without prestige among hundreds of disgruntled internees. Then came announcement of repatriation. This meant a new committee with a preponderance of British, since mostly Americans were leaving. The more palatable food, as carefully prepared as possible, and the sure knowledge of a new camp chairman, cheered the internees who knew they had to remain.

The diary reopens in mid-August.

August 13, 1943—(Inside camp after nearly six months). Tsurumi ordered internees "to begin to pack for repatriation" today. This is actually the first move toward home. The Japs named the repatriation "categories" up through number 5. This includes the men who sent their wives home before the war in accordance with the Department of State's request. I've never seen such excitement as swept through camp this afternoon. It's the greatest moment in our lives. But out of the 1051 in this camp, not more than 350 will go.

*August 14—*Missionaries held extra prayer meetings today—praying about repatriation for those not on the list. All day long people had their heads deep in duffle bags, suitcases, and trunks. One "wag" walking down the narrow hall in the east building where everyone was bent double, their heads in their luggage, commented, "It's evident the *end* is in sight."

Marjorie and I haven't even permitted ourselves to think about what freedom will mean; what it will mean to be clean; to turn a tap and get all the water you want that doesn't have to be boiled; to eat again; to be free to speak your mind; to be rid of the heavy feeling that somebody's going to punish you for something you have or haven't done—to be rid of these little monkeys and their planned brutal treatment of the aged and women and children.

*August 17—*Tsurumi called me to his office this afternoon to "invite" Carl Mydans and me to his "home" to tea—of all things—on Thursday. He asked me to supply him with a list of all accredited foreign correspondents to be checked at the Japanese Embassy office, "to be sure none of your friends are left behind." He continued, "You are undesirables. We do not want you here any longer." That suits me. I'm delighted to be an "undesirable." Of course Tsurumi is just trying to save face because he knows our government has asked for us. I gave him the names of Brines (AP); Covit (UP); Karl von Weigand and Lady Drummond-Hay (Hearst); and of course Carl and Shelley Mydans (*Time and Life*), and Marjorie and me. Tsurumi said that our group "will be treated as number two to diplomats." It makes no difference to me how we're treated as long as we get on that boat.

Jack and Dorothy don't come under any of the present categories. Jack is still ill.

*August 18—*Wouldn't you know it! Tsurumi announced today that "repatriation has been temporarily cancelled." What a wallop in the solar plexus. I went to see Tsurumi to find out what had happened. He was enjoying the camp's deep discouragement. He says the ship has been temporarily postponed "due to U.S. wishes." He doesn't know why. He says, "I think this is only for short time; maybe two or three weeks."

There's a strange reaction among some of the internees who are not likely to go anyway. It's a kind of jealous reaction. They say, "I told you so . . . the boat will never go, so what are you getting all excited about?" I remember there was something of this same attitude at Manila just before we were transferred to Shanghai.

August 19—Tsurumi said this morning that he wanted Carl and me to come to tea anyway—"even if repatriation temporarily postponed." We left camp about two-thirty in the commandant's car. This is class, after the recent handling by the gendarmerie during questioning. Now that we're going home—or are we?—they're trying to leave us with a good taste in our mouths.

Tsurumi lives at 37 Great Western Road—one of the larger British homes with a long garden in back. There are still stickers on the furniture, remnants of the Japanese seizure. The place smells musty and is covered with dust despite a little Japanese maid slipping in and out. The garden is overrun. But Tsurumi is very proud of it. "How you like my luxurious home?" he asked us two or three times. Mrs. Tsurumi, who had been with Tsurumi when he'd been Consul at Vancouver and Bombay, served us tea and cakes and I found a small piece of white bread with what actually proved to be butter on it. After we had cleaned the sandwich tray, Tsumuri opened up with, "Wull-wull, Mr. Gun-san, Mr. Mydans—we have been in two camps together. Now I will ask you some questions."

He reached in his pocket and pulled out a few sheets of paper on which questions had been written in longhand in English. I asked him if this was an "official questioning" and whether or not he was going to quote our answers to the newspapers for Japanese propaganda. He protested that this was just a friendly discussion. The questions were general and not too difficult to answer—or evade answering. He asked what America's ideas of "an honorable peace" would be, how America would accept Japan's "gracious granting of independence to the Philippines and Burma" and what our attitude was toward Wang Ching-wei and the Nanking puppet government.

August 20—This has been a bad day. Gordon Ball (National City Bank) was caught trying to pass a note through the fence to the outside. This is the worst crime you can commit. Tsurumi ordered the entire camp to assemble in front of the west building. He posted guards with drawn revolvers around the entire group. He delivered a speech stating that he knows of others who have been smuggling out notes. He threatened serious punishment for anybody caught.

He sentenced Ball to nine days' confinement to his quarters and ordered the entire camp to remain in their quarters for two days "with no showers, no washing." Fortunately Ball's note merely asked for clothes stored on the outside to be sent to him before repatriation. I've seen Tsurumi's boys work over people who communicated with the outside at the Manila camp. Ball is lucky.

August 21—The entire camp remained indoors today. It was hot and stuffy. Inaba made an inspection today during which he came into our room.

"Hey, Gun-san," he shouted, waving a Japanese newspaper in his hand, "you are writer for *Collier's* magazine. Your magazine says Japan already win the war. Now no need for you to go home."

I asked him how he knew all this. He adjusted his oversized horn-rimmed glasses, sat down on my rickety iron cot, pulled up his green-checked trousers to the knees, and began to translate from the Japanese newspaper.

"Clark Lee—you know this man?—he writes in *Collier's* that Japan has already won its war. This is true. Why your government is not so smart as Clark Lee? Why they don't stop fighting?"

He continued with the Japanese translation of parts of Lee's article. When he finished he said, "My brother in Solomons. He say Americans cannot live like animals in jungle—like Japanese. Americans cannot fight."

"Mr. Inaba," I asked, "if Americans poor fighters, then how come Americans keep advancing in Solomon Islands like Premier Tojo admits? Maybe your brother he make one mistake?"

"Never mind," he said petulantly. "Never mind. It makes no difference if Americans take Solomons. Too far away Japan. You never get Japan. Too far. We never get America. Too far. No one will win war. I think better pretty soon both countries quit." He laughed.

Inaba told us September 2 was the original date for the repatriation. He says a new date has been set, but I couldn't get any more out of him.

August 22—The *Shanghai Times* quotes Sumner Welles from Washington stating the *Gripsholm* will sail from New York with 1500 Japanese about September 1. Boy, does that look good in print! That means we leave here about September 15, as it takes the *Gripsholm* two weeks longer to get from New York to Goa, Portuguese India, than for us to make the trip from here.

August 26—Edouard Egle (International Red Cross Delegate) made his first visit to an internment camp in North or Central China today when he came here. I ran into him in the supply room where he was asking questions about babies' milk and eggs of Inaba who was conducting the tour.

Watson stood trembling in the background. He's even more fearful recently. Egle asked how much milk we received for the babies. Inaba replied that the Japanese Government was supplying milk now but intended to supply more later. I spoke up and said, "Mr. Inaba means that he is permitting *us* to buy our own milk in limited quantity—isn't that what you mean, Mr. Inaba?"

Inaba didn't reply. Egle said, "I see what you mean." Egle asked how much we were paying for the eggs we have. Cliff Flook, in charge of camp supplies, answered, "$3 an egg." (That's about 3 cents U.S. but very expensive for China.) "That's too dear," Egle commented. Inaba tried to change the subject and get Egle out of the storeroom but Egle wanted to talk.

"You're awfully thin," he said to me. "What are you doing now?"

"Since I'm no longer on the committee," I replied, "I've been working outdoors and cleaning toilets. But what I'm actually doing is waiting for the boat to go." He just nodded.

August 27—The *Shanghai Times* announces the *Teia Maru* as the Japanese repatriation ship. That's the former French liner, the *Aramis*, that they took over from the French at Saigon. Tsurumi told me today, "You will be served luxury food on this trip." I remember clearly that he said the trip from Manila to Shanghai last September 'tween decks with the rats and horses on that troop transport would also be "a luxury trip."

August 29—Frank Mortimer's (building monitor) plan for a special diet for forty-seven permanently sick prisoners was turned down cold by Watson today who stated, "I won't permit catering to individuals." These are people who need food free from fat and grease. They have sprue, dysentery, and other forms of food poisoning. This dictatorial attitude on Watson's part is a defense mechanism—he's afraid of people, particularly since the kitchen scandal blew up in his face. I'm sorry that Ben veered off after the good start he made when he first came into camp. He was badly advised and influenced by the former kitchen gang from the *President Harrison*.

August 31—Here's an amazing thing. The *Shanghai Times* reports that the Imperial Japanese Navy has checked a plan by the U.S. Navy to set up a submarine base north of Foochow at Santuoa in Samsu Bay. The story said that a Japanese landing party had surprised the construction of this secret American sub installation—

just across from the northern tip of Formosa—and had captured some personnel. This sort of news, true or false, bolsters prisoners' morale. If there's a base at Santuoa, there are more elsewhere.

Queen Wilhelmina's birthday. Our eighty-nine Dutch held a quiet picnic supper in the "Dutch Garden" that they have cleared near the baseball diamond.

September 1, 1943—A cool day for a change. Six long, black navy cars with Japanese photographers and reporters rolled into camp this morning. They took hundreds of pictures for a pre-repatriation series of propaganda stories on how well the Japs are treating us. Fifteen of these monkeys crowded into our 10 x 17 room. Tsurumi and Inaba brought them in. Inaba said, "This man *Collier's* man. He make broadcast from U.S. He will tell how nice we treat Americans." Tsurumi said, "This room very nice. Only four people. This like special compartment on train."

September 3—Heavy rain, the grounds are nearly flooded. Tsurumi "invited" Mydans and me to tea again. This time it was shorter, but more questions, much like those he asked us the other day.

Tsurumi told us "confidentially" that the sailing date of the *Teia Maru* will be September 20. We will go down to the boat the night before. Carl and I asked permission to take our typewriters, stating that it would be too bad if we returned home to tell people that the Japanese had "confiscated" our typewriters which, to us as correspondents, are the same as toothbrushes to the average internee. The toothbrush gag seemed to appeal to him. At first he said no. Later he said, "I will consider this."

September 4—Everyone is greatly relieved today. The *Shanghai Times* reports that the *Gripsholm* actually sailed from New York on September 2 with 1330 Japanese on board, that she will stop at Rio and Montevideo and Port Elizabeth, South Africa. Now it's sure. Thank God! After two years!

September 5—Jimmy James has been formally appointed food controller by Tsurumi. That ends the kitchen revolution and Watson's and the Room 110's power over the kitchen. The people are still boiling over the revelation that for all these months the children got none of the beef kidneys that came in on the buffalo hindquarters. The kidneys went to the butcher shop gang. No one minds extra cuts of meat for the butcher shop and kitchen crews, but the best cuts should go to the children. Everyone is relieved that James will be preparing the food. Now we all believe that each prisoner will get his proper ration.

September 6—Very little in the paper about Allied action in Italy.

This signifies successes on our part. No word from Jack, who's now at General Hospital.

September 7—Tsurumi reports "absolutely no written matter of any kind—marriage licenses, birth certificates, school diplomas, contracts, papers of identification—or even baby pictures" may be taken by repatriates. He states that no receipts from the Japanese Government or firms (like Mitsubishi) for what I call "robbery" may be taken home.

September 8—More regulations. All "heavy" baggage must be ready for final inspection Sunday the 12th. We are limited to three pieces not to exceed 30 kilos total. Tsurumi says this is reciprocal— U.S. doing the same thing. Still no names as to who are actually going. This is a continuation of their war of nerves. People are packing who obviously won't go. The Japs are enjoying all the speculation. They'll enjoy the disappointments more. Word from Jack at General Hospital that the Swiss doctor as well as the Italian superintendent of the hospital have recommended that due to his physical condition he be placed on the sick list and sent home. Now the Japs have to pass on it. Dorothy is frantic and is packing in hopes of a last-minute okay. It doesn't look very hopeful to me, but it is better to be prepared.

September 9—Underground reports from outside that "Italy has capitulated to Allies." The *Conte Verde* has been scuttled in the Whangpoo River. Wow! No newspapers came into camp today. I asked Tsurumi about the newspaper and he said, "Maybe some mistake," and let it go at that. Everybody's relieved now that it is to be the *Teia Maru* instead of the *Conte Verde* that is scheduled to repatriate us. Wouldn't that have been something—ten days before sailing and our ship scuttled—if we *were* to have gone on the *Conte Verde*.

September 10—International Red Cross comfort parcels—made up by the friends of the I.R.C., not to exceed 20 pounds—arrived in two trucks about three o'clock. Captain Sugahara began inspecting immediately. Last month he insisted on keeping the parcels two days under the hot tin roof of the east shed, before he got ready to inspect them. These parcels always cause great jubilation. Usually what you get in one parcel gives you more vitamins than you get for a whole month from the low-grade chow the Japs supply.

Blackout tonight. I don't know whether this is due to the "upset political condition in the city of Shanghai," or whether it's just the autumn blackout practice. Japanese planes flew over at only a few hundred feet. They dropped flares where there were any lights noticeable. We watched the blackout for a short time from the roof of the west building, until the guards chased us down. The city is really well blacked out. But from the air, you'd always be able to spot it because of the winding river.

September 12—Tragedy today. Miss Dawson, missionary woman age seventy-nine who lived right across the hall from us, was taken out of camp in a coma; nearly dead. She is one of the type, I argued, who never should have been interned.

The attitude taken by the American Association officers then was, "Let them all go in. We'll get them out later." No one has been permanently released yet and nearly seven months have passed since we got in this dump. A number of people are in outside hospitals.

September 13—Tsurumi announced more names today which he said "are unofficial until tomorrow." This relieves many families who have been split, with names of only part of the family appearing on previous lists. Inaba has asked me two or three times, "How do you like our war of nerves on repatriation list?" I always answer, "What war of nerves?" There are some pleasant surprises in this new list since it goes into categories 7 and 8—men with contracts signed in the United States. Bud Kilbourne, the missionary from Japan who has done such a swell job of interpreting for the committee, is on the new list. His wife is so overjoyed that she breaks into tears when anyone congratulates her on their good fortune.

September 14—The *Times* reports the *Teia Maru* sailed from Yokohama with seventy-eight Americans on board. This is the first day we have received the newspaper since the Italian fold-up. There is mention of Mussolini's escape. It seems incredible to us that he could get away.

Twelve more names were added to the repatriation list today. This includes several young couples without children. Dorothy is holding up marvelously. We've heard nothing from the Japanese or from Jack about the success of his petition for repatriation on the sick list.

Tomorrow the heavy baggage will be inspected beginning at 9 P.M. It's really close now. May nothing go wrong this near to freedom. But I'm still going to try to get this diary "out."

This was the last entry in the journal. I had to secrete it at this time for smuggling.

XLVIII

THE first official news regarding repatriation came on July 4. Everyone considered that a good omen and thereafter all camp life seemed to hang on the hope of going home. "Who would go? Whom would the Japs hold back?" Out of three thousand Americans in North and Central China perhaps nine hundred would go. You had an awful, sinking feeling when you thought of the possibility that you might not make it.

In spite of the discouraging reports the Japs kept giving us, we went ahead and put on a camp show called "The Repatriation Review." The east shed, which was used for all camp activity—church services, debugging rice, school classes, library and recreation—became the theater. Tables were roped together for a stage, a few 60-watt bulbs were put in line for footlights, our six-piece pianoless camp orchestra rehearsed for weeks, and the show went on—with the first three rows full of Japs. We put them right next to the orchestra so that the noise of the music would prevent them from hearing the words to some of the more satirical songs.

It was a wonderful feeling when the commandant finally called us in officially and said, "I have pleasure to tell you your name is on list of persons being repatriated to America." And then he had the crust to ask us, "Do you want to go?"

Several smart quips came to mind, but I merely answered, "Yes, indeed."

Marjorie and I were hilarious. But our hilarity was dampened when we saw those who were unfortunate, those who had to stay behind. Only about one-half of all the Americans in China were repatriated at this time, and only 151 out of the entire Philippines-American internee list of some six thousand. We were caught between two fires—our own joy at being released, and disappointment at leaving some of the people who had become our closest friends, and with whom we had been through difficult times.

The day we left camp, the commandant lined up the entire repatriation group in front of the main building. He kept every one with hats off in the hot sun while he passed down the long lines. He insisted on shaking hands with each internee.

Those staying behind crowded the windows and the pillared porch, waving handkerchiefs, dabbing wet eyes, shouting last-minute messages. The camp musicians played "Auld Lang Syne" and "Aloha." Tears flowed freely and unashamedly. Many families were being divided, probably for the duration. Many people were left behind who had expected to go. In Shanghai alone, fifteen people originally agreed upon by the Japanese and American governments were struck off the list by the Japs after the *Gripsholm* had left the United States and South America. Negotiating through the Swiss, the United States salvaged some face by getting thirty-six reinstated out of the fifty-one names the Japs had eliminated.

Those left behind in this group of fifteen included some topflight and average businessmen, and even one entire family. The United States did not want to cancel the whole repatriation, which was based on "humanitarian need," by holding out for the final inclusion of the fifteen whom the Japs had scratched off the list at the last moment. Thus, the *Teia Maru* sailed on schedule. The ship had been held up so many times during the past year that everyone, including those left behind, agreed that it was better to get the ship off and speed at least fifteen hundred homeward. Then another ship, or ships, might be worked out.

During the week just before sailing, as baggage inspection was taking place, a telephone call from the Japanese gendarmerie stopped the inspection momentarily while some baggage was pulled from the line and set aside. This order from the commandant's office appeared to be a bad sign for someone. I voiced this opinion to Norris Wood, who was standing next to me.

"I agree," Norris said. "It happens to be my baggage."

Norris Wood was the top Standard Oil executive in Shanghai. After his bags were put aside the commandant informed him that a gendarme would call for him at eleven the next morning to take him into town. Wood, who had been a very sick man prior to this, nearly had a relapse that night worrying over what could have come up in his record to keep him off the boat. Tsurumi told him he didn't know what it was all about, but that he would send Wood's baggage to the customs jetty if he were able to clear himself at the gendarmerie. Wood said that he knew by the tone of his voice that the commandant didn't have the slightest idea that he had any chance of being cleared. This was only two days before sailing.

At eleven the following morning Norris Wood was ready at the commandant's office. He was in a state of terrific jitters when the gendarme guard showed up. Wood noticed considerable back chatter between the commandant and the gendarme before he was led away.

The whole camp watched the gate all afternoon, hoping against hope that Wood would return. And when he did come back late in the day, we had only to look at his face to know that it was all right.

"A social occasion," Wood told us as we crowded around him incredulous! He was grinning all over.

"What do you mean, 'social'?" someone asked.

"A luncheon date," Wood laughed. "The Japanese supervisor who took over our office gave a farewell luncheon for me and some of the other boys from the firm who came from the Pootung camp."

"A bon voyage! Can you beat it!" someone snorted.

A typical Japanese trick, based on the theory that last impressions are the only lasting impressions.

PART SEVEN

Going Home

XLIX

"A FLOATING concentration camp" is what we 1503 American repatriates aboard the *Teia Maru* called the former French motorship that carried us on our month-long voyage from the Far East to Goa in Portuguese India.

Certainly few, if any, of us expected luxury or even much comfort on this first leg of our two-and-one-half months' 16,000 mile trip more than half-way round the world to home. We were overjoyed at getting away. But in our anticipation we overlooked Japanese psychology. The Japanese gave us all something more to remember them by. They indicated before we left our camps ashore that we must remember we were still under "the authority of His Imperial Japanese Majesty, the Emperor" until the exchange took place.

Frankly, I don't know exactly what I expected. But I did not expect to be jammed into the forward hold between decks with 477 other men where we were told to sleep, eat on the hatch cover, and wash ourselves as best we could with what trickle of water was provided. There was no consideration for age or physical condition. During most of the trip through the tropics, the few portholes were bolted shut and no attempt was made to give ventilation in these smell holes despite the protests by the repatriates' committee through the Swiss Government delegate aboard. I know, for I not only was assigned to the hold but served on the committee and helped to frame the almost daily protests over this and other clearly unhealthy, unsafe, and uncalled-for situations.

Of course, we were on our way home. That factor overshadowed all others. There were no demonstrations; no open indication of how high the feeling actually ran. Although forbidden through the purser's office, hundreds of these men took their straw mattresses and slept on deck. And not only men, but hundreds of women as well.

There were 240 women and children mass-bunked in the upper and lower tiers in what had been the ship's forward glass-enclosed social room. Marjorie was assigned to this section which was on the top deck but was so closed in that the center of the room was stifling and sleep was impossible for many of the older women. The age average of this group of repatriates was over forty and these people, middle-aged and older, were not in even average good physical condition. They couldn't be after the extremely rigorous camp life under the Japanese.

The Japanese Ministry for Greater East Asia saw to that. Just as the Japanese permitted no complaint against maltreatment in the camps, making their own international law, so it was aboard the repatriation ship.

In many ways the exorbitant "squeeze" exacted by the crew for drinking water, regular ration of food, baths, baby food, and cleaning the public toilets, among other things, was no less than highseas robbery. Some of the cabins set aside for the Japanese officers at the outset were sold to the passengers instead of being turned over to the sick and aged. In some cases overpayment and overtipping by the repatriates who were able to secure large amounts of money aggravated the condition. Inequalities in the kinds and general amounts of foods served in the four dining spaces were unnecessary. Those of us in the unventilated hold were served staler and different food from even the third-class dining room. However, all food served aboard was better than camp food.

The constant overcrowding and sleeping on deck—in fact, anywhere with or without covering or pillow—brought on even further lowered physical condition. And by the time we reached Goa, this was increasingly noticeable. For instance, when the ship wallowed even slightly, hundreds became seasick. Just over five hundred— one-third of the passenger list—were in cabins, with at least one or two on the floor. On deck you had to pick your way carefully over prostrate bodies or between the few deckchairs available. At night it was almost impossible to move anywhere on deck. When tropical downpours occurred, as they did two or three times during the night, you always had to scramble for the limited cover; then back out to the wet decks again. A month of this with extremely limited bathing and clothes-washing facilities wears down even the healthiest person.

A careful checkup by a group of repatriate sea captains showed the ship's lifesaving and other safety equipment to be in "questionable condition." This was obvious even to the landlubber. A checkup, again by repatriates, was made on the lifebelt equipment. It was not possible to find a belt for each passenger. Negligence atop this came when the repatriates' general committee finally felt that in the interest of safety we must recommend fire and lifeboat drill and stated we would carry it out ourselves to co-operate. The Japanese captain listened to the Swiss delegate's recitation of our recommendation, bowed politely, sucked in his breath and replied that "maybe later" he would find it convenient to hold such a drill. But none occurred through the entire trip. Yet, seafaring men remember the conflagration with many lives lost in the Red Sea of the sister ship of the *Teia Maru* (the *Aramis*) on its maiden voyage. We repatriates ourselves put out several small fires due to defective wiring.

The main point, as seen by this repatriates' general committee and by other practical repatriates who anticipate other repatriations from the Far East, is that a precedent was being established in this first of the total-civilian non-diplomatic repatriations between belligerent nations. One of the reasons behind this ship's delay of nearly one year was the inability of the governments to agree on principles establishing future exchanges of nationals.

There was no one aboard who would have agreed to stay in camp rather than to have made this trip homeward, even under worse conditions. As it was, the *Teia Maru* was an improvement over camp conditions.

The repatriates' committee on board the *Teia Maru* was chairmaned by Claude A. Buss, former Executive Secretary to the High Commissioner in the Philippines. This committee of seven was established on direct orders from the State Department in Washington. Active Government representatives of the committee were United States Consul General N. P. Davis; Dr. Juan Marin, Consul General Chargé d'Affaires in China from Chile; Frederick Sullivan, representing the Canadian Government. The rest of us on the committee were civilians—Cornell Franklin, former Chairman of the Shanghai Municipal Council; LeRoy Pharis, Shanghai Power Company; Dr. Paul Mayer, missionary from Japan; and I.

We acted in exactly the same capacity as the camp internee committees except that we had no direct contact with the Japanese. According to agreed practice, all of our communications—and these were largely complaints—had to be made through Mr. H. Abegg, Swiss Minister Delegate. There was aboard the *Teia Maru* Prince Shimazu, Vice-President of the Japan Red Cross who was making the trip to Singapore for inspection of conditions there. The Japanese delegate aboard was Baron Hayashi, a Japanese Foreign Office official.

Informally I had several talks with Prince Shimazu and Baron Hayashi. Neither of these Japanese was particularly concerned about the filthy conditions on the ship or the lack of safety equipment and precautions, although their own people were returning on the same ship. Prince Shimazu remained in his comfortable cabin throughout most of the trip, as did Baron Hayashi, except to take an occasional turn back and forth across the bridge in the cool of the early morning.

As the voyage drew to a close, it was apparent to us on the committee that our duty was to make a protest to the Japanese through the captain of the ship. It would never have done to leave the ship without making such protests in writing. This was not only face for us, but showed that we would not accept willingly conditions which the Japanese knew to be contrary to international law and agreement. As well as constant verbal protests made through Mr. Abegg, who represented our government, we made two written protests. But so far as results went, we might as well have saved our breath and our ink.

L

WHEN we arrived at Goa in Portuguese India—just a few hundred miles south of Bombay—the *Gripsholm* was nowhere in sight. In fact she was reported to be a full twenty-four hours late. A great groan of disappointment went up from the repatriates, who had expected to exchange their prisoner status for one of free citizens the day after we arrived.

But the disappointment was forgotten the next afternoon when every American, Canadian, and South American crammed the *Teia Maru's* rail as word flashed around, "The *Gripsholm's* in sight." Tears of emotion blurred the blue and gold markings of the great white Swedish ship as she inched her way past the stone breakwater, moved slowly through the brown harbor water, and was warped into the quay only a few hundred feet ahead of the *Teia Maru.*

As we stood drinking in the sure knowledge, for the first time, that we soon would be free, the Japanese repatriates aboard the *Gripsholm* gave a great cheer as the Japanese colors at the *Teia's* masthead were dipped in recognition of the *Gripsholm's* arrival.

There wasn't a sound from the crowded decks of the *Teia.* But late that night several hundred missionaries met on the forward deck to sing hymns of gratitude for their deliverance. The excitement of the *Gripsholm's* arrival was felt long after midnight aboard the filthy old *Teia Maru.* Already Red Cross supplies and comfort parcels from the *Gripsholm* for our Far East camps had begun to pile up on the quay. And the Jap's parcels for their internees in America were already awaiting loading into the *Gripsholm.*

We began to get indications from worried American Red Cross officials and International Red Cross delegates on the quay that the Japanese captain of the *Teia Maru* might leave a day early, without fully loading all the American Red Cross supplies. There had been some such trouble at the first exchange down in Lourenço Marques in 1942. We wanted no such repetition here, and our camp ship committee heartily agreed to postpone the exchange to the *Gripsholm* until all the Red Cross supplies were unloaded and at least on the quay-sides nearest the *Teia Maru.* We well knew of the Japs' attitude on delivery of parcels if the mood didn't happen to suit them at the moment.

We knew what the delivery of even half of these parcels would mean to the war prisoners and the civilians left behind. What were a few more hours of the dirt of the *Teia* for us compared to what these parcels would mean to the people back in camp? There wasn't a grumble from one of the 1503 on the boat.

But everyone was anxious to get off to have a closeup of the *Gripsholm.* Port authorities did not permit wholesale visits to the quay until after the exchange. The Japs were just as anxious to see what the *Teia* was going to be like as we were to get aboard the *Gripsholm.*

When the Japanese baggage gang came aboard the *Teia Maru* the night before we traded ships with them, even their allegedly inscrutable Oriental faces showed pretty plainly their surprise at the living accommodations aboard ship.

Russ Brines and I talked with one of the Japanese who spoke American without trace of an accent. He was grousing about the "small trickle of water" that came from the water faucet in his cabin aboard the *Gripsholm*. We merely told him that water aboard the *Teia Maru* was "rationed," letting him find out for himself that he'd be lucky to get twenty minutes of water out of each twenty-four hours, once the *Teia* sailed. These Japanese expressed great enthusiasm at the prospect of getting back into the "co-prosperity sphere" and of leaving behind them the land of labor unrest, strikes, deserters from the armed forces, widespread inflation and unpatriotic black markets.

When one Japanese told me this I merely replied that I was certain he had a great revelation in store for him when he actually experienced the much-talked-about "prosperity" that was now supposed to be available for the Japanese people due to their invasion in East Asia. He didn't miss my point.

I talked to another Japanese who said, "You'll be surprised at the great scope of your country's war effort. It's tremendous." I was more amazed at his attitude, which was entirely American. He told me that he hadn't been in Japan since he was a baby. And he asked me what it was like in the co-prosperity sphere. I gave him the only answer possible. I said, "I think you'll be more surprised at your country's war effort and activities to try to win the war than I will be when I reach the United States."

Another smiled grimly when he saw the ship in which he was going to return to the "co-prosperity sphere." "People in your country don't know what war is," he snorted at me. "You complain about conditions on a ship like this. We are glad to suffer for our Emperor. We'll show you what a war is before this fight is over."

The day following the exchange hundreds of the Japanese repatriates took their laundry down on the quay to the small-handled water pump, and "reverted to type," washing and wringing out their clothes while seated on the rails of the narrow-gauge railroad track, and then proceeded to bathe themselves. Carl Mydans tried to make a picture of this for *Life*, but was chased away by water-throwing Japs. Hundreds of Americans watched the little by-play.

But the dramatic incident of the actual exchange of these three thousand American and Japanese nationals climaxed our entire twenty-two months of imprisonment. The two ships were lying one behind the other along the quay. The great white *Gripsholm* was forward of the stubby gray *Teia Maru*. The Portuguese port authority arranged a line of boxcars just off the quay-side running the full length of the two ships. The Japanese disembarked from the *Gripsholm* and passed along the shore side of these boxcars, while we got off the *Teia* and filed over to the *Gripsholm* on the harbor side of the cars. Unless you were high on deck of either ship you couldn't see the exchange take place.

I stayed on the top deck of the *Teia Maru* to watch the exchange until almost the very last. Despite the number of people and the baggage, of which the Japs had the greatest amount, the actual exchange took only one hour and thirty minutes.

The first event of the morning exchange occurred when the Japanese Minister from Chile and his staff left the *Gripsholm* some fifteen minutes ahead of the others. They carried with them the picture of His Imperial Japanese Majesty the Emperor, which was being returned from the closed Japanese legation at Chile. A picture of His Majesty must never be left behind. Many a Japanese officer has been lost in sea action going back into the captain's quarters after the Emperor's picture.

The captain of the *Teia Maru* and all his officers were at the gangway bent double in homage as the Minister and his staff paced through the quay-side warehouse, stumbled across the railway tracks and handed the precious picture to Baron Hayashi, the Japanese representative. It was a large picture and the Baron had difficulty carrying it up the narrow gangway. Meantime, the *Teia's* officers and men remained bent over in reverence until the picture, wrapped in white tissue paper, was safely aboard.

This ritual completed, the exchange of prisoners began.

Our people began to straggle across the gangway on the quay and hoisted their sacks and few belongings onto their backs for the short walk to the *Gripsholm*. We Americans and Canadians were a sorry-looking lot. We were thin, and pale for the most part. I hadn't particularly noticed before the ragged condition of our clothes and shoes. We were refugees in every conceivable sense of that word.

But our spirit! That was indescribable. I won't try.

The Japs streaming over to the *Teia Maru* from the *Gripsholm* presented a most vivid contrast. I don't know what I expected, but I was certainly surprised at first to notice the well-fed, well-groomed appearance of the Japanese men, women, and babies.

There was a spring to their step. They carried their small handbags with ease. The children frolicked along the route. Our people just dragged themselves and their few belongings across to the *Gripsholm*. To see these two long lines of human beings, one moving along easily, quickly, and the other a slow-motion process, only re-emphasized the fundamental differences between the way we treat our enemy aliens and the way the Japanese treat theirs.

Although we few correspondents aboard the repatriation ships were practically censored out of filing any copy on the exchange, the correspondents who came down from Bombay and New Delhi cleared many thousands of words.

We all were particularly glad to find Frank Hewlett of the United Press waiting on the quay. The last time Marjorie and I had seen Frank was just before he had joined General MacArthur at Corregidor and I had remained behind in Manila to make my last broadcast. Frank had come all the way to India from MacArthur's Southwest Pacific headquarters because he had expected his wife—who had been at the High Commissioner's Office in Manila—to be aboard. Due to unfortunate circumstances beyond her control, Virginia didn't get aboard. Frank, the great guy that he is, carried right on, getting his stories and filing them, keeping busy day and night. Keeping busy is a great help at a time like that.

Tillman Durdin of the *New York Times* was there, healthier looking than ever. He didn't recognize me at first, I'd lost so much weight (over 40 pounds). The last I'd seen Durdin was in Singapore just before Pearl Harbor. "The voice sounds like Gunnison . . . and it must be you . . . but you don't look like you . . ." he said when we first met.

Johnny Morris of the United Press, formerly of Shanghai, had chartered a plane from Bombay. Arch Steele, the *Chicago Daily News* former North China correspondent, covered the exchange, as did Jim Brown from INS en route from Russia to Burma. Preston Grover (AP), out from the Middle East desert, was there with a camera and typewriter for Brines and Cronin, and Gardner from the *Sydney (Australia) Morning Herald* was down. It was like old home week in the City Room. I think we picked up more information about what had happened since the war started than we did through all the reading we attempted aboard the *Gripsholm* the rest of the trip home.

Morris and Frankie Hewlett filed my first piece for *Collier's* for me, which never got through the British censors; nor did their check-messages to me. Between our own State Department and the Bombay censors we were well bottled up. And after waiting twenty-two months to get the first story out, it seemed a crime to us.

Two days after we had moved over to the *Gripsholm*, the *Teia Maru* sailed, loaded with every Red Cross parcel the *Gripsholm* had brought out. Our delay was worth while.

As the *Teia Maru* slipped her lines and the Portuguese tugs pushed

er out, I was amazed to hear some singing from the *Gripsholm's*
deck. And, from the expressions on the faces of the Japanese packed
onto the forward deck of the *Teia Maru*, so were the Japanese. It
sounded like a hymn to me. I turned to the person nearest me.
"What are they singing?" I asked.

"Wouldn't you know it?" the man replied. "The —— missionaries
are singing 'God Be with You till We Meet Again.' "

They tried to sing some other hymns, but the Japs aboard the
Teia Maru countered strongly, typically, and effectively, with their
national war anthem.

That was our "*tag*" to twenty-two months of Japanese imprisonment.

LI

TO US aboard the *Gripsholm*, who arrived at Port Elizabeth,
South Africa, and later at Rio de Janeiro, after a perfect cruise-
ship passage from Goa, it seemed longer than a few weeks since we
had left everything Japanese behind us. The present and future
freedom was what counted.

Censorship regulations were stiff. Correspondents were not permitted to tell even a little about the hardships some of the repatriates had been through. (Release of atrocity stories in the United
States and Great Britain in January 1944 lifted this censorship.)

However, we were allowed to tell about what went on aboard the
Gripsholm which had been transferred into a twenty-four-hour-day
health center. You might say we were crowded. But it's all in the
way you look at it. We had all reached the stage at which we could
have opened a can of sardines and said, "Move over—there's still
plenty of room."

After the first two weeks at sea everyone's health began to improve. The ship's doctors and the twenty-odd civilian doctors from
the camps were pleased with the upswing in weight and general
appearance of the repatriates. The more than one hundred serious
sick cases showed marked progress during those first two weeks
aboard the *Gripsholm*. And little wonder. Sunshine, fresh fruit,
milk, eggs, and cereals took the pallor away. The children perked
up especially. You noticed this from the increased activity of children underfoot. We had over two hundred under the age of twenty.

The Swedish crew were particularly helpful. They had been ever since the *Gripsholm* pulled into Goa, and the crew members brought oranges, apples, sandwiches, and cakes onto the pier and handed them to the baggage gangs, the children, and others of us who got ashore. If those Swedes were as helpful to the Japanese repatriates, the contrast of returning from what the Japanese propaganda department called the "war-starved United Nations areas" into their own "co-prosperity sphere" must have been unmistakable the moment the Japs boarded their avowed luxury liner, the *Teia Maru*, to return to "prosperous" Japan.

We had movies once or twice aboard the *Teia Maru*—movies of the Japanese capture of Singapore. But it rained during this showing out on deck and we never saw the finish. One Canadian repatriate said that was significant because the Singapore-Malaya incident wasn't finished anyway. "And when it is," he concluded, "we'll be showing the Japanese movies."

Aboard the *Gripsholm* we had movies—and what movies! Most of us hadn't seen a motion picture for nearly two years. We hadn't heard a new popular song for the same period. We hadn't seen an American magazine for longer. Although listening was strictly forbidden, and we were supposed to have had no radio equipment, we had heard a few broadcasts from the United States, England, India, and Chungking, but no movies.

The first picture shown aboard the *Gripsholm* was *Yankee Doodle Dandy*. As in any George Cohan production there were a few emotional spots, and they hit this repatriate audience right in the teary places. Especially when the American flags appeared at the end. We were people who hadn't seen an American flag for nearly two years. This repatriation audience was absolutely silent when the first flag sequence appeared on the screen. There was the American flag— *the* flag—all forty-eight stars and thirteen stripes: red, white, and blue. But the realization had to sink in that now you could give voice to your feelings. There was no one to stop you, no one who wished to stop you. Once that realization sank in, once that fact clicked, well, the lid was off. You ought to have heard the applause, the cheering, the whistling.

I tell these things because, although they may seem unimportant at the first hearing, they were *big* in significance in the lives of these fifteen hundred Americans who were returning from the severest kind of imprisonment any non-criminal civilian can possibly have passed through. These people were coming home full of resentment toward the enemy and filled with more appreciation and respect for their America than it is possible for anyone to understand who hasn't experienced two such years of Japanese domination.

Here's another example of what I mean. The first night at sea—out of Goa—someone, I don't know who, dug down in his pocket and champagne was served just at the end of dinner. Someone stood up and started singing "The Star-Spangled Banner," and when that was finished, "God Bless America" . . . and then a toast was drunk to the United States of America . . . and when that was finished there was scarcely a dry eye in the dining room. Overemotional strain at being released? Well, maybe that's the medical terminology. But we were realizing—experiencing—what the word *America* means; what the word *freedom* means. We will never forget.

There were fifteen hundred happy and only a few sad repatriates when the first mail was distributed, mail from all the folks at home. You could tell the few who had received bad news of deaths of loved ones. But most of the news was good news. The point that caught my attention first was the number of war marriages; and secondly, the very efficient censorship of names of places where men were training for various branches of the service. Of course, the numerous Government agency initials, and the WACS, the WAVES, and the others particularly puzzled the women aboard. The women naturally grabbed for the magazines distributed by the American Red Cross, to see how styles had changed. They had expected the styles to appear strange to them, but my impression was that most of the women were surprised at the lack of any fundamental change in dress in the past two years.

The American Red Cross, besides distributing magazines, huge chocolate candy bars, and cigarettes, outfitted those in need with clothing and shoes. A survey was made by a repatriate committee from each camp of their neediest cases, and those repatriates were outfitted first. That took the better part of a week. After that, others less needy were given clothes. You must remember that a majority of those repatriates, with the exception of the Shanghai people who had experienced for the most part only seven months of internment, had been unable to get any clothing at all for two years, and that most of their clothing was tropical wear. We arrived home in winter weather. So the Red Cross was properly prepared to have some winter as well as tropical clothing aboard.

The little store aboard the *Gripsholm* was probably one of the busiest corners on the ship. Every day there were long lines of repatriates in front of it, patiently waiting to get near the counter in order to buy toilet articles, writing paper, sweaters, bathing suits, and all the hundred and one little things that we had almost forgotten existed.

We settled down into a pretty routine shipboard life. The over six hundred missionaries were the busiest with their meetings, their religious services, and their adult education classes. There were many classes in Chinese on deck each day. Most of those missionaries, when asked what they would do when they got home, told you in four words. "Return to Free China."

We came to expect new questionnaires every day or so from the hard-working State Department staff aboard the *Gripsholm*. But, as I overheard a repatriate say one day, "I've had plenty of practice in filling out questionnaires from the Japs the past two years, and since I'm going home, and I've got nothing else to do—and it doesn't interfere with my eating three times a day—I'll fill out a questionnaire a day, and like it."

There were birthday parties with ice cream and cakes, the like of which we'd almost forgotten. And just to indicate that we were back into the luncheon belt, the members of the Rotary Clubs in East Asia had a meeting. They found over thirty members aboard, and the chairman, the senior Rotarian from Canton, China, planned other meetings to hear reports from the different areas represented. The largest contingent was from Shanghai with sixteen members.

We had a smattering of the world's news each day from the radio in the bar. You had to get in there early to hear London or New Delhi—it was news and it wasn't forbidden and we weren't going to be imprisoned if we were caught listening to it.

The repatriates aboard the *Gripsholm*, with a few exceptions, when asked what they planned to do when they reached home, answered, "I've lost too much time already as a prisoner. Just let me find something to do to help win the war."

LII

AFTER two and a half months across 16,000 miles by sea with only three days ashore, 1503 repatriates stood out on deck in the cold damp drizzle of the first day of December. They were staring across New York Harbor at "The Old Lady with the Torch."

New York Harbor loaded with gray and camouflaged ships—the likes of which we'd never seen anywhere in Occupied East Asia— slowly slipped by. Just as slowly came the realization that "this was it." We were home. This was that faraway place to which a lot of us aboard the *Gripsholm* had had cause to wonder whether or not we would return.

It's no good trying to describe your reactions, your feelings, or your friends' attitude at such an emotional moment as this. It's bound to be "corney" in print. But "corn" or not, here it was: one hundred per cent America and we all were straining our necks and eyes to see over the crowd at the rail, and through the mist, to catch a glimpse of something familiar.

The press boat came alongside while we were still in the stream. Not permitted aboard, frozen-fingered photographers flashed bulbs at the waving crowds along the ship's rails. The Navy, the FBI, the State Department officials moved all too slowly—for us—up the gangway to the upper lounges and promenade decks where they set up identification and interrogation files and tables. Lines formed automatically—our last "camp line." And this last line wound around corridors, deck after deck, deep down inside the ship.

Everyone was impatient to get ashore. "They say they can get us all off before midnight . . ." was what you heard all along the line. It seemed an impossible task. But the customs and other officials had learned since the first 1942 *Gripsholm*. And they accomplished the impossible. Nearly everyone was cleared. Of course there were a handful who were held for further questioning. There was a suspicion that obviously the Japanese must have slipped at least one or two people aboard who were "friendly" to the Japanese; people who might be expected to peddle subtle propaganda that the "Japs aren't so bad after all . . ." *ad infinitum*. And others who might even do a bit of espionage for Hirohito. The only way of telling was to examine carefully anyone who was at all likely to be suspect. Some missionaries, some bamboo-Americans, and even a few prominent Far Easterners were among those last released from Ellis Island to which they had been transferred from the *Gripsholm*.

But the rest of us were back in the middle of things within twelve hours. To Marjorie and me it meant customs inspection; a hurriedly written and quickly censored "glad-to-be-home" radio interview over the Mutual Network, with Dave Driscoll, War News Services director of WOR, asking the questions; flash bulbs; mail from the Red Cross; our first ration books; a speedy ride up the North River side of Manhattan with Christopher Cross from Mutual (a quick mental note that the *Queen Mary* was in . . . the last time we'd seen her was in 1941 off the Heads in Sydney Harbor loaded with Anzac troops headed for Singapore), and finally, reunion with our families.

If anyone asked specifically what happened the three days following our arrival, I'd say we ate and slept and tried to tell our bewildered mothers—Marjorie's and mine—between mouthfuls what it was like to be free, to have all the food we wanted (even on meatless Tuesday), and to be able to see American flags instead of Jap banners.

We couldn't pass hamburger joints. Without saying a word we'd automatically turn in and sit at the counter. And coffee and doughnuts? Those were things you dreamed about behind barbed wire and spent hours trying to recall exactly what the taste of a dunked doughnut actually was. And on an empty stomach between burps from rotten Japanese fish that was real heroism.

Everyone asked, "How does it feel to be back?" There's no answer but the trite old word, "Swell!" But when we said it there was nothing trite about it. People looked at us as though we'd just been released from the zoo. And the way the Japs had thronged to the camps to peer at us, we had been. You'd hear people say in a heavy whisper, "Yeah . . . just back from a Jap prison camp . . . kinda thin, huh?" I guess we did look a little on the underfed side. I was still 35 pounds underweight—even after all the butter, bread, cereals, meat, and ice cream aboard the *Gripsholm*.

The first chance we had, Marjorie and I slipped out alone for a walk down relighted Fifth Avenue, and to elbow our way through the throngs of furloughing service people and chippies on Uncle Sam's greatest midway—Broadway and Times Square.

Tojo's propagandists had told us, and everyone else in Occupied East Asia, that half the stores along Fifth Avenue had boarded up their windows and gone out of business. No stock for sale due to extreme war rationing. They said Broadway was closing down— practically no night life in New York any more; America's morale had dulled with the dimouts.

We wanted to see for ourselves. There may have been fewer lights. But there were more people than we'd ever seen along Broadway pre-Pearl Harbor! And Fifth Avenue! The windows were never more loaded with necessities *and* luxuries! If New York stores were an indication of America at war, we were fighting amid luxury. While we both were delighted to see for ourselves what we knew was true, despite Tojo's propaganda, I somehow couldn't seem to adjust myself. It was hard to realize, coming from a bare, war-strained Asia, that what I was seeing, on the surface at least, was America at war.

There were strikes, and more threats of strikes. The President stepped into the middle of the threat of the nation's railways to strike. I had believed Tojo's boys when they had reported a few strikes: it wouldn't be an alive U.S.A. if we weren't griping at something. But I had scoffed at the constant stress in the Japanese propaganda on the undermining of American morale through more and more strikes. Certainly these strikes and threats of strikes raised Japanese morale. Then to come home and find that the Japs weren't exaggerating the situation, that their reporting of strikes was pretty accurate, caught me with my guard down.

Friends said, "You'll never know a war's going on here—after what you've been through. These people here need a bombing, or something to wake them up. They don't know what war is."

Somehow this analysis didn't seem right to me. It sounded again too much like Tojo's patter for patent victory. Yet what I saw *appeared* to give proof to the point that Americans didn't know they were at war; didn't fully realize a war was on. There was no use taking anyone's word for it. The only answer was to go and find out for myself; to go around the country to large cities and small towns; to war plants and farms, to ship yards, aircraft factories . . . and even further to talk with GI Joe himself in the camps and training stations.

And after going out and seeing for myself—from coast to coast, from north to south—there's still no complete answer, "yes" or "no," for our nation of 135 million people. We've got them all from draft-dodgers to broken-hearted 4Fs; from successful blackmarketeers and ".01 of 1 per cent profiteers" to the most unselfish war-bond and war-work contributors. On the surface—at first glance—you'd be justified in saying, "They don't know a war's going on. Look at the way they play. Look at the money they spend. See all the laughter. Witness the wastefulness. . . ."

On the other hand, dig a little deeper. Nearly everyone in America has someone close to them in the Service. Look, for example, at the thousands of women of all ages doing drudging work in war plants. A good percentage are GI Joe's wives, sisters, mothers.

Think for a moment of the ingenuity of the small and middle American businessman and factory owner in transforming his unit into a war plant. Ingenuity and idea-men are the modern "Minute Men" of America, all the way from the GIs to the top industrialist and transport executives who plan the over-all support for the war.

A British journalist friend shakes his head and laughs incredulously after a trip across the United States—the same kind of trip I have made. His answer is, "Well, old boy, I don't know how you do it. You are at war all right. You'd be more war conscious if bombs dropped in America, it's true. But you've reached only about 60 per cent war speed. You haven't had to go into high gear. It will prove a post-war blessing not to have been forced to strip your gears, like some of the rest of us. All I can say is that God protects babies, drunks, and Americans. . . ." Inadvertently perhaps he did put his finger on one of the reasons for American success. Talk with some of the boys back from hairbreadth escapes; talk with prisoners of the Japs who are now free. See if they don't give credit to something besides good luck. I do. Prayer pays off.

To be absolutely fair, you can't say America doesn't know there's a war on; nor can you say that we all are fully conscious that we are fighting an enemy. It's because so few of us have ever seen an enemy, or believed there could be a real enemy who would deprive us of "life, liberty, and the pursuit of happiness," that we aren't "fighting mad" the way the British, Poles, French, Dutch, and others are.

I've often been asked this question: "You've been away. You're seeing the U.S.A. with a fresh viewpoint. If you were to make a terse observation about American attitudes toward the war—especially toward the Far East (Japan, China, and Russia)—what would you say?"

I'd say this, generally:

In Eastern United States: Russia is wonderful. All is forgiven. We misunderstood Russia's aggressive action prior to the time the Soviets joined with England. Base all future peace for us and the world upon the Soviets' word that they will do what they say. China is comprised of four hundred million people who somehow resemble a cross between the delightful, politically vital Madame Chiang Kai-shek, the corner laundry man and the local chop-suey joint operator. China is a democracy, and only needs Chiang Kai-shek back in Nanking as "President" to restore China to a powerful position, similar, say, to the restoration of France to a new status in Europe. Japan is a secondary nation, populated by a group of toothy, smiling, inscrutable, incredible prehistoric little people who need to be spanked . . . but "handling the Japanese" will be relatively easy compared to what we have to do to Germany. Germany is the real world menace.

In the Far West: Beware of Russia. If they won't fight Japan with

us then obviously they must be against us. Don't accept any of that
Soviet Asiatic double-talk. Watch them like hawks. Get along with
them, but don't follow any Soviet leads too far without guarantees
that the Soviets are going to fulfill their promises. Pat them on the
back and praise them for their gallant and amazing ability as fighters,
but remember they can fight us some day too. As for China—get in
and help the Chungking people hard and fast. Support Chiang Kai-
shek to the hilt or it may be too late. Be careful of certain monopo-
listic business trends in China. But support China; get back into the
Philippines; demand complete control of all the islands in the Pacific; take a strong lead in all Asiatic politics and economics; our
economic future (West Coast) is in the Far East. Japan: "All Japs
are bastards." Don't trust all American-born Japanese; at least until
the fighting stops and we've smashed Japan to a pulp. Occupy Japan
until kingdom-come if necessary.

In the Mid-West: Beware of Britain. Otherwise the reaction is
somewhere in between the East and the West, with extremes noted
in loud minorities demanding American aloofness from "entangling
alliances."

Over-all attitude: "Co-operate with every nation in the world
toward one goal: Maintenance of peace. Prevent any more wars that
will pull our boys away again. Enforce the peace. Don't give Germany or Japan a chance to breathe a warlike breath—or anyone else,
for that matter. Join and participate—lead—in a World League or
Council of Nations. Quit following Britain's, France's, or anyone
else's lead in world economics or politics. Let's not follow; let's
make history! But let's get this war over quickly and get the boys
home again!"

But everywhere I have gone, the question I've been asked the
most is: "How did the Japs treat you? Are the atrocity stories we
hear really true?"

And when I reply that in the first place: "The treatment we civilian prisoners received was generally bad, and was not in accordance
with the fair treatment specified in the Geneva Convention, under
which the Japanese agreed to operate civilian camps. . . ." And that
in the second place: "Many of the camps operated by the Japanese
were atrocities in themselves . . ." I have been asked another question:

"Do you believe we, in America, are giving fair treatment to our
Japanese prisoners (the Japanese internees and the openly *dis*loyal
American-born Japanese) or do you think we are pampering and
coddling these Japanese? Shouldn't we be tougher on the Japanese

prisoners in retaliation for what the Japs are doing to our people who are still over in East Asia?"

Again, there was only one way to answer that question. Go and visit Japanese enemy alien camps here in the United States, and see for myself.

So I made a trip to the Tule Lake camp in California, the camp holding some nineteen thousand Japanese enemy aliens and openly disloyal American-born Japanese. This is one of the ten War Relocation Authority civilian camps in the United States opened in 1942. But it differs from the other nine in that it is set up to keep "on ice" the troublemakers, and certain Japan-born Japanese, for the duration. The others are temporary camps for American-born Japanese to be operated only so long as it takes to relocate these American citizens, most of whom were removed from the Pacific Coast "due to military necessity." Incidentally, this Tule Lake camp is the one in which the Japanese Government protested that their nationals were not receiving proper treatment. And this is the same camp which the Spanish Government checked on for the Japanese, and found to be operated under the rules of the Geneva Convention. The Japanese might take note that at least we permitted the neutral government representing them to inspect the camps. The Japs don't permit the Swiss Government representatives in the Far East to visit all of the camps containing American, British, Dutch and Filipino internees.

But apart from what the officials say, here is my own first-hand report: I was permitted to go anywhere in the camp I wished, and to talk with whomever I wished, including the Japanese prisoners. Let me make several comparisons between the treatment we received (and what our people are still receiving at the hands of the Japanese) and the way the United States Government is treating the Japanese held here.

First: The food is good. The Japanese prepare it themselves in well-stocked and well-equipped kitchens. Sometimes they cook it Japanese style, sometimes American style. They have rice at each meal. They have good fish at least three times weekly. They have plenty of milk, fruit, and vegetables. They have meat three times weekly when it is possible, based upon availability of rationed meat in the community. And they usually have meat. They have canteen stores, which are run by the Japanese themselves. Prices charged are the same as outside the camp. And they can purchase nearly anything they desire.

Our people, on the other hand, in the Japanese camps, live on a bare minimum of food. We were always hungry. The fish we got was usually very old. Meat, when we got it, was usually blue and covered with flies. And where there were plenty of fresh vegetables in the community, the Japanese said it was "too much bother" to get the vegetables for us. The small canteen stores we were permitted to have charged very high prices for everything—higher than outside the camps.

On food content and quality we in the Japanese camps received the equivalent of about 1900 food calories per day. The Japanese in American camps have been receiving between 3000 and 5000 food calories daily.

As a matter of fact, I believe the Japanese in the Tule Lake camp actually look better physically than the free Japanese I saw around Japanese Occupied East Asia. Obviously the Japs out there are living a restricted wartime life. They are tightening their belts to try to prevent us from landing in Japan too quickly.

Another point of comparison. We had less than an average of 30 square feet of space per person in the camps in Manila and only a bit more in Shanghai. That means you are jammed so close together that you can't turn over in your sleep without hitting the person next to you. The Japanese in our camps here in America have approximately 110 square feet per person. I saw their living quarters. Where we had anywhere from fourteen to one hundred persons in a room, they have (here in America) small family units in special family rooms.

Where we lived in old broken-down school buildings and missionary compounds, the Japanese here live in well-built U.S. Army barracks with all the facilities of showers, toilets, washrooms, and clean eating halls and well-lighted rooms for recreation. They have library facilities and schools, their own camp newspapers, and are permitted daily newspapers and national magazines from the outside. Some of them are even paid from between $12 and $19 U.S. dollars per month for working on the camp farm, in the schools, and around the camp.

There are many other points in favor of our treatment of our enemy civilians. But these points should be in our favor. We are operating under the rules of the Geneva Convention, to which the Japanese have agreed but never fulfilled, just like everything else they promise. They are great on promising, but you seldom find Japanese fulfilling their promises.

It may be felt in the United States that because the Japs are badly treating and slowly starving the United Nations' civilian prisoners, and giving them practically no medical treatment at all, that we here should treat the Japanese we hold in the same way; that we should retaliate. I have talked to our people here about this. Let me tell you how Secretary of Interior Harold L. Ickes (the Cabinet officer in charge of W.R.A.) answered my question on these camps, and you can judge for yourself.

In his office in Washington, D.C., Mr. Ickes said, "Gunnison, we are fighting for certain principles in this war. One of them is living up to the laws of humane, fair, honest treatment of people the world over. It would be destroying one of these principles for which we are fighting to maltreat the Japanese enemy aliens we are holding here, just to retaliate for what they are doing to our people. At least," he said, "we are going to be honest and strictly law abiding. The Japanese will have to pay for breaking the law later . . . and they will, in the defeat we are now beginning to hand them!"

I think that is a fair statement of how most Americans feel. Don't think for a moment that we are pampering these Japanese in our camps. They are living behind barbed wire. They are living what Tojo-san would call a "non-luxurious life," but nowhere nearly as non-luxurious as if they were free and back in Japan at this very moment.

We have Army guards around the Tule Lake "segregation" camp. We have strict rules which the Japanese must obey. But they are fair rules. And I'm satisfied, from my own experience as a prisoner of the Japanese, that if I were placed in charge of the Japanese camp at Tule Lake I'd run it pretty much as I found it was being run when I visited it.

In final analysis—and yet you can't really be "final" about anything these days—my only real fears regarding the war are (1) that if it continues much longer, enough of our own people will become "war weary," thereby slowing down an ultimate smashing victory. One of the greatest dangers is the psychological effect of over-publicized "leveling off" wartime production peaks. Should the Asiatic war continue well past the closing date of European fighting the lift in morale due to the victory over Germany may result in a letdown in the homeside attitude in fighting Japan. We'll relax. It's a natural reaction. Certainly this will be true with the British. After Europe, to the Britisher (except the Australian and New Zealander) the war in Asia will be merely a matter of face-lifting for the Empire.

And (2) I am apprehensive that the Japanese will make the utmost of this psychological letdown here and in Britain to quit suddenly, and to make full use of their already carefully laid plans for the next phase of the fight against the "foreigner" in Asia. I fear we shall become "benevolent victors" all too soon. That's the danger, as I see it, against which we Americans—we in the United Nations— must guard for our own self-preservation in the future.

PART EIGHT

After This, What?

LIII

I WATCHED Uncle Sam's chin-whiskers take an awful jerking
for the first two years of the war in the Far East. Although the
whiskers sometimes came out in handfuls, Uncle Sam never lost his
feet or his dignity. Hirohito's international jiujitsu wasn't good
enough. Even in the darkest days no thinking American ever doubted
that eventual military victory over Japan would belong to the
United Nations.

But victory, as everyone knows equally well now, will be only
the beginning. What good is it going to do to win the fighting if
we don't win the peace? That would mean that we had lost the war.
We must make history in the Far East. We must not let history be
written and enacted by the Japanese. Their plan is ready. Ours
must be formulated and promulgated without delay. And any such
plan, to be effective, must be based upon a deeper understanding
than we now have of Japan, China, and Russia—of their peoples,
their complex internal politics, and their own plans for the future.

First, and always, there is China—China with all its smiling graft,
its traditional corruption, and inefficient handling of the Burma
Road—China so "misunderstandable" to the foreigner; so exasperat-
ing under many different conditions. And yet—this China stood
up to the Japanese for long and weary years while we "talked" a
lot of moral support and sent Bibles, at the same time permitting
bombs and gasoline to go to its enemy (and our enemy) the Jap.
During those years the Chinese tried to understand us, and couldn't.
We didn't even try to understand them.

In spite of our early mistakes, of all the United Nations giving
help to China, and fighting with China against the Japanese, I be-

lieve the United States should gain most in immediate post-war opportunity for business expansion. But "business" in China—as the Old China Hand knew it—will never return to the same old stand. Extraterritoriality, national legal rights, and special foreign concessions inside China are gone forever. And rightly so.

China from now on will be a Chinese monopoly, not a foreign concession, if the Chinese have anything to say about the Pacific stability peace settlement. I believe China is likely to come out way ahead when the Far East economic-political bargaining is finished and Japan is boxed within its own islands.

When Generalissimo Chiang Kai-shek went to Cairo in 1943 (accompanied by Madame Chiang, peace-planner Dr. Wang Chunghui, General Shang Chen, chief liaison officer to the Allied military personnel, and his other staff officers) he carried a chip on his shoulder. America was by then pouring millions of dollars' worth of equipment, and more millions in lend-lease loans, into China to fight the Japanese. But the Japanese still had Free China pretty well corralled. Frankly and openly, Chiang and his military staff admitted that even at that date, unless they were given more assistance from the air, and more military supplies for China's ground forces, the Japanese might turn on China in an all-out offensive to knock her out of the war—and that it *could* be successful.

To assist them in a decisive attempt to finish off China, Japan has been depending upon at least two factors: quick military action in Central China, and internal civil war.

As to civil war possibilities, the Japanese have noted with some satisfaction, first, growing American confusion over who the so-called Communist armies are and what they stand for in China; and secondly, the propaganda from discontented internal Chinese groups to secure exclusive American lend-lease support for forces led by such Communist functionaries as Mao Tse-tung, chairman of the Central Executive Committee of the Chinese Communist Party, and Chou En-lai, Communist member of the Chungking Peoples' Political Council.

The rather opaque theory behind this attempt is: If the British and Americans can switch leaders in Yugoslavia (Mikhailovitch to Tito) to accede to Russian wishes, why not shift support in China (Chiang to Mao Tse-tung) to show Far East good will toward Stalin? It has been an attempt to create a kind of Yugoslavia in Central China. One main trouble with this theory is primarily that Stalin has never nodded toward Mao Tse-tung over Chiang. What's more, this is an obvious move to prevent a united front in China. We have picked our horse in the China race (Chiang Kai-shek) and regardless of inevitable trouble makers, we will back Chiang.

We have tried to insist that Chiang and Mao and other politicians bury their hatchets, not in each other's backs, but under the Great China Wall—at least until Japan is driven from China.

We sent the first and subsequent B-29 "Super Flying Fortress" squadrons to China actually to strike heavy Allied blows at Japanese war industry and military installations in Japan proper; secondly, we fully recognized that these powerful planes and supplies for China's armies were sent specifically to aid Chiang Kai-shek liberate China from Japanese aggression. If these arms had to be used by Chiang against disrupting civil influence, including Communists, we had no objection although we might prefer otherwise. But winning the war is the first objective.

But to return to the time of the Cairo Conference. In China leading war lords and money men were needling Chiang with the disturbing charge that while he was promised tremendous help, very little of it had arrived in China. Secondly, these influential Chinese pointed out to Chiang that if America brought its own troops and planes into China and cleaned out the Jap, America would want too much "cumshaw" in economic opportunity after the fighting was over. These men told Chiang they wanted to see some Chinese do some successful fighting. They wanted to see some Chinese airplanes. They wanted China to save its own face in the Orient. America, as an ally, should supply the equipment and the training instructors—even tactical leaders—but the Chinese should do the successful fighting.

Chiang and his staff look at Britain and America in entirely different lights. They believe that the British are out to get back every square inch of lost British territory and prestige in the Far East. They believe that Churchill and most of his advisors plan to have the Crown Colony of Hong Kong returned to the British Empire. They believe the British will do everything in their power to get back economic power and control in China, equalling in practice, if not in name, the pre-war concession setup. And Chiang and his group are determined that this is not going to happen.

A strong point in Chiang's position is his realization that in the Far East showdown he can depend on the Soviets for strong moral support. To understand why, it is necessary to examine the thinking which Russia is doing in terms of the future.

Any résumé of Soviet basic aims must include the following:

1. To avenge Russia's defeat by Japan in the Russo-Japanese War,

and to regain areas taken by Japan at that time, including Port
Arthur.

2. To establish Russia as the dominant commercial and shipping
nation on the East Asiatic Pacific.

3. To become the dominant Asiatic military and naval power; to
police East Asia; to keep to a minimum any U.S.-British naval and
air strength in East Asia.

4. To replace gradually U.S.-British political influence in China.

5. To supply China gradually with most of its needed outside
supplies, systematically shutting out all American, British, and Dutch
economic strength.

Chiang and his advisors, who also take a long-range point of view
in nearly everything they do, believe that they can play the Anglo-
American force against the Russian force—for the present—to make
political-economic progress for themselves.

The Free China group believes that it can safely give Americans
a good post-war deal economically, while still holding onto most of
the controls through Chinese monopolies. America will be able to
furnish the strongest economic and financial assistance when the
war is over. But Russia will grow in strength. Russia will constantly
press the Chinese to open up more economic opportunities in China
for imports and exports. And as always with the Soviets, with trade
comes strong political influence. With America and Russia both
giving China support, Chiang's group hopes to be able to shut Britain out with a minimum of influence.

Meanwhile there is not only Japan but the puppet government of
Wang Ching-wei and his group at Nanking with which to reckon.

The agents of Chungking are busy deep inside the Far East Axis
camp; deep inside the Nanking puppet government; deep within the
Japanese official civilian administration. Chungking secret societies
have marked puppet Wang Ching-wei for assassination. They have
offered huge rewards for him dead or alive. Of course all this is
known to the Japanese and Wang. Wang's no fool. He has his
counter-spies, and his counter-offers out for Chiang and Madame
Chiang. And he is waging a terrific propaganda war for popular
support—a war which in some quarters has apparently achieved success. In this propaganda Wang represents himself as China's cham-
pion against the Western foreigner with Japanese support—a support which will be engulfed in a Greater China when enough of
China is united. And this statement, superficial as it may seem to
us, is convincing to many Chinese who do not like China's close
relations with the Western nations.

To the man on the street in America and Britain, part of the situation at least seems clear. The position of the United Nations is plainly taken: Chiang Kai-shek is the leader of Free China. With him we shall defeat Japan. To him we shall look for Chinese leadership after the war. Wang Ching-wei is a traitor. We foresee a clear victory over Japan, in China as elsewhere, the elimination of Wang and his group, and the triumphant establishment of Chiang's government over a liberated and united China. But the situation is not so simple as that.

I have watched complicated forces at work in China—many of them powerful, many disconcerting, and all of them generally confusing to the foreigner. Out of them all, these facts seem to emerge:

We may assume the victory over Japan, the elimination of the Japanese army from China, and continue, in peace, to support the government of Chiang Kai-shek and the other Free China leaders. But whether or not the general mass of fickle, swirling Chinese public opinion led by provincial dictators is going to accept Chiang or reject him amid a series of inside murders, wars, and general internal disruption, is an unanswerable question. There are forces at work already to cause just such internal combustion.

My awareness of this bigger China problem was sharpened considerably by my transfer from the Manila concentration camp to Shanghai. My Shanghai freedom was enough to give me a closer glimpse of what is going on inside Japanese-occupied China. Inside Wang Ching-wei's territory, I watched some of the reaction to Wang-inspired propaganda.

To the United Nations, and to Chungking Chinese, Wang is clearly a traitor. But to other Chinese, both in Occupied and Free China, who have not been quite sure as to the long, rough outcome of the China affair, and who have listened to Wang propaganda, it has been convenient to call Wang names but to withhold their own final judgment.

All Chinese recall Wang's hop out of Chungking into French Indo-China; how attempts were made upon his life, and how, in early 1940, he puppeted into Nanking on a Japanese latchstring. But the skillful Nanking propaganda constantly reminds them that Wang was extremely close to the revered Sun Yat-sen, founder of the New China program, and tells them endlessly how Chiang and Wang were Dr. Sun's choice to head the military and political sides of the new republic after his death. It is also pointed out that these two Chinese revolutionaries were always competitors, and that Chiang's army and his military skill gave him an early, and not necessarily logical, advantage over Wang.

It seems clear to us that on the day of complete victory over Japan—or even before—Wang Ching-wei will be eliminated, probably through assassination by Chinese loyal to the Chiang Kai-shek government and the Free China ideal. But so successful has Wang propaganda become in some quarters that it has given use to a theory which foresees quite a different destiny for the Nanking puppet leader.

According to this theory, accepted by some Chinese who feel that they are more than usually well informed, Chiang and Wang together planned Wang's jump into the Jap tent. They assert "there is close liaison between the two, and when the moment comes, Chiang and Wang will emerge arm-in-arm victorious for Sun Yat-sen's China, just as the father of China would have wished his two protégés to do." That is the "happy-ending" school of thought. And Wang propagandists further this kind of talk with wise nods. It doesn't make much sense to me—but it is a point of view that must be recorded.

I talked with responsible civilian Chinese inside Occupied China and elsewhere who contend they "know" how Wang Ching-wei thinks. Maybe they do, maybe they don't. I have interviewed Wang's close advisor and Foreign Minister Chu Min-yi.

Enemy newspapermen inside barbed-wire internment camps usually don't interview puppet Foreign Ministers—not when the Japanese know about it. But due to an unusual coincidence, this was possible during Chu Min-yi's visit to the Chapei camp after I was interned. As a member of the Internee Executive Committee I was appointed "tour director" for all visiting firemen. And we had plenty of them—all eyes from Japan see the white man behind barbed wire. Because our camp at Chapei started out as headquarters for the commandant of all internment camps in North and Central China, most bigwig officials from Japan came out to look us over, slup tea with the chief commandant, R. Tsurumi, and grin toothily at our discomfort.

On this special day, I was told, "Great preparation must be made for most distinguished visitor." So, as usual, we did nothing. In a cloud of dust, three large shiny cars, confiscated from enemy aliens, pulled in through the camp gate. I noted a very tall, bald man who led the party upstairs; "pretty big for a Jap," I thought. When he came into the office, I recognized him immediately—Chu Min-yi, puppet Chinese, come to see and report to puppet Wang how Americans and British were faring behind barbed wire. The committee, as usual, was introduced to the "great man" and, as usual, was unimpressed. Then I was pushed into the fore as tour director and we started on our usual visitor's tour of rooms—the most crowded rooms, of course: the filthy scullery, the maggoty butchery, the inadequate kitchen, the hopeless camp hospital, the supplyless storeroom. . . .

I soon saw that Chu's English was next to impossible, his French was fair. Here was my chance, for the commandant did not speak French and was very much embarrassed that he couldn't speak in Chinese to Chu. I kept the pace of the tour down to a slow walk, spurting ahead with Chu only when I wanted to ask a question where my English had to come in.

In the half-hour visit Chu told me these things:

1. It was inevitable that the Chungking and Nanking people must get together for a New China. He told me that he felt enough strength could be assembled behind Wang Ching-wei to make Wang "head of the State," but with Chiang Kai-shek as prime minister and active generalissimo. "Chiang and Wang are not fundamental enemies," he said. (This is an amazing statement when you examine it. So far as I know, he was unaware that I was a newspaperman.)

2. Japanese military support for the Nanking Government would immediately dissolve once Chiang's forces realized that they were retarding China's unity and political economic progress, and quit fighting Wang and Chu. If Chiang's forces would "stop fighting this civil war," he said, and "unite in a joint force, all China could be peaceful again," This, he insisted, would not mean any loss of face for Chiang. (This was typical puppet propaganda.)

3. Under a new "National China" as visualized by Wang, no nation would be given any special political rights in China and no nation—not even Japan—would be given any special economic privilege in China. America and Britain and Russia would have equal opportunity to help rebuild the New National China. (This last is not out of tune with the Chungking policy.)

There was more before we made the final round to the baseball field where the ponderous Chu Min-yi watched the game for a few minutes before driving away. His replies to my questions follow the general trend of Wang propaganda that there is considerable thought in Nanking about making some kind of a compromise between the Nanking and the Chungking leaders. But is Chungking going to take a new benevolent attitude toward Nanking, once the victory over Japan has been won? Anything can happen inside China. I won't be amazed if we get several Far East surprises before this is all over. And some of these surprises may come through the so-called Communist leaders and their mercenary armies. We know pretty well what Chiang's attitude is. He wants to keep all forces, including these so-called Communist red armies, with him without internal bickering. Chiang insists there be no discussion of internal differences until Japan is defeated.

Chiang is an old soldier. He is a dictator disciplinarian according to his own Chinese lights. In the tight spots he has faced and survived he could not afford to show any signs of weakness. It is not likely that he is going to now.

Chiang promises an end of internal bickering, and a "full rice-bowl" when all Chinese join with him to wipe out the Japanese menace and clean the disloyal from Nanking. He tells the population that the American and Britisher are China's friends, but that they will receive no special political or economic positions when this war ends. He emphasizes that he, Chiang, is no "tool" of the white man. Rather, he is utilizing the strength of the foreigner to drive out the Japanese octopus. And he adds that there is no Chinese who cannot become a "loyal son of Free China." And in "Christian spirit," to which Chiang sometimes alludes, he urges them to come back into the fold.

If Chiang says there is no Chinese who cannot repent, what about Wang Ching-wei in case the time comes when Wang feels it would be fruitful to repent and strike out at the Jap? "Is this an invitation?" Wang Ching-wei people ask. If so, what is the rest of the offer?

Certainly the Japanese do not look upon Wang Ching-wei as a died-in-the-wool Hirohito lover. They take care to see that Wang's Japanese-trained national armies of some two million are interspersed with enough well-equipped Japanese troops to prevent an overnight *coup d'état.*

Meanwhile Wang's propaganda makes attractive promises to the people. The Nanking home program promises to improve the conditions of the average Chinese through public works, educational and agricultural projects, and controlled international trade. Wang's public attitude toward the Japanese is one of avowed friendship as a Japanese ally against the United Nations. (He declared war against the United Nations January 9, 1943.) But he seldom fails to point out that he and his administration are "pure Chinese" in every thought and action, "following closely the principles of Dr. Sun

Yat-sen." To be exceedingly frank, it is considerably confusing to the intermediate Chinese to have two men trying to sell him different brands of Sun Yat-sen.

Privately, one hears Wang supporters imply that since Wang is not too friendly to the British, Wang felt originally that the Japanese could give China a better start on the road to united independence—freeing China from all foreign (white) domination. It is implied that Japan must be eliminated from China but that Orientals should be used to help each other. East is East and West is West.

None of Japan's brutality in China is condoned by Wang. He keeps quiet about this evil. I am speaking now about Wang's personal propagandists, not the Japanese-inspired Nanking propaganda corps of fanatical-minded Sino-Jap students hopped-up by Japanese promises and special privileges. These youngsters are the menace to New China. In many instances, they are more Japanese than the Japs. These 10 per cent puppets are causing 100 per cent trouble. This is the crew which must be destroyed quickly when it can be found after fighting ceases.

Wang's attitude (not his official Japanese attitude) toward foreign nations is held to run the gamut from wishing close friendly cooperation with Soviet Russia, a certain amount of economic reconstruction assistance from the United States, and Chinese-controlled business relations with the United States, to a pretty careful freeze-out for his pet dislike—the British. He is willing to consider economic equality for all foreign nations in China, based on equality of opportunity and treatment to be accorded the nation to which he would offer the least inducement to come back—the British.

That the Generalissimo might be magnanimous toward Wang, with victory achieved, is indicated by Chiang's former treatment of the young Marshal Chang Hso-liang who abducted Chiang in the Sian incident. The "Young Marshal" is still alive—or was the last I knew. He has even been mentioned for a spot in the new Free China government after victory in order to pull into the Chiang fold some rather vitriolic radical groups.

Following is a typical observation from occupied areas. This is the kind of idea that is being "sold" today by the Wang propagandists—one that has grown in acceptance. This is what Chiang and the Soong family have to counteract:

"Both Chiang and Wang had place, honor, and responsibility next to Sun Yat-sen. Chiang was related to Dr. Sun through marriage. Both men dislike the Japanese but Wang has gone inside the invader's tent in an attempt to ease him out. Chiang has stayed outside to bring in foreign assistance. Why can't they get together after Chiang wins military victory?"

You get this along the seaboard in the larger cities where the Wang propagandist has had an opportunity to do some concentrated work. What attitude is in the interior, I make no pretense of knowing.

However, I have not stressed the true strength of public opinion gathered behind Chiang, a strength which is far greater than Wang's. Chiang's guerrillas are cutting away beaverlike at the Japanese invaders. The city and country guerrillas take their toll of the Chinese whom they believe to be pro-Japanese. But there are millions of Chinese who are tightlipped and wear their "inscrutable masks" so that neither Chiang nor Wang know which way they will jump.

LIV

RETURNING to the United States after two years of Japanese imprisonment, I seemed to sense an underestimation of the Japanese in the stories I read in our American magazines and in O.W.I. overseas communiqués. Not that I'm afraid of the Jap, nor have I ever had any doubts of our military-naval success. But I've seen the Jap in action. He's tenacious. We can't afford to guess him wrong during the fighting, nor during the surrender and peace-adjustment period to follow.

As I write this (June 1944) the Japanese are in the third critical stage of their attempt to hold Greater Pacific Oceania, and entering the fourth. They need a "lift" at home. They need something besides reiteration of "glories of our victorious war gods." The first period was "the offensive stage," from December 7, 1941, through December 1942. Enough has been said about that.

The second was "the prestige from victory" period, which coasted along with flying flags and *banzai* celebrations from December 1942 through July and August 1943. Tojo's trip through the southern Asiatic regions was a definite attempt to bolster prestige, then beginning to wane.

The third has been the "population awakening period." The populations of occupied areas daily have become more swiftly aware of the growing power of the United Nations' forces. And what is just as important, these people have been waking up to the Japanese failure to pay off on pre-war and present promises. Skeptical at first, the native peoples are growing certain that the only pay-off is what they pay to the Japs.

The fourth is "the guerrilla period" in which planned internal revolt begins within occupied zones, revolt which will open jungle and mountain trails to the final offensive period.

The fifth is the "full out United Nations offense and mopping-up period." Here the final blow against Japism will be struck from air, sea, and land. No Japanese slap and admonition will suffice, but a complete knockdown and drag-out is most vital to the Pacific's future.

For the Japanese military and civil administrators in occupied areas, the 1943 third period was a growing nightmare. In the first place, reports kept coming back to Japan that the peoples of the occupied territories were not giving full, voluntary co-operation to the co-prosperity movement. Reports showed that these peoples say they don't understand the Japanese method of counting "one for you and two for me." This attitude worries the Greater East Asia home office administration. And what has proved even more disconcerting, there's U Ba Maung and his demands for Burmese assistance. There have been Thai requests for monetary assistance and assurance of military assistance "if Japanese forces aren't able to hold against the Anglo-British-Chinese powerhouse at Burma's border."

In the Netherlands East Indies native leaders have constantly sought more local autonomy, and a large Chinese trader group—formerly predominantly pro-Chungking—has been a constant source of worry from the first. The Netherlands Indies Archipelago is scattered; its defense by Japan never was too secure with supply sources distant and enemy air superiority growing.

Furthermore, no one in Japan is sure of Admiral Jean Decoux in French Indo-China. He is French above all else. After all, what has he done to assure the Japanese of anything but three bows toward Tokyo and a few polite *banzais?*

To the Philippines, Tojo-san has already sent three top-flight generals—one of them General Tanaka. And the Tojo-Hirohito ("I and God") combine awarded the Filipinos their "independence." But Tojo never has been sure that the Filipinos aren't just waiting for the day they can cry "death to the enemy" and murder every Japanese within reach.

Actually feelings run higher in the Philippines against the Japanese now than at any former time, even than at the height of the battle for Bataan and Corregidor. Guerrilla sniping is continuous and effective. It is no secret—particularly to the Japanese—that constant short-wave radio contacts are maintained between MacArthur's headquarters in the Southwest Pacific and "opposition" forces in Luzon, Mindanao, and the other islands. Anti-Japanese propaganda and anti-Japanese activity has risen to a higher stage of efficiency in the Philippines than in any other place in the Far East. The Japs have the occupation jitters and have tried feverishly "to mop up" what they call "the remainder of the decimated Filipino-American forces living like foxes in the hills."

The feeling against most of the framers of the new Japanese-Filipino constitution is particularly high among literate Filipinos, who know or intuitively feel the difference between "independence" and serfdom.

As for China: It is obvious that the bombs from General Claire Chennault's 14th American Airforce have begun to prove to the average Chinese that Uncle Sam, not Hirohito, is stronger.

These are indications—growing indications—that have worried the conqueror of the Southwest Pacific.

Go one step forward from the third period of "population awakening" (of official Japanese perplexity and reorganization) to the fourth or "guerrilla period" which began slowly, early in 1944, when the peoples of occupied countries realized that Japan was actually being defeated. When enough of the occupied population catch this idea, the big change will begin to take form. The guerrilla period means the start of an open internal uprising taking the place of the passive underground resistance. Dammed-up resistance, due to lack of food, to harsh treatment, and stricter and more unsympathetic Japanese domination, will give the fundamental impetus to the breakthrough. This will take the form of widespread assassinations, increasing guerrilla activity in all occupied zones, with emphasis first in French Indo-China, the coastal areas of China, the Netherlands Indies, and the Philippines, where organizers of guerrilla forces are biding their time.

Add only one more feature to this picture for Hirohito and his staffs to mull over. When the United Nations conclude the European war—and the Japanese expect "a costly United Nations' victory"—again the question: What attitude will an unexpectedly strong Russia take toward Japan? This has worried Tojo-san from the first. Japan's Pacific strategy has been based on an exhausted, weak-kneed Russia, a Stalin without sincere American or British friends; a Russia without strength when the Axis breaks.

Overwhelming strength is the only thing the Japanese can or will recognize. Anything else—even consideration of a wily offer through Russia of a political arrangement—would be a sign of Occidental weakness. If there is any sign of weakness (and it could come only from the political side) we will have lost the Far East war.

When the Empire falls it will be Tojo or whoever is at the sword handle—not Hirohito—who falls and loses the nation's face. It is likely that since Tojo and Hirohito have done what no others have accomplished in the world's history—taken over the South Pacific and most of East Asia in a before-breakfast campaign that missed only Australia, New Zealand, Hawaii, and India by a slight miscalculation—there will be a move afoot to save their face for posterity. This would give Japanese historians an inspiration to hand on to future Japanese in the next, and already planned, Japanese white and yellow war.

Philosophically they'll learn from this war and use what they learn in their next. And one wonders: Is Russia included among the nations the Japanese intend to squeeze out of the Far East?

What is it worth to Stalin to "mix it up" in the Pacific? The Japanese still have a wallop left and that is being saved for the force that first gets close to Japan. Stalin's Far East espionage is superior to that of any other nation. Stalin, too, has seen that the Jap has been on the defensive—admittedly so since August 1943.

Although the Jap won't exactly admit it, he'd like to figure out some way for a "political arrangement" to hold what he has grabbed or at least a portion of it even if he has to turn to Stalin as the "mediator."

In order to visualize Stalin as an eventual ally of the United Nations in the war against Japan and in the post-war Far East, it is well to examine the position of Russia in relation to Japan, as we have already examined her point of view in regard to China. We must try to understand the fundamentally Oriental thinking processes of the Russian, who, after all, *is* an Asiatic.

For our war and post-war purposes Russia can be envisioned as two nations—European and Far Eastern. In Europe Stalin has been our fighting ally—thank God! But Stalin and his counsellors may be the cooks who spoil Britain's and America's post-war recipe.

In the Far East, where Russia—our European ally—has remained in a state of suspended belligerency with Japan, one fact has been clear. Russia is not friendly toward Japan. Russia has refrained from fighting Japan for Far Eastern supremacy only because it has been too busy with Germany. But Russia, up to the time this was written, had not signified its desire to ally itself with anyone (except possibly China) to fight against Japan. Yet in its fundamental aims Russia has well-thought-out plans concerning its post-war positions in both Europe and Asia. Here are some of them: "Do we get special trade concessions—especially in North China and western China?"

Russia is in the unique position of coming out ahead regardless of whether it enters active fighting against the Japanese or not.

Japan's attitude toward Russia has been one of acute suspicion from the beginning; one of acute fear that the Russian would permit Americans to establish bases from which Japan itself could be attacked. With this possibility constantly in view, the Jap has kept a large force at hand in Japan, and along a few of the northern islands leading into the Kurile group "just in case."

But the Far East War is so complicated in its beneath-the-surface political swells, so Orientally complex as regards face and political prestige, that in an extended war in the Pacific after Germany is defeated, Russia must inevitably be drawn in. Under the sixteen-autonomous (Commonwealth Soviets) state plan promulgated by Stalin early in 1944, it is entirely feasible for a few of the East Asiatic Soviet States eventually to take on a shrinking Japan, without the entire Russian nation becoming embroiled.

This, if it takes place, is the typical Oriental approach. And the Russian is first of all Oriental—and proud of it. An Oriental maxim is that "the end justifies the means." If it's going to suit Russia's own individual aims better to fight even briefly against Japan, Stalin will enter against Japan. If the Soviets feel they can gain just as much in the future by staying out then no amount of wheedling and promising will bring Moscow pilots over Tokyo—if the war does not continue too long.

Russia's Pacific area aims are few but potent. Russia considers itself the protector of the Asiatic, and supports the doctrine that Asia is a spot eventually to be inhabited by Asiatics only. This sounds strangely familiar. Hirohito's boys at Moscow are playing this shrill note close to the Stalin-Molotov window. "Powerful Asiatics—while they may disagree—never should quarrel except perhaps superficially. Don't," say the Japs in Moscow, "don't make the mistake Chiang has made in turning to the English and the Americans for aid in Asia. Perhaps you had to in Europe. But you don't have to out here. Present a peace program—a political arrangement—for Japan to America and Britain; play along with Japan for a time; and—who knows?—maybe we'll have 'Asia for the Asiatics' after all?"

LV

WHAT will happen inside Japan—inside each Japanese when he finally realizes that Japan has been defeated in battle; that "honorably" or "dishonorably," the Divine People have been licked by the hated foreigner?

The first reaction will be to blame the military group who have defiled the name of the Emperor by leading him along the wrong trail. But there will be certain militarists who will seek to keep a hand in the ranks of the new government group that makes the peace with the United Nations. Others will don white kimonos and disembowel themselves in disgrace.

The patent propaganda inside Japan, before our counter-propaganda forces can get at the Japanese mind, will be to establish—to fix indelibly—that the white man has won an unfair victory; that the white man has taken unfair advantage of Japan after Japan won its war. This trend had already begun in late 1943.

It may be alleged that the Japanese have an inferiority complex. Perhaps that's what it is. But on the other hand, I seem to notice what I would term definitely a "superiority" attitude. And it stems from the primary Japanese reaction that we, "the foreigners" (and the Russians are not included in that category since they are Asiatics), will be "suckers when it comes to enforcing the terms of the peace and post-war pact." The Japanese are superbly confident that we British, American, and Dutch "whites" are not capable of enforcing our "weak democratic methods" of opening up Japanese thinking to the rest of the world. They feel certain they can out-organize us, out-last us, out-guess us, out-delay us. Therefore their leaders—Mitsui and Mitsubishi and the military and naval men—feel superior. They admit we *might* be able to control them "briefly." But they insist we not only lack the stamina, but do not have the sustained interest in the Far East to carry on such an extended, highly organized and intense occupational campaign as will be necessary to accomplish what our idealistic planners seek.

And certainly, in part, any thinking person who has had anything to do with the Japanese must admit that this view has a basis in fact. Therein lies the greatest danger for our loss of the physical victory, and the basis for a new "Asia for the Asiatic" war inspired by, and including, the Japanese.

The programming Japanese look upon the fighting in this war as only the first phase of the plan to drive the hated foreigner out of Greater East Asia. The loss of the first phase by the Japanese Government of Tojo and Hirohito can be interpreted by the government in power at the moment of cessation of hostilities as a "temporary setback achieved by the foreigner through dishonorable use of superior strength."

The Japanese undoubtedly will point out that this phase of the war was successful for the glorious forces of His Imperial Japanese Majesty. They will also point out that it was a victorious war because of the vast Oceanic and Asiatic territory originally taken by the Imperial Forces during 1941–44 from the Solomons and Burma back up into Central China. The very fact that the Japanese took this territory even momentarily is "victory." The Japanese state: "Victory was complete. Japan had what was rightfully hers. We have suffered a temporary setback."

And the people will be instructed to wait for that moment when the foreign occupational strength in Japan and Greater East Asia will "weaken" because of "decadent living and self-satisfaction which will grow out of what they [America and Britain] consider their striking victory."

This opinion is based upon my knowledge of the Japanese awareness of the attitude of the so-called Pacifist-Isolationist segments of our own people and the British. It is upon the misdirected attitudes of these Pacifist-Isolationists that the Japanese are already constructing their plans for the second phase of their war against us.

Both the Germans and the Japanese are depending upon us to soften up quickly (within a decade) after victory, just as if we'd won a baseball game or a cricket match.

To be successful we must plan now for at least a generation ahead. Japan must be minutely organized by our allied Control Commission, or Allied Military Government (including the Russians whether they fight or not). We must "out-Jap the Japanese," out-organize him and superimpose this organization on him in a typically forceful, Japanese-Oriental manner the moment our first occupational forces arrive in the islands following surrender.

Such a move would surprise the Japanese. It would throw him off balance. He doesn't expect us to treat him as another Oriental nation would in victory. He expects us to do what we are doing in reoccupied Europe—"improvise," or as Mr. Hull says, "keep flexible to the point where the man in charge can deal with any group within the reoccupied country which appears to be strongest." But we can't "improvise" with the Jap. He's not built that way. Let him see that our only plan is to improvise and keep flexible and he'll out-organize *us*.

If the German is an expert at organization, at regimentation of his national life, the Japanese is a super-expert. The Japanese Neighbor-hood Association, for instance, completely overshadows the German organization of the same type. The German Gestapo is a ruthless spy-police organization. The Japanese gendarmerie and its accom-panying tentacles are a fatalistic setup that makes the Nazis look like country boys when it comes to cold-blooded action from spying to atrocities. One fundamental reason is that the German is basically an Occidental. The Jap lives under the veneer of a code of polite-ness. But beneath he has been trained in animal hates and reactions from childhood.

This training is what we of the Occident must clearly root out, over a period of time, through out-organizing the Japanese under-ground, and above-ground, government; through reorganizing the Japanese educational system, rewriting the Japanese textbooks in a subtle manner acceptable to the type of Japanese mentality now capable of absorbing only a semi-feudal form of thought; super-vising Japanese business through a "Business Foreign Service" com-prised of experienced Far Eastern American-British-Russian-Chinese-Dutch businessmen who will work together under some kind of commission or United Nations League that will back them up in their strong decisions.

Japan must have a high commissioner, preferably American, who should, in the experienced opinion of others besides myself, have a rank higher than that of a new Japanese prime minister. He must have access to the Emperor at all times. I suggest he be an American, at least at first, for several reasons. Primarily, while the British fleet will play a large part in the reoccupation of East Asia, it will be the American forces that will have done the majority of the work. The Japanese recognize this. They respect the nation with greatest force. Obviously America has that greatest strength in the Pacific. To have a Britisher, Chinese, or Russian take over the administra-tion of a surrendered Japan would give the Japanese what he would feel "a psychological advantage" in that the Americans had sur-rendered a rightful privilege to an "inferior ally." These small points loom large in psychological victory which must play an equal part with the physical victory.

The situation has now grown so critical in the long-range Asia *vs.* Occident struggle that it is no longer a matter of whether we *want* to do this organizing, or whether we consider it non-idealistic, unChristian, or aggressively militaristic and "Empiristic." We have passed the stage where we can afford to have scruples in dealing with our enemy, who will himself remain our enemy when the fighting stops. We can't expect the Jap or the German to accept defeat in a "sportsmanlike" Anglo-American fashion.

The stability settlement for Japan seems to me infinitely more important to the United States than the thorough clean-up that obviously must be carried out—also for generations—in what was once a Greater German Reich. The difference lies in race and color—in the fact that the German is a Westerner, and the Japanese an Oriental. But today the world is so small that, regardless of race or creed, the only way in which we will be able to keep from annihilating great segments of our population, and ruining our already lowered living standards, is to band together to prohibit war.

Only a handful of Japanese see this. These are sometimes mistakenly called "liberals." But there are no liberals, as we know the word, in Japan. The Japanese with whom we will deal will be sincere Japanese patriots. We must not make the mistake of believing that these men are pro-Ally. We must never forget that even these Japanese will feel deeply the "dishonor of defeat" at the hands of the Westerner; even these Japanese will feel that some day this defeat must be avenged. But the difference, as I visualize it, between these few "realists" and the militaristic Japanese who will pose as "liberals" and "anti-militarists," is this:

The "realists" can see that Japan's only hope for survival is to get along quietly in a world shrunk to the size of a Japanese plum. They know that military conquest—for generations to come—is less likely to bring new face and prosperity to Japan than a slow acquisition of economic power. And I really mean slow. This is the typical so-called "practical" Japanese long-range view. But it will not be the popular point of view.

. The great danger is that we will do business politically on a continuous basis with that group which Mr. Hull asserts is "friendly" to us: namely, the feudal, dictatorial business tycoons of Mitsui, Mitsubishi and a few others. I feel that some of our business interests who want to get into Japan and do business there immediately will use any subterfuge to get in on the ground floor with these tremendous commercial interests. This is not a pretty picture but it is a danger.

The Japanese government with which we will deal, and which will at first be made up of a commercial group, will attempt to organize Japan so tightly from the underground through many types of associations—cultural, political, and others—that it will be impossible for us to organize the nation and operate it. The Japanese are exceedingly capable organizers.

We must go into Japan with an organization that we will superimpose upon them. We must forbid *any* type of organization on their part and forcefully insist upon it. We must occupy Japan, Korea, and "Manchukuo" (Manchuria) for an indefinite period.

The first group to go in would be the military and naval occupational forces. At the same time, an Allied military government would enter. With them should come an official but civilian "Business Foreign Service" group as well as an "Education Foreign Service" group and a "Propaganda Foreign Service" group.

These groups and others should supervise and co-operate intimately with the "Allied Military Government" and high military control in Japan. There should be a general or admiral as ambassador or the super-high commissioner who will outrank the Japanese prime minister. This must be an organization that will remain in Japan probably for a couple of generations.

To preserve our future in the Pacific, to preserve our own shores from attack by an Oriental power—Japanese or any other—and to enforce a "no fighting" program in Asia for our good, and the Asiatic good, there are certain fundamentals to which we of the United Nations must adhere. There are three points of focus in any approach to the Far East, beginning with the final days of the fighting.

First, there is the broad focus that includes Asia in a world picture. The Far East must be visualized as functioning harmoniously in the broad world society. And it isn't going to function harmoniously if it isn't co-ordinated into the entire picture by persistent effort.

Second, there is the closer focus bringing into clearer vision the Far East alone. Here to the observer it becomes a pulsating, integrating, complicated Orient. The nations of this Orient must live in peace among themselves.

Third, there are the individual nations, with special focus on the most difficult one at the moment—Japan.

Regardless of how victory is accomplished, whether Japan folds quickly, once it is evident to the average Jap that he's going to be pulverized by superior force; or whether the Jap fights to the last until we swarm onto the beachheads of the Japanese islands themselves (which I believe will never happen, because the Jap will quit first), an entirely new "everyday life" philosophy must be injected into Japan.

Orientalists and experts in Shinto will say, "You're crazy even to suggest such a thing." But someone's got to be "crazy" enough not only to suggest that there must be change inside Japan but to propose that it is possible to bring about such change. If the attempt isn't made now, it will have to be made later, after the Japanese have had another crack at us. And however difficult it may be now, it will be more difficult later. Now is the time. We must face it. We must accomplish the "impossible," for it means our own preservation.

Regardless of what an Allied military government does with the physical assets of Japan, the successful approach to creating a new Japan that can be held in line in the Orient *is the psychological approach*.

First, we must not forget that the fundamental education of the Japanese has made him a bold-faced liar in any dealings he has with the Westerner, and in most dealings with himself. That's part of his psychology. His code does not necessitate his living up to statements made to the Occidental. To go to work in Japan on any other premise than this is to invite failure, to insure another war.

To change the Japanese way of life into one that will enable him to get along with the outside world's way of life (heretofore the Japanese has lived pretty much in a language, cultural, and political-economic vacuum) the approach must be carefully conceived and executed. The change-over must be done through existing Japanese methods, and with a complete Japanese approach. To be successful, it cannot have any foreign flavor.

Several forceful change-over methods have been recommended. Two of them are extremely practical. But practical or not, they are impossible of execution because of the kind of people we Westerners are. And because we live according to certain principles.

The first of these "successful methods" of changing the Japanese and the islands more quickly to a live-in-the-world-harmoniously system recommends killing off all Japanese in the surrendering armed forces. (Plenty of them will commit suicide anyway, it is argued—and truly.) This approach is Oriental, all right, and certainly would solve many problems. But that's not our way of life.

The second suggestion, and one with considerable backing particularly in China, is to eliminate the Shinto worship and debunk the mythical divinity of this Emperor, or any Emperor to come. This is another efficient idea, and one that the Japanese would be likely to apply were he conquering America or the Island Kingdom of Britain.

However, one of the prime foundations of our democratic Western life is freedom of religion. Shinto—whether called a cult, a racket, or a way of life—is the religion of nearly every Japanese. Despite what the missionaries assert, their work in Christianity has merely scratched the surface in Japan. But it has done some good. Through the study of Christianity a few Japanese have come to understand a little better the way of life lived outside of Japan. Most of these have used this understanding of us against us. But on the basis of that understanding and the war a few Japanese have come to see that perhaps the Japanese must re-gear their way of life to mesh into the world's system; that they will never be able to re-gear the world's system to fit theirs. This second suggestion then is out, if we are to stick to our own principles—and we must.

What then? In the first place, Tojo and the subsequent militarists will either commit suicide or face trials.

As the time grows closer for a final decision on what to do with His Imperial Japanese Majesty, Emperor of Japan (once we have won the fighting against Japan), two points of view block action by the planning agencies of America, Britain, China, the Netherlands, and Russia. It seems from this distance that before Japan surrenders there will be in operation some kind of an active United Nations League or Council. It will doubtless be to this League that the Japanese will surrender. This League or Council will decide the fate not only of Hirohito but of the mystic-political-state-sect or religion, Shinto.

The two points of view which must be adjusted into one firm policy are these:

First, that the "person" of His Imperial Japanese Majesty must remain inviolate after the fighting stops; that we can "do business" with Hirohito, because, although a puppet, he allegedly expressed a desire before war broke out in December 1941 not to go to war with the United States.

The reason it is held Hirohito should sign the Imperial Rescript for the stability terms—and that "we should use him as our puppet for good just as the Japanese Military used him for bad purposes"—is this:

"Under the present formula of Japanese life, the Emperor is a symbol of political 'spiritual inspiration' for each Japanese. To refuse to 'do business' with him would irritate the Japanese. The Throne or the Emperor Symbol can do no wrong. Thus the Emperor himself is not held responsible for the loss of the War." (Although it is *admitted* he and his "era" would be given positive credit if the war had been successful.)

The second and more controversial point of view is that the United Nations must *not* "do business" with the person of Hirohito under any circumstances:

1. Because Hirohito is the personal symbol of furious hate and aggression against the white man.

2. Because he is the person visualized in the mind of the individual Japanese civilian and fighting man as the "personal symbol" of leadership against the "foreigner."

3. Because this hate can be more capably carried on into the peace through the retention of the warring Emperor.

It is argued, according to the "keep Hirohito" point of view, that since the Emperor is "only a symbol" the symbol himself cannot be held responsible in the Japanese mind for doing wrong—for losing the war; for urging hate of the foreigner. If this is true—that the divinely descended Emperor, no matter who he is, can do no wrong—then I for one firmly believe it will be infinitely safer and preferable to "do business" with Hirohito's successor. Obviously this would involve the immediate elimination of Hirohito, through his death, and the acceptance of whatever member of the Imperial family is slated for the Throne. Allowing Hirohito to remain alive and on the throne would be to take grave chances of inspiring the Japanese to support him in a future struggle to "avenge the dishonorable" action taken against Hirohito by the United Nations—especially the American forces. With Hirohito dead, his logical successor would be the Crown Prince whose youth would make a regency necessary. The regents, though appointed according to Japanese tradition, would have to be approved by the United Nations, who, backed by overwhelming force, would actually dictate to them, and thus, through them, to the Emperor and the Japanese people.

I foresee nothing but accentuated trouble if Hirohito remains alive after our Army of Occupation takes over Japan proper. It is quite conceivable that the Emperor may make the "supreme sacrifice" of his Imperial body as a result of the dark cloud that has passed over his heretofore aggressive happy "era" or reign. If he

does not do it himself—since he is really not supposed to have any
corporeal life to lose—he could certainly be "discovered" some
morning to have become "indisposed" and have passed along to the
Imperial Shrine to join his ancestors.

Hirohito has been to the Japanese civilian and soldier in this race-
hate war against the white man even more of a symbol of hate and
aggression against us than Hitler has been to the fighting Nazi. If
Hitler and Mussolini and lesser Hitlers must go, Hirohito must
follow. Our former Ambassador to Japan, Mr. Joseph Grew, apparently believes that since any Japanese emperor is virtually a
puppet, and since Hirohito was reputed to have indicated he didn't
want war with us, Hirohito should be permitted to carry on. If Mr.
Grew's suggestion (adhered to at present by Mr. Cordell Hull) is
followed, we have lost before we get started. Hirohito is just the
symbol the inevitable future underground will need on which to
hang continued race hatred and heroization for the next war.

His lineal successor, directed by the regents who are instructed by
our own councils, will take a new attitude toward his subjects. His
subjects who revere him as a Divine Person will continue in their
reverence to follow his newly "enlightened" Imperial Rescripts as
they did those of his unfortunate predecessor, Hirohito. To be sure
these rescripts will have been dictated by the United Nations Council through the regents. But the new Emperor—not the United
Nations councils—will talk to the average Japanese something like
this:

"A new Japan has been born due to circumstances necessitating
our taking a position of responsibility in a new and peaceful world.
Hirohito did great things for Japan. But I will accomplish greater
things for Japan and each Japanese. I will bring the world to Japan
in a better life for each individual—instead of ordering Japan to rule
the world."

A new Emperor, under a new constitution, under a redefinition of
what Shinto actually stands for (a religion *per se*, not a personalized
State religion) would give the United Nations Control Commissioner and the new Japan something positive upon which to begin
to base new responsibilities for a disarmed, demobilized Japan in
what we insist shall be a more stable world than pre-1939. This
new "enlightened" Emperor (enlightened by us) must carefully
point out to his subjects that there is going to be a division between
the religion (the personal worship of the Emperor) and the political functions of the actual Government itself.

A new Japan must be constructed, through a government imposed by the United Nations, upon the framework of what—since Emperor Meiji—has been called Modern Japan. But we must insist, through the so-called liberal Japanese in defeated Japan, that the Emperor make a clear and wide cleavage between the religious and the economic-political responsibilities within the State, and with international affairs.

Specifically, among other stipulations in a new constitution, the Prime Minister and his Government shall be responsible to the public—and not a feudal public—for the actual operation of the State. And in order to awaken the submerged thinking of a feudal people, United Nations commissions, including Japanese members, even some American Nisei, shall outline roads along which the Japanese people shall travel for generations to come. And the emphasis in laying out these roads should be at least fourfold:

First: Economic—with United Nations supervision over all Japanese industry and endeavor, especially to check all raw material entering Japan, and what it's used for.

Second: Educational—with United Nations supervision and revision of textbooks and teaching methods that have developed the type of thinking causing the present war-minded Jap. The Press and Radio—to continue to be utilized just as at present but to carry the new slant: the division of personal responsibility to the Emperor; the Prime Minister's responsibility to the individual. The Press and Radio would stress Japan's new attitude toward the Westerner; that the Japanese must get along in the world with the Westerner without the idea of eventually wiping the white man off the earth.

Third: Political—with careful check on political agitation; with clear-cut emphasis and drill on division of the religious and political responsibilities to the public by the Emperor and the Prime Minister.

Fourth: Military—with reduction of all armed forces to mere local police force size in the beginning. Then Japan would be required to provide its quota in an International Army or Police Force, if one is established.

I know how fantastic this whole plan may sound to many who see no possibility of Westerners "instructing" an Emperor of Japan or re-educating the Japanese people in the direction of those freedoms which are the basic goal of Western democracy. I confess that I do not propose it with anything like complete conviction that it will succeed. I suggest it only as a basis, finding in no other plan so far proposed anything which to my mind offers a promise of future stability.

To put the international stability machinery into operation at once, Japan, as well as Germany, must be immediately placed in the world organization and told in no uncertain terms what their responsibilities are. None of this "you may enter when you are properly qualified" business, as in the formation of the former League of Nations. (As an AP correspondent in Geneva covering the old League, I watched political stickiness over who was "qualified" to be members gum up League machinery to the point of self-sabotage.) Every nation must belong.

If the result of victory in the Far East is going to be the outlawing of future fighting, and an attempt to establish a certain economic and political stability, then every nation's responsibility must be clearly defined and understood. All nations must see to it that their neighbors carry out these responsibilities.

We must attempt to stick to fundamentals in the Far East—fundamental principles that we agree upon before the end of fighting. I weaken my point, I realize, by saying we must "attempt" to stick to fundamentals, but the frailty of human determination when principles are involved is notorious. I want to be practical.

This must be for us a selfish peace. As strong victors, we, the United Nations, cannot afford to slacken off in decades to come; to become wishy-washy benevolent victors. But we must send understanding businessmen (our Business Foreign Service) and wise politicos into Japan; wise educators (our Educational Foreign Service) and cultural leaders to try to steer the thinking of the new and rising Japanese generations away from their elders, who will be constantly hammering for a new, an avenging war against the Westerner.

We must not forget—we can never afford to become tired of our role as supervisors of a planned "stability" in East Asia. Our work will go on, not merely for years, but for generations.

We are forewarned by the Japanese. They are frank to tell us what they plan, what they'll get away with if they can find the possible loophole. They say this—and they aren't kidding:

"We will fight until every white man is driven out of Asia. If we can find a neutral government through whose 'good offices' we can work out a political arrangement to terminate the present fighting, we will do so to prevent your getting into Japan proper. But this will not be the end. If you accept this peace, we will begin where we left off in preparing for a continuation of this 'one-hundred-years' war.'

"If you don't accept this peace, when hostilities do cease we will continue the fight underground. We will continue the fight from deep inside our spiritual and our ancestral bodies. We will avenge the peace, because it will not be honorable.

"We are so sorry—but there can be no peace as long as white men seek political or economic power in Asia."

This is Japan's warning. Either we heed it now, and act accordingly in imposing a supervised, planned stability on the Japanese, incorporating them by force into the new policed world setup, or we will fight again, and again.

ROYAL ARCH GUNNISON

is now Radio News Analyst for the Mutual Broadcasting System. Before the year is out he will be once again in the Southwest Pacific with General MacArthur and in the China-Burma-India war theater with General Chennault's 14th Air Force as *Collier's* Far East correspondent.

He has traveled almost all over the world, has been a correspondent for the Associated Press, North American Newspaper Alliance, *The Christian Science Monitor*, *Collier's*, and has contributed to *Time* and *Reader's Digest*.

He was born in Juneau, Alaska. His name comes to him, through his father, from the Royal Arch Degree in Masonry, which his grandfather received on the night of his father's birth.